A-Z CANTERBURY, MARGATE and RA...

C000269649

CONTEN...

REFERENCE

Motorway	**M2**	Car Park (Selected)	P
A Road	**A28**	Church or Chapel	†
Tunnel		Cycleway	
B Road	**B2052**	Fire Station	■
Dual Carriageway		Hospital	H
One-way Street	⇒	House Numbers A & B Roads only	48 113
Traffic flow on A roads is also indicated by a heavy line on the driver's left.	⇒	Information Centre	i
Restricted Access		National Grid Reference	630
Pedestrianized Road		Park & Ride	Wincheap P+
Track		Police Station	▲
Footpath		Post Office	★
Residential Walkway		Toilet:	
Railway — Level Crossing, Station, Tunnel		with facilities for the Disabled	▽
		without facilities for the Disabled	▽
		for the Disabled only	▽
Built-up Area	EAST LA	Educational Establishment	
Local Authority Boundary	— · — · —	Hospital or Hospice	
Posttown Boundary		Industrial Building	
Postcode Boundary (within Posttown)	· — — —	Leisure or Recreational Facility	
		Place of Interest	
Map Continuation	8	Public Building	
Airport	✈	Shopping Centre or Market	
		Other Selected Buildings	

SCALE

1:15,840

0 — ¼ — ½ — ¾ Mile

0 — 250 — 500 — 750 — 1 Kilometre

4 inches (10.16) to 1 mile or 6.31cm to 1 km

Copyright of Geographers' A-Z Map Company Limited

Fairfield Road, Borough Green, Sevenoaks, Kent TN15 8PP
Telephone: 01732 781000 (Enquiries & Trade Sales)
01732 783422 (Retail Sales)

www.a-zmaps.co.uk

Copyright © Geographers' A-Z Map Co. Ltd.

 Ordnance Survey® This product includes mapping data licensed from Ordnance Survey® with the permission of the Controller of Her Majesty's Stationery Office.

© Crown Copyright 2003. All rights reserved. Licence number 100017302

Edition 2 2004, Edition 2B 2007 (Part Revision)

NORTH

B2008

Warden

B2231

Leysdown-on-Sea

ISLE OF SHEPPEY

THE SWALE

HERNE BAY
Bel

WHITSTABLE
Tankerton Swalecliffe

14 1

10 **11** **12** **13**
Herr

Seasalter Chestfield
South Street

A291

Oare
FAVERSHAM
42 **43**

26 **27**
Yorkletts

A299

A290

Hers

Ospringe

A2

Blean

Sturry West

M2
6

7
A2

Boughton under Blean

34 **35** **36** 3

University of Kent Fordwich

P+

A251

Harbledown **CANTERBURY**

A2

Sheldwich

38 **39** **40** 4

P+ Bekesbo

P+
Patrixbourne

Chartham

A2

N O R T H

A252

Chilham

Bridge

A252

Challock

Stour

Great Stour

A28

B2068

A252

A28

D O W N S

M20

A251

Wye

SEA

MARGATE

Westgate on Sea

4   **5**   **6**   **7**   Cliftonville   **8**   **9**

Birchington   Garlinge   Kingsgate

ISLE OF THANET   St. Peter's

stone   Reculver   Lydden   *NORTH FORELAND*

17   **18**   **19**   **20**   **21**   **22**   **23**   **24**   **25**

St. Nicholas at Wade   Kent International Airport (Manston)   Manston   **BROADSTAIRS**

Dumpton

Monkton   **Minster**

Upstreet   **28**   **29**   **30**   **31**   **32**   **33**

Cliffsend   **RAMSGATE**

River   *Stour*   *PEGWELL BAY*

Richborough Port

Stour   *Little Stour*

Great   *SANDWICH BAY*

Great Stonar

44

Ash   **SANDWICH**

ourne   **Wingham**

Woodnesborough

Eastry

DEAL

Aylesham

Eythorne

Ringwould   Kingsdown

A2

SCALE

0   1   2 Miles

0   1   2   3 Kilometres

❶

❷

71

❸

N O R T H

❹

¹70

Grenham Bay

MINNIS BAY

❺

Birchington

Putting Grn

The Minnis

Birchington-on-Sea 🚉

❻

DARYNGTON AV.

ROAD   DANE

DANE

CT7

Gore End Farm

BIRCHINGTON

69

NORTH SEA

WESTGATE ON SEA

Westbrook

Westgate Pav. & Thtre.

St. Mildred's Bay

Children's Pool

Putting Grn.

WESTBROOK

ESPLANADE

ROYAL ESPLA

PROMENAD

Westbrook Centre
Victoria House

The Gardens

ST. CLEMENTS RD.

ESSEX RD.

ST. MILDRED'S GS.

ST. MILDRED'S RD.

Tennis Cts.

OLD BOUNDARY RD.

BOWES AV.

EDMANSON AV.

FITZMARY AV.

GRESHAM AV.

BARNES AV.

PEMBROKE AV.

WESTONVILLE AV.

CLIFFE AV.

GDNS

Westgate Bay

ROWENA RD.

ETHELRED RD.

BAY

SQUARE

SHERWOOD GR.

ADRIAN SQ.

BETHEL

ROXBURGH RD.

CONIFER CT.

SAXON RD.

NORMAN RD.

AVENUE ROAD

SEYMOUR AV.

TYSON AV.

COURTS

WESTMINSTER

BOLEYN AV.

AUDLEY AV.

MUTRIX AV.

ORCHARD RD.

BARN CR.

CROSSING RD.

LANGHAM GDNS

MEADOW RD.

Mutrix Rd.

OLD

CANTERBURY

Westgate Bay

WEST BAY

CEDRIC RD.

THANET RD.

Cin.

STATION RD.

Westgate-on-Sea

CHESTER RD.

QUEENS RD.

HOCKEREDGE GDNS.

ST. JAMES PARK

BRIDGE RD.

MAYNARD AV.

S.

CARLTON RD. EAST

DOMNEVA RD.

CUTHBERT

Westgate Coll.

ELM CT.

Harold AV.

GROVE RD.

ESSEX AV.

248

BRIARY CL.

ALICIA

257

NOBLE CL.

ROSE LAWN

EDINBURGH

CORONATION RD.

AMELIA AV.

193

RYDER'S RD.

DANE END RD.

Pav.

ELM

Jun. Play. Sch. Fld.

A28

ROAD

Rec. Grd.

Playing Field

MICHELLE AV.

DENT-DE-LION RD.

OAK GS.

DRIVE

LEYBOURNE RD.

BALMORAL RD.

GLEBE RD.

CROW HILL

AVENUE

KINGST

Club House

CANTERBURY

St. Augustine's Coll.

COUNTESS MOUNTBATTEN CT.

Lib.

STREETE CT.

BELMONT RD.

Dent-de-lion Castle (remains of)

GS.

DENT-DE-LION

KING'S

ST. FISHER'S GDS

WELSDENE RD.

LENHAM

GLEBE RD.

LESLIE AV.

ELLINGTON

BROOKE AV.

HUNDREDS CL.

CHARING CR.

REDHILL CL.

GUILDFORD AV.

OSBORN AV.

LINDEN GROVE RD.

ST. LUKE'S RD.

Sch.

LINDEN

Comm. Centre

RECULVERS RD.

RICHBOROUGH RD.

Dent-de-lion Farm

Dent-de-lion

Dent-de-lion Farm Cottages

GARLINGE

THROWLEY COTTS.

STEPH.

CHILHAM AV.

SUDBURY

ST. CRISPIN'S AV.

ST. MARGARET'S RD.

WELLINGTON RD.

ST. BENET'S RD.

WINDSOR M.

GOLDEN ACRE LA.

LINKSFIELD RD.

SOUTHWOLD PL.

St. Crispin's Prim. Inf. School

PROSPECT RD.

ST. JEAN'S RD.

CROFTON RD.

WELLESLEY CL.

Fulham Farm

Zeila Farm Cottages

Zeila Farm

HIGH

ROAD

ABBEY RD.

LINKSFIELD RD.

Hengrove Farm

10 08 Ⓐ Ⓑ 09 Ⓒ Ⓓ

68

1

2 *NORTH SEA*

67

3

4

THE OAZE

66

5 *WHITSTABLE BAY*

WES C

The Battery

SEASALTER *PARADE* ADMIRALTY WK SEASALTER BEACH

6 FAIRWAY CR GEORGE'S AV FLORENCE AV SHAMROCK AV SUN RAY COLUMBIA GENESTA AV METEOR SOPHIE AV BRITANNIA

GROVE ROAD ASHLEY DR HAZLEMERE MEDINA AV ALFREDE CL SOMERSET CL

PRESTON CORYLUS DR EDEN ROAD SHAMROCK AV DORSET CL FIELD VW

BLUE ANCHOR CARAVAN PARK ALLAN RD HODGSON RD MARY ST BOWLER'S RD LUCERNE DR WAUG EDEN ROAD PARADE ROAD

65 FAVERSHAM FOXDENE DR GATE RD ACRE RD MACDONALD INGHAM RD CORD CL CAROLINE ANTHONY SANDPIPER

08;iding Centre Ⓐ ALBERTA CARAVAN PARK ROAD Ⓑ FARLEY RD UCERNE Comm Cen 26 09 FAVERSHAM Hall Ⓒ THE GRANGE VICTORIA Ⓓ

INDEX

Including Streets, Places & Areas, Hospitals & Hospices, Industrial Estates,
Selected Flats & Walkways, Stations and Selected Places of Interest.

HOW TO USE THIS INDEX

1. Each street name is followed by its Postcode District and then by its Locality abbreviation(s) and then by its map reference;
   e.g. **Abbey St.** ME13: Fav . . . .3F **43** is in the ME13 Postcode District and the Faversham Locality and is to be found in square 3F on page **43**.
   The page number is shown in bold type.

2. A strict alphabetical order is followed in which Av., Rd., St., etc. (though abbreviated) are read in full and as part of the street name;
   e.g. **Bayview Rd.** appears after **Bay Vw. Hgts.** but before **Bay Vw. Rd.**

3. Streets and a selection of flats and walkways too small to be shown on the maps, appear in the index with the thoroughfare to which it is connected
   shown in brackets; e.g. **Albert Ct.** CT11: Ram . . . .3E **33** (off York St.)

4. Addresses that are in more than one part are referred to as not continuous.

5. Places and areas are shown in the index in BLUE TYPE and the map reference is to the actual map square in which the town centre or area is located
   and not to the place name shown on the map; e.g. BELTINGE 2H **15**

6. An example of a selected place of interest is **Bleak House & Smuggling Mus.** 3H **25**

7. An example of a station is Bekesbourne Station (Rail) 5F **41**

8. An example of a hospital or hospice is **CHAUCER BMI HOSPITAL, THE** 6G **39**

GENERAL ABBREVIATIONS

All. : Alley	**Flds.** : Fields	**Nth.** : North
App. : Approach	**Gdn.** : Garden	**Pal.** : Palace
Arc. : Arcade	**Gdns.** : Gardens	**Pde.** : Parade
Av. : Avenue	**Ga.** : Gate	**Pk.** : Park
Bri. : Bridge	**Gt.** : Great	**Pas.** : Passage
Bungs. : Bungalows	**Grn.** : Green	**Pl.** : Place
Bus. : Business	**Gro.** : Grove	**Prom.** : Promenade
Cvn. : Caravan	**Hgts.** : Heights	**Ri.** : Rise
Cen. : Centre	**Ho.** : House	**Rd.** : Road
Circ. : Circle	**Ind.** : Industrial	**Shop.** : Shopping
Cir. : Circus	**Info.** : Information	**Sth.** : South
Cl. : Close	**Intl.** : International	**Sq.** : Square
Comn. : Common	**La.** : Lane	**St.** : Street
Cnr. : Corner	**Lit.** : Little	**Ter.** : Terrace
Cott. : Cottage	**Lwr.** : Lower	**Trad.** : Trading
Cotts. : Cottages	**Mnr.** : Manor	**Up.** : Upper
Ct. : Court	**Mans.** : Mansions	**Vw.** : View
Cres. : Crescent	**Mkt.** : Market	**Vs.** : Villas
Cft. : Croft	**Mdw.** : Meadow	**Vis.** : Visitors
Dr. : Drive	**Mdws.** : Meadows	**Wlk.** : Walk
E. : East	**M.** : Mews	**W.** : West
Est. : Estate	**Mt.** : Mount	**Yd.** : Yard
Fld. : Field	**Mus.** : Museum	

LOCALITY ABBREVIATIONS

Acol : **Acol**	Fav : **Faversham**	P'hm : **Petham**
Ash : **Ash**	G'ney : **Graveney**	Ram : **Ramsgate**
Bek : **Bekesbourne**	Harb : **Harbledown**	Rec : **Reculver**
Birch : **Birchington**	H Bay : **Herne Bay**	R Comn : **Rough Common**
Blean : **Blean**	Hernh : **Hernhill**	St N : **St Nicholas at Wade**
Brid : **Bridge**	Hoath : **Hoath**	S'wch : **Sandwich**
B Oak : **Broad Oak**	L'brne : **Littlebourne**	Seas : **Seasalter**
B'stairs : **Broadstairs**	Lud'm : **Luddenham**	Shel : **Sheldwich**
Cant : **Canterbury**	Mans : **Manston**	Sturry : **Sturry**
Chart'm : **Chartham**	Mgte : **Margate**	T Hill : **Tyler Hill**
C'let : **Chislet**	M'sde : **Marshside**	Up Harb : **Upper Harbledown**
C'snd : **Cliffsend**	Minst : **Minster**	Wgte S : **Westgate-on-Sea**
Clift : **Cliftonville**	Monk'n : **Monkton**	Whits : **Whitstable**
Darg : **Dargate**	Oare : **Oare**	Wdchu : **Woodchurch**
Dunk : **Dunkirk**	Osp : **Ospringe**	Wdboro : **Woodnesborough**

Craddock Ho. CT1: Cant 1H 39	Dane Cres. CT11: Ram 1E 33	Dickens Av. CT1: Cant 6A 36
Craddock Rd. CT1: Cant 1H 39	Danecroft Ct. CT1: Cant 1F 39	Dickens House Mus. 3H 25
Crampton Ct. CT10: B'stairs 3G 25	(off King St.)	Dickens Rd. CT10: B'stairs 2H 25
Crampton Tower Mus. 3G 25	Danecroft Ho. CT1: Cant 1F 39	Dickens Wlk. CT10: B'stairs 3H 25
Cranborne Wlk. CT2: Cant 5E 35	(off King St.)	(off Eldon Pl.)
Cranbourne Cl. CT11: Ram 1F 33	Dane End Rd. CT8: Wgte S 5H 5	Dilnot La. CT7: Acol 4F 21
Cranbrook Cl. CT9: Clift 4E 9	Dane Gdns. CT9: Mgte 5B 8	Discovery Wlk. CT1: Cant 3A 40
Cranleigh Ct. CT5: Whits 5G 11	Dane Hill CT9: Mgte 2H 7	Doggerel Acre CT5: Whits 6H 11
Cranleigh Gdns. CT5: Whits 5G 11	Dane Hill Gro. CT9: Mgte 3H 7	Dolphin Cl. CT10: B'stairs 3G 9
Cranmer Cl. CT4: Brid 6F 41	Dane Hill Row CT9: Mgte 3H 7	Dolphin Ct. CT6: H Bay 2C 14
Cranmer Ho. CT2: Cant 1D 38	Danehurst CT8: Wgte S 4A 6	Dolphin St. CT6: H Bay 2C 14
Craven Cl. CT9: Mgte 5E 7	Dane John Cotts. CT1: Cant 3F 39	Domneva Rd. CT8: Wgte S 5H 5
Crawford Gdns. CT9: Mgte 3B 8	Dane John Ct. CT1: Cant 3F 39	CT12: Minst 3F 29
Crawford Rd. CT10: B'stairs 2F 25	Dane John M. CT1: Cant 3F 39	Donegal Rd. CT1: Cant 2A 40
Creighton Flats CT13: S'wch 4B 44	Dane John Wlk. CT1: Cant 3F 39	Donnahay Rd. CT12: Ram 4C 24
(off School Rd.)	Dane Mt. CT9: Mgte 5C 8	Donnithorne Ho. CT6: H Bay 2G 14
Creine Mill La. Nth. CT1: Cant 2E 39	Dane Pk. Rd. CT9: Mgte 3H 7	(off Brunswick Sq.)
Creine Mill La. Sth. CT1: Cant 2E 39	CT11: Ram 1E 33	Dorcas Gdns. CT10: B'stairs 1G 25
Cremer Pl. ME13: Fav 3C 42	Dane Rd. CT7: Birch ....1H 19 & 6A 4	Doric Ct. CT11: Ram 4C 32
Crescent Rd. CT7: Birch 6E 5	CT9: Mgte 3H 7	Dorothy Dr. CT12: Ram 5C 24
CT9: Mgte 3F 7	CT11: Ram 1E 33	Dorset Cl. CT5: Whits 6D 10
CT10: B'stairs 5H 9	Danesmead Ter. CT9: Mgte 3H 7	Dorset Gdns. CT7: Birch 6D 4
CT11: Ram 2C 32	Dane Valley Rd. CT9: Mgte 4B 8	Dorset Pl. ME13: Fav 4E 43
ME13: Fav 4F 43	(not continuous)	Dorset Rd. CT1: Cant 3B 40
Crescent, The CT2: Cant 5F 35	CT10: B'stairs 6D 8	Douglas Av. CT5: Whits 4G 11
CT5: Whits 5A 12	Daniels Ct. CT5: Whits 4E 11	Douglas Cl. CT10: B'stairs 2E 25
Cress Way ME13: Fav 4C 42	Darenth Cl. CT6: H Bay 4F 15	Douglas Rd. CT6: H Bay 3E 15
Cresta Cl. CT6: H Bay 1F 13	Dargate Rd. CT5: Seas 4C 26	Douro Cl. CT1: Cant 1B 40
Crinan Ct. CT11: Ram 6F 25	Dark Hill ME13: Fav 3D 42	Dove Cl. CT5: Whits 6E 11
Crispe Pk. Cl. CT7: Birch 6F 5	Darnley Cl. CT10: B'stairs 4F 25	Dovedale CT7: Birch 6F 5
Crispe Rd. CT7: Acol 3C 20	Darrell Cl. CT6: H Bay 4A 14	Dove Dale Ct. CT7: Birch 6F 5
Crispin Cl. ME13: Fav 3F 43	Darren Gdns. CT10: B'stairs 5F 25	Dover Rd. CT13: S'wch 6B 44
Crofton Rd. CT8: Wgte S 6A 6	Darwin College	Dover St. CT1: Cant 2G 39
Croft's Pl. CT10: B'stairs 3H 25	University of Cambridge 3E 35	Down Barton Rd. CT7: St N 6D 26
Cromwell Rd. CT1: Cant 4G 39	Darwin Rd. CT2: Cant 3E 35	Downings, The CT6: H Bay 5E 15
CT5: Whits 3F 11	CT7: Birch 5D 4	Downs Av. CT5: Whits 4G 11
Cross La. ME13: Fav 4E 43	Daryngton Av. CT7: Birch 6A 4	Downs Pk. CT6: H Bay 3E 15
Crossley Av. CT6: H Bay 1F 13	David Av. CT9: Clift 3D 8	Downs Rd. CT2: Cant 4E 35
Cross Rd. CT7: Birch 5E 5	David's Cl. CT10: B'stairs 4H 25	CT11: Ram 3A 32
Cross St. CT2: Cant 1E 39	Davidson Rd. CT2: Cant 1D 38	Downs, The CT11: Ram 4D 32
CT6: H Bay 4B 14	Davington Cotts. ME13: Fav 3E 43	(off Royal Esplanade)
Crossways CT2: Cant 4F 35	DAVINGTON 3E 43	Dragoon Ho. CT1: Cant 1G 39
Crossways Av. CT9: Mgte 2A 24	Davington Hill ME13: Fav 3E 43	(off Artillery Gdns.)
Crow Hill CT10: B'stairs 2H 25	Dawsons Row ME13: Osp 5C 42	Drapers Av. CT9: Mgte 5H 7
Crow Hill Rd. CT9: Mgte 5D 6	Daytona Way CT6: H Bay 1G 13	Drapers Cl. CT9: Mgte 5A 8
Crown Gdns. CT2: Cant 1E 39	Deal Rd. CT13: S'wch 6B 44	Drapers Homes CT9: Mgte 5A 8
Crown Hill Rd. CT6: H Bay 3A 14	Dean Ct. CT1: Cant 1G 39	Drapers Windmill 4A 8
Crundale Way CT9: Clift 4E 9	Dean Cft. CT6: H Bay 5F 15	Dreamland Cinema 3F 7
Crystal Bus. Cen. CT13: S'wch 3D 44	Deane Cl. CT5: Whits 6G 11	Drive, The CT1: Cant 4H 39
Cudham Gdns. CT9: Clift 3E 9	Deans Mill Ct. CT2: Cant 1F 39	CT5: Whits 5D 12
Culpepper Cl. CT2: Cant 4G 35	Deansway Av. CT2: Sturry 1C 36	Drove, The CT2: Cant 4E 37
Culvert, The CT6: H Bay 2D 14	Deborah Cl. CT5: Whits 6H 11	CT5: Whits 5D 12
Cumberland Av. CT1: Cant 3B 40	De Havillands CT4: Bek 6H 41	CT12: Monk'n 2A 28
CT10: B'stairs 2G 25	Delacourt Cl. CT12: C'snd 4E 31	Druidstone Pk.
Cumberland Rd. CT9: Clift 2B 8	Delaware Cl. CT2: Sturry 2D 36	(Enchanted Woodland & Sculpture Pk.)
CT11: Ram 3D 32	Delfside CT13: S'wch 5C 44	...............................1A 34
Cundishall Cl. CT5: Whits 5E 11	Delf St. CT13: S'wch 4B 44	Drybeck Av. CT10: B'stairs 2H 31
Cunningham Cres. CT7: Birch 6C 4	Delmar Cl. CT5: Whits 2D 12	Dryden Cl. CT1: Cant 3A 40
Curlew Cl. CT6: H Bay 5G 15	Denbigh Rd. CT12: Ram 6A 24	Drying Shed La. CT1: Cant 2E 39
Curlinge Ct. CT11: Ram 3A 32	Dence Cl. CT6: H Bay 2F 15	Duck La. CT1: Cant 1G 39
Curtis Way ME13: Fav 4E 43	Dence Pk. CT6: H Bay 3F 15	Dudley Av. CT8: Wgte S 5G 5
Curzon Ho. CT11: Ram 3D 32	Dene, The CT1: Cant 5H 39	Duke St. CT9: Mgte 2G 7
(off Alpha Rd.)	Dene Wlk. CT9: Mgte 6H 7	.................................5F 25
Cushman Rd. CT1: Cant 3E 39	Dengrove Pk. CT2: B Oak 2B 36	Dumpton Gap Rd. CT10: B'stairs ...5G 25
Cuthbert Rd. CT8: Wgte S 5H 5	Denmark Pl. CT1: Cant 1G 39	Dumpton La. CT11: Ram 5G 25
Cuttings, The CT12: Ram 1C 32	Denmark Rd. CT11: Ram 1E 33	Dumpton Pk. Dr. CT10: B'stairs ...6G 25
Cypress Cl. CT5: Whits 6E 11	Denne Cl. CT2: Sturry 1D 36	CT11: Ram 1F 33
Cyprus Rd. ME13: Fav 4G 43	Denstead Ct. CT2: Cant 4C 34	Dumpton Pk. Rd. CT11: Ram 1E 33
	DENSTROUDE 6E 27	Dumpton Park Station (Rail) 6F 25
	DENT-DE-LION 5C 6	Duncan Cl. CT5: Whits 6F 11

D	Dent-de-Lion Ct. CT9: Mgte 5C 6	Duncan Dr. CT7: Birch 5C 4
	Dent-de-Lion Rd. CT8: Wgte S 4A 6	Duncan Rd. CT5: Whits 6F 11
	CT9: Mgte 5C 6	Duncombe M. CT1: Cant 6H 35
Da Capo Studios CT1: Cant 4C 38	Denton Way CT9: Mgte 4C 8	Duncon Rd. CT11: Ram 3D 32
Daigor La. CT12: Mans 6F 23	Dering Rd. CT6: H Bay 3D 14	Dundonald Rd. CT10: B'stairs 3H 25
Daimler Av. CT6: H Bay 2H 13	Derwent Av. CT11: Ram 2A 32	CT11: Ram 2C 32
Dalby Rd. CT9: Mgte 2A 8	Desmond Cres. ME13: Fav 6H 43	Dunedin Rd. CT12: Ram 6A 24
Dalby Sq. CT9: Clift 2A 8	D'este Rd. CT11: Ram 2F 33	Dunoon Ct. CT11: Ram 6F 25
Dallinger Rd. CT7: Birch 5D 4	Detling Av. CT10: B'stairs 6G 25	Dunstan Av. CT8: Wgte S 6H 5
Dalmally Vs. CT2: B Oak 3B 36	Devon Gdns. CT7: Birch 1D 20	Durban Cl. CT12: Ram 6A 24
Dalmaney Cl. CT10: B'stairs 2H 25	Devon Rd. CT1: Cant 2B 40	Durban Rd. CT9: Mgte 4A 8
Dalmeny Av. CT9: Mgte 4D 8	Devonshire Gdns. CT9: Clift 3B 8	Durham Cl. CT1: Cant 4F 39
Dalton Ct. CT11: Ram 2E 33	Devonshire Ter. CT10: B'stairs ...2H 25	DURLOCK 4G 29
(off Belmont St.)	Dexter Cl. CT2: Cant 6F 35	Durlock CT12: Minst 4G 29
Damerham Cl. CT2: Cant 5E 35	Diamond Ho. CT5: Whits 6F 11	Durlock Av. CT11: Ram 4B 32
Dan Dr. ME13: Fav 3C 42	(off Diamond Rd.)	Durnford Cl. CT1: Cant 6E 35
Dane Ct. Gdns. CT10: B'stairs 2D 24	Diamond Rd. CT5: Whits 3G 11	Durovernum Ct. CT1: Cant 3G 39
Dane Ct. Rd. CT10: B'stairs 6C 8		

Dymchurch Ho. *CT1: Cant* 2H **39**
  (off St Martin's Pl.)

E

Eagle Hill CT11: Ram 2D **32**
Ealham Cl. CT1: Cant 5H **39**
Earlsmead Cres. CT12: C'snd 4E **31**
Eastchurch Rd. CT9: Clift 3E **9**
E. Cliff Pde. CT6: H Bay 2E **15**
E. Cliff Prom. CT6: H Bay 2F **15**
  CT10: B'stairs 3H **25**
EAST DUMPTON 6G **25**
Eastern Esplanade CT9: Clift 2A **8**
  CT10: B'stairs 1H **25**
Eastfield Rd. CT7: Birch 6E **5**
Eastgate Cl. CT6: H Bay 4F **15**
E. Kent Retail Pk. CT10: B'stairs 2B **24**
EAST NORTHDOWN 4E **9**
E. Northdown Cl. CT9: Clift 4E **9**
East Northdown Farm & Gardens 4E **9**
East Ri. CT12: Ram 6B **24**
East St. CT1: Cant 5A **36**
  CT6: H Bay 2E **15**
  ME13: Fav 4F **43**
Eaton Hill CT9: Mgte 3G **7**
Eaton Rd. CT9: Mgte 3G **7**
Ebbsfleet La. CT12: Ram 4C **30**
Eddie Willett Rd. CT6: H Bay 2H **13**
EDDINGTON 3D **14**
Eddington Bus. Pk. CT6: H Bay 4D **14**
Eddington La. CT6: H Bay 4B **14**
Eddington Way CT6: H Bay 4C **14**
Edenbridge Ho. CT1: Cant 2H **39**
Eden Ct. CT6: H Bay 3B **14**
Edenfield CT7: Birch 6F **5**
Eden Rd. CT5: Seas 6C **10**
Edgar Cl. CT5: Whits 2D **12**
Edgar Rd. CT1: Cant 1H **39**
  CT9: Clift 2A **8**
  CT12: Minst 3F **29**
Edge End Rd. CT10: B'stairs 3F **25**
Edinburgh Rd. CT9: Mgte 5D **6**
Edinburgh Wlk. *CT9: Mgte* 5D **6**
  (off Edinburgh Rd.)
Edith Rd. CT8: Wgte S 4B **6**
  CT11: Ram 3C **32**
  ME13: Fav 5E **43**
Edmanson Av. CT9: Mgte 4C **6**
Edward Dr. CT7: Birch 6F **5**
  (Canterbury Rd.)
  CT7: Birch 6E **5**
  (Neame Rd.)
Edward Rd. CT1: Cant 2G **39**
Effingham St. CT11: Ram 3E **33**
Egbert Rd. CT8: Wgte S 4A **6**
  CT12: Minst 3F **29**
  ME13: Fav 5E **43**
Egdert Rd. CT7: Birch 5B **4**
Egerton Dr. CT9: Clift 3E **9**
Eider Cl. CT6: H Bay 5B **14**
Elbridge Hill CT3: Sturry 4H **37**
Elder Cotts. CT6: H Bay 4H **15**
Eldon Gro. CT11: Ram 3D **32**
Eldon Pl. CT10: B'stairs 3H **25**
Elfrida Cl. CT9: Mgte 5C **8**
Elgar Bretts Ct. CT1: Cant 3F **39**
Elgar Pl. CT11: Ram 1E **33**
Elham Cl. *CT9: Mgte* 4C **8**
  (off Lyminge Way)
Elham Rd. CT1: Cant 4E **39**
Elham Way CT10: B'stairs 5G **25**
Eliot College
  University of Kent at Canterbury . . .4E **35**
Elizabeth Ct. CT6: H Bay 2D **14**
  CT10: B'stairs 6H **9**
Elizabeth Kemp Ct. CT12: Ram 6C **24**
Elizabeth Rd. CT11: Ram 3F **33**
Elizabeth Way CT6: H Bay 4F **15**
Ellen Av. CT11: Ram 6E **25**
Ellenden Ct. CT2: Cant 4C **34**
Ellington Av. CT9: Mgte 5D **6**
Ellington Pl. CT11: Ram 2C **32**
Ellington Rd. CT11: Ram 2C **32**
Elliot Cl. CT1: Cant 5A **36**
Elliot Ct. CT6: H Bay 3G **15**

Elliotts Pl. ME13: Fav 4F **43**
Ellison Cl. CT5: Whits 4C **12**
Ellison Ct. ME13: Fav 5G **43**
Ellisons Wlk. *CT1: Cant* 2A **40**
  (off Nonsuch Cl.)
Ellis Rd. CT5: Whits 2A **12**
Ellis Way CT6: H Bay 5G **15**
Elm Ct. CT8: Wgte S 5A **6**
Elm Gro. CT2: Cant 5C **34**
  CT8: Wgte S 5H **5**
  CT12: Mans 6F **23**
Elmley Way CT9: Mgte 6H **7**
ELMS 2D **32**
Elms Av. CT11: Ram 2D **32**
Elmstone Gdns. CT9: Clift 3E **9**
Elmstone Rd. CT11: Ram 2D **32**
Elm Vs. CT2: Cant 6C **34**
Elmwood Av. CT10: B'stairs 5G **9**
Elm Wood Cl. CT5: Whits 3C **12**
Elmwood Cl. CT10: B'stairs 6F **9**
Elm Wood W. CT5: Whits 3C **12**
Emelina Way CT5: Whits 1D **26**
Emmerson Gdns. CT5: Whits 2C **12**
Empire Cinema 4B **44**
Empire Ter. CT9: Mgte 5G **7**
Ennerdale ME13: Fav 5G **43**
Enterprise Rd. CT9: Mgte 1H **23**
Enterprise Way CT9: Mgte 1H **23**
Enticott Cl. CT5: Whits 4A **12**
Epping Cl. CT6: H Bay 5F **15**
EPPLE 5F **5**
Epple Bay Av. CT7: Birch 5E **5**
Epple Bay Rd. CT7: Birch 5D **4**
Epple Cotts. CT7: Birch 5F **5**
Epple Rd. CT7: Birch 5F **5**
Ersham Rd. CT1: Cant 3G **39**
Eskdale Av. CT11: Ram 2A **32**
Esmonde Dr. CT12: Mans 5B **22**
Esplanade CT8: Wgte S 4G **5**
Essex Av. CT6: H Bay 1H **13**
Essex Gdns. CT7: Birch 1D **20**
Essex Rd. CT1: Cant 3B **40**
  CT8: Wgte S 5B **6**
Essex St. CT5: Whits 5F **11**
Estuary Cl. CT5: Whits 2E **13**
Ethelbert Cres. CT9: Clift 2A **8**
Ethelbert Gdns. CT9: Mgte 2H **7**
Ethelbert Rd. CT1: Cant 4G **39**
  CT7: Birch 5B **4**
  CT9: Mgte 2H **7**
  CT11: Ram 3D **32**
  ME13: Fav 5D **42**
Ethelbert Sq. CT8: Wgte S 4A **6**
Ethelbert Ter. CT8: Wgte S 4A **6**
  CT9: Mgte 2H **7**
Ethelred Ct. ME13: Fav 5E **43**
Ethelred Rd. CT8: Wgte S 4A **6**
Ethel Rd. CT10: B'stairs 2F **25**
Evelings All. *CT5: Whits* 3F **11**
  (off Middle Wall)
Everard Way ME13: Fav 3D **42**
Eversleigh Ri. CT5: Whits 6H **11**
Eynsford Cl. CT9: Clift 3F **9**

F

Fairacre CT10: B'stairs 3E **25**
Fairacres Cl. CT6: H Bay 3G **15**
Fairfax Dr. CT6: H Bay 2B **16**
FAIRFIELD 3D **24**
Fairfield Pk. CT10: B'stairs 3E **25**
Fairfield Rd. CT10: B'stairs 3E **25**
  CT11: Ram 5E **25**
  CT12: Minst 2F **29**
Fairlawn CT5: Whits 4D **12**
Fairlawn Rd. CT12: Ram 4B **24**
Fairlight Av. CT12: Ram 1B **32**
Fairoaks CT6: H Bay 3F **15**
Fair St. CT10: B'stairs 3E **25**
Fairview Cl. CT9: Mgte 3A **8**
Fairview Gdns. CT2: Sturry 2E **37**
Fairway Cres. CT5: Seas 6C **10**
Fairway, The CT6: H Bay 5B **14**
  ME13: Fav 5C **42**
Falala Way CT1: Cant 1H **39**
Farleigh Rd. CT2: Cant 5G **35**

Farley Rd. CT9: Mgte 6H **7**
Farm Ho. Cl. CT5: Whits 5H **11**
Farrar Rd. CT7: Birch 1E **21**
Farthings Ct. CT2: Cant 4C **34**
Faulkners La. CT2: Harb 2A **38**
FAVERSHAM .4F **43**
FAVERSHAM COTTAGE HOSPITAL 4E **43**
Faversham Ind. Est. ME13: Fav 4H **43**
Faversham Reach ME13: Fav 2F **43**
Faversham Rd. CT5: Seas 6A **10**
  ME13: Osp 5A **42**
Faversham Station (Rail) 5F **43**
Faversham Swimming Pool 4E **43**
Favourite Rd. CT5: Whits 1D **26**
Fellowship Wlk. CT13: S'wch 5B **44**
Fenoulhet Way CT6: H Bay 2E **15**
Fern Cl. CT5: Whits 4C **12**
Fern Ct. CT10: B'stairs 2H **25**
Ferndale Ct. CT7: Birch 1E **21**
Ferndown CT7: Birch 5B **4**
Fernlea Av. CT6: H Bay 3C **14**
Field Av. CT1: Cant 5B **36**
Fielding St. ME13: Fav 4E **43**
Field Vw. CT5: Whits 6D **10**
Field Way CT2: Sturry 3D **36**
Fiesta Wlk. CT1: Cant 3A **40**
Fife Rd. CT6: H Bay 3H **13**
Fifth Av. CT9: Clift 2B **8**
Fig Tree Rd. CT10: B'stairs 6F **9**
Finch Cl. ME13: Fav 5F **43**
Finches, The CT7: St N 5E **19**
Finlay Cl. ME13: Fav 4D **42**
Finsbury Ct. *CT11: Ram* 1E **33**
  (off Finsbury Rd.)
Finsbury Rd. CT11: Ram 1E **33**
Firbank Gdns. CT9: Mgte 6F **7**
Firbanks CT5: Whits 5H **11**
First Av. CT9: Clift 2B **8**
  CT10: B'stairs 3F **9**
Fir Tree Cl. CT11: Ram 3C **32**
Firtree Cl. CT2: R Comn 5A **34**
Fisher Rd. CT2: Cant 1D **38**
Fisher St. CT13: S'wch 4C **44**
Fishermans Wharf CT5: Whits 3G **11**
  (off Diamond Rd.)
Fitzgerald Av. CT6: H Bay 4A **14**
Fitzmary Av. CT9: Mgte 4C **6**
Fitzroy Av. CT9: Mgte 4B **8**
  CT10: B'stairs 3F **9**
  CT12: Ram 5B **24**
Fitzroy Rd. CT5: Whits 2H **11**
Flagstaff Ct. CT1: Cant 3G **39**
Flamingo Dr. CT6: H Bay 5C **14**
Fleets La. CT2: T Hill 1D **34**
Fleetwood Av. CT6: H Bay 3B **14**
Fletcher Rd. CT5: Whits 4B **12**
FLETE 2F **23**
Flete Rd. CT9: Mgte 3F **23**
Fleur de Lis Heritage Cen. 4F **43**
  (off Preston St.)
Flex Appeal 2H **11**
Flood La. ME13: Fav 3E **43**
  (not continuous)
Flora Rd. CT11: Ram 1E **33**
Florence Av. CT5: Whits 6C **10**
Florence Ct. CT9: Clift 2B **8**
Florence Rd. CT11: Ram 3D **32**
Foads Hill CT12: C'snd 3F **31**
Foads La. CT12: C'snd 5F **31**
Fodbury Ct. *CT8: Wgte S* 4A **6**
  (off Ethelbert Sq.)
Forbes Rd. ME13: Fav 5E **43**
FORD 6A **16**
Ford Cl. CT6: H Bay 1G **13**
Ford Hills CT3: Hoath, H Bay 6A **16**
  CT6: H Bay 5B **16**
Fordoun Rd. CT10: B'stairs 2F **25**
Ford Wlk. CT5: Seas 4C **26**
FORDWICH 4E **37**
Fordwich Gro. CT10: B'stairs 6E **9**
Fordwich Pl. CT13: S'wch 5B **44**
Fordwich Rd. CT2: Cant 3D **36**
Fordwich Town Hall 4E **37**
Foreland Av. CT9: Mgte 3D **8**
Foreland Ct. CT11: Ram 4D **32**
Foreland Hgts. CT10: B'stairs 6H **9**
Foreland Pk. Ho. CT10: B'stairs 6H **9**

M

R

S

The representation on the maps of a road, track or footpath is no evidence of the existence of a right of way.

Editor:
Richard West

Advertisement Manager:
Lawrence Brown

Advertising Executive:
Ellie Lawson

Production Assistant:
Gina Mitchell

A Link House annual published by IPC Country & Leisure Media Ltd (part of the IPC Group of companies) from:
Link House, Dingwall Avenue, Croydon CR9 2TA.
Tel: 020 8686 2599
Fax: 020 8781 6044

Distributed by:
MarketForce,
247 Tottenham Court Road,
London W1P 0AU.
Tel: 020 7261 5555

Pre-press by CK Litho; printed by Millennium Offset Ltd

© IPC
Magazines Ltd
1999 All Rights reserved

ISBN 0-86296-174-2

BRITISH COINS MARKET VALUES

CONTENTS

The Millennium Crown from the Royal Mint, featured on the front cover

Market Trends

COIN collecting in the United Kingdom is as popular as ever, we can again report. There are new faces at the coin shows up and down the country and the leading numismatic societies and clubs are also attracting a number of new members. We also have the attractive and well produced monthly magazine, *Coin News*, supporting this renaissance, and seemingly selling very well. Sadly the recent arrival *Coins and Antiquities* has announced it has ceased publication.

The coin auction scene this year has been dominated by two highly important sales. First, the wonderful King George III collection of Herman Selig sold by Spink (on March 2, 1999), and then the Larry Stack collection, a superb accumulation, of Celtic, Anglo-Saxon and English Hammered coins sold by Sotheby's (on April 22 and 23, 1999). It was good to see that Mr Stack, one of the famous New York numismatic family, chose to sell these coins in London rather than New York. We will return to both these auctions later.

We can see that the demand for coins will continue to strengthen into the new Millennium and, with that in mind, we will take a look at the current situation in each of the areas of collecting covered by COINS M<ARKET VALUES. We should remind you that COINS MARKET VALUES remains the only one volume annual price guide which deals with all the coins of England, Scotland, Ireland and the Channel Islands.

Celtic Coinage

The demand for good quality coins is growing at a pace and this is reflected by the fact that even secondhand copies of Robert Van Ardsell's large tome on the subject (which surprised

everyone and sold out some time ago) are much sought after.

Undoubtedly the Stack sale at Sotheby's was the highlight of the year, for that part of the auction was the most keenly contested. For example: a Tincomarus gold quarter stater (VA 378-1) realised £2,100; a Verica gold quarter stater (VA 525-1) £3,300; an Eppilus gold quarter stater £1,050; and an Addedomaros gold quarter stater for £780. But there were many highlights; the superb illustrated catalogue produced by Sotheby's will become a yardstick for prices for quite a while. We urge you to obtain a copy — it will become a collector's item in years to come.

English Hammered Gold

There is a definite growth of interest in

Four gold quarter staters in the Stacks sale at Sotheby's. The prices realised were:
TINCOMARUS £2,100;
Verica £3,300; Eppillus £1,050;
ADDEDOMAROS £780.

Six superb pennies of Edward the Elder in the Stack sale at Sotheby's. Prices realised (top to bottom, left to right): £3,600; £3,600; £2,700; £5,000; £3,4000; £3,600.

this area in the United Kingdom, but there is even increased demand within Europe in general which is more surprising. In our opinion this is due to the impact made by Volume 1 of Herbert Schneider's collection (dealing with coins from 1257 to 1603). The fact that the next volume (due out before the end of the year) deals with coins from 1603 and the milled series, is likely only to heighten the situation.

Milled Gold
Where have all the good coins gone? There seems to be so little available now in dealers' trays, and, when anything good turns up at auction, prices are very strong. In fact, we have made more changes to the prices in this section of COINS MARKET VALUES than for many a year.

At auction, the sale of Herman Selig's stunning collection of coins of King George III was the absolute highlight. The coin on the cover of the catalogue, an 1817 pattern crown by William Wyon, struck in gold and with the 'Three Graces' on the reverse, sold for £170,000, against an estimate of £40,000 to £50,000.

Hammered Silver

Prices are holding up well in general, although some early Anglo-Saxon pennies are currently a little soft, one might say.

Again, the Stack's auction at Sotheby's represents the highlight of the season. In the sale there was a particularly attractive group of pennies of Edward the Elder, featuring floral and architectural types, which fetched strong prices.

Milled Silver
There are more collectors for this area in the United Kingdom, and around the world, than for any other of our domestic series and it has been consistently stable. There is always a demand for top quality material, and dealers in the know, both in the United Kingdom and in the United States, can place choice coins instantly. Again this year there are many changes in the price columns in COINS MARKET VALUES. It is worth noting that we receive more correspondence about this section than any other.

Copper and Bronze
Each year we make the same comments about the lack of good material and so it continues. This used to be one of the hottest areas of collecting during the change-checking boom of the 1960s, and a number of important collections were formed at that time. In fact, those were the days when Seaby's used to produce a separate catalogue of British Copper Coins and their values, such was the demand.

There is no doubt that copper and

From Sotheby's auction of the Stack collection, Scottish penny of David I sold for £3,600, while a Bamburgh penny of Henry of Northumberland sold for £6,000.

*Hiberno-Norse pennies sold at Spink
(Stack collection):
Phase I - £1,150; Phase V - £1,700.*

bronze need to be very carefully
stored, otherwise they can deteriorate
(see the section of 'Keeping Your
Coins'), but is that the reason for the
decrease in the numbers of collectors
interested? Whatever, it is still a wonderful area to collect.

Just take a look at the marvellous
half pennies and farthings of Charles II,
or the farthings of Anne and George I,
the cartwheel pennies of King George
III and the copper pennies of Queen
Victoria — if you need convincing!

We suggest an investment
in a secondhand copy of

Peck's superb British Museum catalogue of copper, tin and bronze coins
(a plea to the British Museum to
reprint it, with a good colour plate),
and a whole new world will open up.

Scottish coins

The demand for Scottish material continues unabated. This has been going
on for the last few years and probably
reflects the political position there,
since the fresh interest is happily
mainly coming from within Scotland.
In the past, many of the prominent collections were in England and even the
United States of America. However
you will find few dealers have much in
the way of stock at present.

Again, a couple of prices at the
Stack auction at Sotheby's caught the
eye: a David I penny (lot 679) realised
£3,600, while a Bamburgh penny of
Henry of Northumberland (lot 680)
realised a staggering
£6,000.

*Front covers from two of
the major sales of the past
year, and of two
magazines in the United
Kingdom, although sadly
'Coins and Antiquities' has
ceased publication.*

Irish coins

Once again it is noticeable that there is a number of new collectors in the market and slowly but surely things are returning to what they were in the 1970s. That was the peak of the market when the numismatic scene in Ireland was at its liveliest.

Nowadays the annual coin fairs and Whyte's auctions in particular have become the focal point for a new revival of interest within Ireland. There has always been a certain demand for Irish material from North America, for example, but it is only when there is firm support from within Ireland that things really take off. Now that the Irish economy is so strong, it has had an uplifting effect on coin collecting.

In particular, there is keen demand for Hiberno-Norse at present, and prices at the Stack sale at Sotheby's showed this dramatically.

Incidentally, as with Scottish and Anglo-Gallic coins, COINS MARKET VALUES offers you the only up-to-date annual guide to prices (the last Seaby catalogue on the subject was published in 1984).

Anglo-Gallic coins

The demand for Anglo-Gallic coins continues to be small but enthusiastic. It appears that there is a small number of keen aficionados spread thinly around the world. Prices can be quite strong when a rarely offered piece comes on the market, but there is in-depth support to buy numbers of these pieces. It is worth noting that collectors of purely English hammered coins like to have one example of Edward the Black Prince in the collection, as well as a denier of Richard the Lionheart, because they read 'RICAR-DUS' while his English coins have the name of his father.

The peak of the market remains the sale of the Elias collection in 1990, and all newcomers to the series must obtain the catalogue which is still available.

How to Collect

A few words of advice for those who have recently discovered coin collecting.

How much is it worth?

There was a time when newcomers to coin collecting would ask the question 'What is it?'. Nowadays certainly the most common question dealers hear 'What is it worth?'. It is a sign of the times that history takes second place to value. The object of COINS MARKET VALUES is to try to place a value on all the coins produced in what is known geographically as the British Isles, in other words England, Wales, Scotland and Ireland, and the Channel Islands, as well as the Anglo-Gallic series.

This is a difficult task because many coins do not turn up in auctions or lists every year even though they are not really rare. However, we make a stab at a figure so that you the collector can at least have an idea of what you will have to pay.

How to sell your coins
Auction

In England we are well served with a number of auction houses, giving the potential seller considerable choice. In

Price lists and auction catalogues will prove invaluable.

London alone we have, in alphabetical order, Baldwins, Bonhams, Dix Noonan Webb, Glendinings, Sothebys, Spink and Vecchi; while there are smaller companies up and down the country, such as Croydon Coin Auctions. In Ireland Whyte's of Dublin hold the pole position.

The best approach for the seller is first of all to compare all their catalogues and if possible attend the auctions so that you can see how well they are conducted. Talk it over with their experts, for you may have special cataloguing requirements and you could find that one of the firms might look after them better than the others.

An obvious coin, like say an 1887 £5, requires little expertise and will probably sell at a certain price in almost any auction; however, if you require expert cataloguing of counter-marked coins or early medieval, then you need to know what the company is capable of before you discuss a rate for the job.

You should remember though that while it is not complicated to sell by auction you may have to wait at least three or four months from the time

you consign the coins to the auctioneers before you receive any money. There are times when auctions manage to achieve very high prices, and other times when, for some inexplicable reason, they fail to reach even a modest reserve.

You should also bear in mind that the best deal in the long term is not always the lowest commission rate. Finally, auctioneers will usually charge you at least 10 per cent of the knock-down price, and you should remember that some buyers may also be inhibited from paying a top price by a buyer's premium, also of 10 per cent (indeed, some firms are now charging 15%).

Dealers

The function of a dealer is to have a stock of coins for sale at marked prices. However, they will naturally only wish to buy according to the ebb and flow of their stocks. It is also true to say that dealers infinitely prefer fresh material, and if you strike at the right time it is possible that you could achieve a better price than by waiting for auction, since of course you will receive the money immediately. Generally speaking, both dealers and auctioneers will not make any charge for a verbal valuation, but you should allow for the dealer to be making a profit of at least 20 per cent.

Bullion coins
Relating to Kruggerands, sovereigns, and so on, most newspapers carry the price of gold, which is fixed twice daily by a group of leading banks. Anyone can buy sovereigns, and Krugerrands and other bullion coins, and it is better these days now that there is no VAT on top. Normally, when you sell the bullion coin you expect the coin dealer to make a few pounds profit on each coin, but don't expect a good price for a mounted coin attached to grandfather's watch chain, which will not be worth anything like the same price as an undamaged item.

How to collect coins
You should obviously purchase your coins only from a reputable dealer. How can you decide on a reputable dealer? You can be sure of some protection if you choose one who is a member of the British Numismatic Trade Association or the International Association of Professional Numismatists. Membership lists of these organisations can be obtained from the respective secretaries: Mrs Carol Carter, PO Box 474A, Thames Ditton, Surrey KT7 0WJ (tel: 0181 398 4290; fax: 0181 398 4291) and Jean-Luc Van Der Schueren, 14 Rue de la Bourse, B 1000 Brussels.

However, many dealers are not members of either organisation, and it does not mean that they are not honest and professional. The best approach is simply to find one who will unconditionally guarantee that the coins you buy from him are genuine and accurately graded.

As a general rule you should only buy coins in the best condition available, and on this subject you will at first have to rely on the judgement of the dealer you choose. However, remember it will not always possible to find pieces in Extremely Fine condition, for example, and it can sometimes be worth buying coins which are not quite Very Fine.

In the case of great rarities, of course, you might well have to make do with a coin that is only Fine, or even Poor. If there are only six known specimens of a particular piece, and four are in museums, it seems pointless to wait for 20 years for another

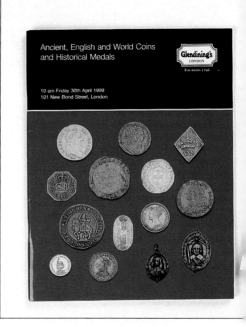

one to be found in the ground. Over the last few years condition has become too important in many ways, and has driven away collectors, because obviously you cannot buy coins only in top condition, since in certain series that would rule out at least 50 per cent of the available specimens. It depends on the type of coin, the reign and so on, so be realistic.

It is worth taking out subscriptions with auction houses so that you can receive copies of all their catalogues, because this is an excellent way to keep up with prices as well as the collections that are being offered.

However, one should not overlook the fact that a number of dealers produce price lists, which in many ways are most useful to the collector, because coins can then be chosen at leisure by mail order. It is also easier to work out what can be afforded to buy than when in the hot-house atmosphere of the auction room.

The most famous list is Spink's

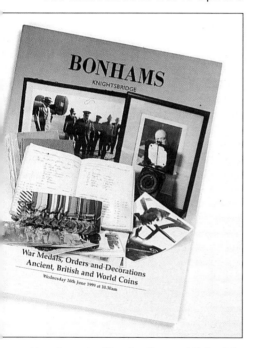

Numismatic Circular first published in 1892, and still going strong with ten issues a year. It is more than a price list being an important forum for numismatic debate and the reporting of new finds, etc (annual subscription £15).

There are also many expert dealers who produce excellent lists; many of them advertise in this publication and obviously we cannot mention them all here, but a good cross section of those who list domestic coins, and not listed

in any order of preference, is as follows:

Lloyd Bennett, PO Box 2, Monmouth, Gwent NP5 3YE. Hammered, Milled, Tokens.

B. J. Dawson, 52 St Helens Road, Bolton, Lancashire BL3 3NH. Hammered, Milled, Tokens, Medals.

Dolphin Coins, 2c Englands Lane, Hampstead, London NW3 4TG. All British.

Patrick Finn, PO Box 26, Kendal, Cumbria LA9 7AB. Hammered English, Irish, Scottish.

Format, 18 and 19 Bennetts Hill, Birmingham B2 5QJ. All British.

Grantham Coins, PO Box 60, Grantham, Lincolnshire. Milled, good on Maundy.

K. B. Coins, 50 Lingfield Road, Martins Wood, Stevenage, Hertfordshire SG1 5SL. Hammered and Milled.

C. J. Martin, 85 The Vale, Southgate, London N14 6AT. Celtic and Hammered.

Peter Morris, PO Box 223, Bromley, Kent BR1 4EQ. Hammered, Milled, Tokens.

S. R. Porter, 18 Trinity Road, Headington Quarry, Oxford OX3 8QL. Milled and Hammered.

Chris Rudd, PO Box 222, Aylsham, Norfolk NR11 6TY. The only specialist dealer in Celtic Coins.

Seaby Coins, 14 Old Bond Street, London W1X 4JL. Hammered, some Milled.

Simmons & Simmons, PO Box 104, Leytonstone, London E11 1ND.

Also don't forget there are specialist dealers who do not produce lists, for example, Chelsea Coins (Dimitri Loulakakis, 0181 879 5501) who, although a prominent dealer in European and world coins, is also the man for Maundy money.

Societies

You should consider joining your local numismatic society, there being quite a number of these throughout the country. To find if there is one near you, contact the British Association of Numismatic Societies, Mr P. H. Mernick, c/o Bush, Boake, Allen Ltd, Blackhorse Lane, London E17 5QP (tel: 0181 523 6531). The BANS organises annual congresses and seminars, and it is a good idea for the serious collector to consider attending one of these. Details are usually well publicised in the numismatic press.

Those collectors who wish to go a little further can apply for membership of the British Numismatic Society, and for their annual membership fee they will receive a copy of the *British Numismatic Journal* which incorporates details of current research and many important articles, as well as book reviews.

Another useful facet of membership of this society is that you can borrow books from its library in the Warburg Institute. The secretary of the British Numismatic Society is C. R. S.

Farthing, 10 Greenbanks Gardens, Wallington, Fareham, Hants PO16 8SF.

Londoners might like to consider joining the London Numismatic Club, which is the best society after the Royal and the British, and is always looking for new members. Newcomers will be sure of a very friendly reception. The secretary is Robert Hatch, c/o P. Rueff, 2 King's Bench Walk, The Temple, London EC4Y 7DE.

Coin Fairs

Whilst it is always important to visit museums to see coins, it is worth remembering that there is often a fine array on show at coin fairs around the country, and most dealers do not mind showing coins to would-be collectors, even if they cannot afford to buy them on the spot.

The BNTA have been very successful with the COINEX shows, and the annual event at the Marriott Hotel should not be missed (October 9 and 10, 1998). Likewise COINEX North held each Spring (in 2000 in Harrogate: for further details contact BNTA Secretary 0181 398 4290).

Howard and Frances Simmons are the popular organisers of the Cumberland Coin shows, held at the Cumberland Hotel, London, since the late 1960s (for details ring 0171 831 2080).

The Croydon team of Davidson/Monk organise the monthly shows at the Commonwealth Institute, Kensington, London W8 (ring 0181 656 4583).

David Fletcher organises the monthly Midland Coin and Stamp Fair, second Sunday every month (enquiries 01203 716160).

There are also fairs held at York racecourse in January and August. For information ring 01268 726687.

Finally for details of the successful Irish coin shows in Dublin ring Peter Sheen (003531 496 4390); and for the annual shows in conjunction with the Irish Numismatic Society ring Ian Whyte (003531 874 6161).

Keeping your Coins

ONCE you have started to collect coins make sure you know how to look after them properly.

Storage

Careful thought should be given to the storing of coins, for a collection which is carelessly or inadequately housed can suffer irreparable damage. Corrosion depends essentially on the presence of water vapour, and therefore coins should not be stored in damp attics or spare bedrooms, but where possible in evenly heated warm rooms.

We should also point out here that one must be very careful only to pick up coins by the edges, for sweaty finger prints contain corrosive salt. The following are suitable methods of storage.

Wooden cabinets

A collection carefully laid out in a wood cabinet is seen at its most impressive. Unfortunately, though, the modern wooden cabinets which are custom built especially for coins are not cheap. Their main advantages are the choice of tray and hole sizes, and the fact that because the manufacturer is often himself a collector, he takes

Coins cabinet produced by Peter Nichols of St Leonards-on-Sea.

Cabinet supplied by Collectors Gallery of Shrewsbury.

care to use only well matured woods, which have no adverse reactions on coins.

Among the makers of wood cabinets are H.S. Swann, of Newcastle (tel: 01661 853129) and Peter Nichols of St. Leonards, East Sussex (tel: 01424 436682).

If one cannot afford a new cabinet, then a second-hand version may be the answer. These can sometimes be purchased at coin auctions, or from dealers, and can be very good value. However, it is not always easy to find one with the tray hole sizes to suit your coins.

Do-it-yourself cabinet makers should also be careful not to use new wood, which will contain corrosive moisture. In this case the best method would be to use wood from an old piece of furniture.

Albums, plastic cases and carrying cases

There are many of these on the market, and some of them are both handsome and inexpensive. There are also

Coin boxes produced by Lindner.

very attractive Italian and German-made attaché type carrying cases for collectors, with velvet lining and different sizes of trays, and so on. These can be obtained from a number of dealers, but Collectors Gallery, 6-7 Castle Gates, Shrewsbury SY1 2AE (tel: 01743 272140) makes a speciality of them.

We would also recommend the coin album, which claims to prevent oxidization. The coins are contained in cards with crystal clear film windows enabling the collector to see both sides of the coins. The cards then slide into pages in an album, and might be a convenient method of storage, especially for the new collector.

Coins International of 1-2 Melbourne Street, Leeds LS2 7PS (tel: 0113 2468855) also offer a large range of albums, envelopes, plastic boxes and capsules, etc.

Lindner Publications Ltd, 26 Queen Street, Cubbington, Leamington Spa CV32 7NA (tel: 01296 425026) supply very useful coin and collecting boxes as well as albums.

In central London, probably the best place to visit is Vera Trinder, 38 Bedford Street, London WC2 (tel: 0171 836 2365/6) who does appear to keep a very good stock. Stanley Gibbons, 399 Strand, London WC2 (tel: 0800 611622) also produce large size coin albums. Phone them for a free brochure.

Envelopes
Plastic envelopes, being transparent, are very useful for exhibition, but we never recommend them for long-term storage purposes. They tend to make the coins 'sweat', which with copper and bronze in particular can lead to corrosion.

Manilla envelopes are much more suitable, since the paper is dry, unlike ordinary paper, and consequently they

are ideal for the storage of coins. Most collectors use them in conjunction with a cardboard box, which makes for simple unobtrusive storage. This is

Coin case from Lindner.

the most inexpensive method of storing coins.

Still the best article we have seen on the storage of coins and medals, which deals with all the materials which are used, was by Mr L. R. Green, who is Higher Conservation Officer at the Department of Coins and Medals at the British Museum. This appeared in the May 1991 issue of *Spink's Numismatic Circular*.

Magnifiers
New collectors will need to have a good magnifying glass to examine coins, and these can be obtained from W. H. Smith or most other stationers; many opticians also offer very good magnifying glasses.

There is now also an excellent and inexpensive binocular microscope on the market, manufactured in the USA and available for less than £200 from Allan Davison of Cold Spring, MN (fax: 001 320 685 8636).

Cleaning coins

In the course of each week dealers examine many coins which some poor unfortunates have unwittingly totally ruined by cleaning. They are, therefore, usually the best people to ask about the subject.

One dealer tells of a bright-eyed expectant gentleman who offered his late father's very useful collection of copper coins, which he proudly said he had 'brightened up' the previous day, so as to be certain of a good offer. The dealer did not enjoy his customer's sad disappointment when he found himself unable to make any offers, but then the coins had been cleaned with harsh metal polish and looked like soldiers' buttons.

We always advise people never to clean coins unless they are very dirty or corroded. Also by 'dirt' we do not mean oxide which, on silver coins, can give a pleasing bluish tone favoured by many collectors.

The following simple instructions may be of some help, but do not, of course, apply to extremely corroded coins which have been found in the ground, for if important they are the province of a museum conservationist.

Gold coins

Gold should cause collectors few problems, since it is subject to corrosion only in extreme conditions. For example, a gold coin recovered from a long spell in the sea might have a dull, rusty appearance. However, in the normal course of events a little bath in methylated spirits will improve a dirty gold coin. A word of warning, gold coins should not be rubbed in any way.

Silver coins

Silver will discolour easily, and is particularly susceptible to damp or chemicals in the atmosphere. A gentle brushing with a soft non-nylon bristle brush will clear loose surface dirt, but if the dirt is deep and greasy, a dip in ammonia and careful drying on cotton wool should do the trick. We should once again stress that there is no need to clean a coin which simply has a darkish tone.

Copper and bronze coins

There is no safe method of cleaning copper or bronze coins without actually harming them, and we would only recommend the use of a non-nylon, pure bristle brush to deal with dirt.

There is no way of curing the ailments peculiar to these metals, namely verdigris (green spots) or bronze disease (blackish spots) permanently, and we would advise collectors not to buy pieces in such condition, unless they are very inexpensive.

Museums

ONE of the best places to see and admire coins is in museums. Many have coin collection, but here are the museums which keep the major collections.

London
The British Museum.
The HSBC Money Gallery illustrates the development, management and production of the coins, banknotes and electronic money in use today. The display ranges over an enormous number of coins and other objects which have been used as money over the last four and a half thousand years. There are 19 specially designed cases displaying many choice pieces, beautifully presented and making the best use of modern lighting techniques.

The Keeper of Coins is:
Dr Andrew Burnett,
British Museum,
Great Russell Street,
London WC1B 3DG.
Tel: 0171 636 1555
Fax: 0171 323 8171
E-mail: coins@british-museum.ac.uk

Some of the attractive showcases in the exhibition at Cardiff (copyright: National Museum of Wales).

A superb £20 piece of 1576 in the National Museum of Scotland (copyright: National Museums, Scotland).

Edinburgh
National Museums of Scotland.
The National Museums house the premier collection of Scottish coins and tokens, but also possess significant collections of English, British, ancient and foreign material. The Scottish coins include the Coats collection, on which Edward Burns based his three-volume standard work, *The Coinage of Scotland.*

Many coins of all periods and of types made or used in Scotland are included in various thematic displays in the Museum of Scotland, opened in 1998.

There is currently no numismatic exhibition in the adjoining Royal Museum, but anyone wishing to view or study specific coins or series is welcome to visit the Coin Room by appointment.

The Curator of Numismatics is:
Mr Nick Holmes,
Royal Museum,
Chambers Street,
Edinburgh, EH1 1JF.
Tel: 0131 247 4061
E-mail: nmmh@nms.ac.uk

Glasgow
Hunterian Museum.
A new permanent gallery devoted to numismatics has

been opened at the Hunterian Museum. It is situated in an upstairs mezzanine gallery off the main hall and features over 2,000 items.

The Hunter Coin Cabinet contains the important 18th century collection of the eminent Scot and royal physician Dr William Hunter, and in the new gallery there are many of the choice specimens from this collection.

The curator of coins is:

Dr Donal Bateson,
Hunterian Museum,
University of Glasgow,
Glasgow, G12 8QQ.
Tel: 0141 339 8855

Cardiff
National Museum and Gallery.

There is an excellent general exhibition of coins, medals, decorations and tokens in the National Museum and Gallery, Cardiff. The displays include many superb and rare pieces, presented with excellent lighting in good showcases. The Tregwynt (Pembs) Civil War hoard of gold and silver coins, found in 1996, provides a spectacular centrepiece.

The exhibition is supported by an entertaining guide by Edward Besly entitled Loose Change, a guide to common coins and medals.

The assistant keeper in charge of coins is:

A view of the new display area at the Ashmolean (reproduced with permission of the Ashmolean Museum).

The famous Charles I Oxford crown showing a view of the city. One of the important pieces at the Ashmolean (reproduced with permission of the Ashmolean Museum).

Mr E. M. Besly,
Department of Archaeology and Numismatics,
National Museum and Gallery,
Cathays Park,
Cardiff, CF10 3NP.
Tel: 02920 573291
E-mail: Eward.Besly@nmgw.ac.uk

Birmingham
Birmingham Museum and Art Gallery

Birmingham Museum has one of the largest regional coin collections in England. Although it is very diverse there are important groups of British Celtic, Saxon/Norman and Medieval coins. The collection is also particularly noteworthy for the products of local mints such as Matthew Boulton's Soho and its successors, including today's Birmingham Mint. There is also a fine collection of commemorative medals.

At present there are no numismatic displays on show, but a new gallery is planned as part of a major re-display programme. A temporary exhibition, 'Money', will run from July 2000 to September 2000.

The curator of coins is:

David Symons,
Birmingham Museum and Art Gallery,
Chamberlain Square,
Birmingham B3 3DH.
Tel: 0121 303 4201

Cambridge
The Fitzwilliam Museum.

The Fitzwilliam in Cambridge houses the famous Grierson col-

*The Numismatics Gallery in the Ulster Museum
(reproduced with the permission of the Trustees).*

lection of European Medieval Coins currently being catalogued in a series of 13 volumes (Volume 1, now available, consists of 674 pages and 65 plates - so you can appreciate the magnitude of the task).

In recent years the Museum has acquired the important collection of Christopher Blunt, which will also be published in due course. There is also a very good exhibition.

The curator of coins is:
Dr Mark Blackburn,
Fitzwilliam Museum,
Trumpinton Street,
Cambridge, CB2 1RB.
Tel: 01223 332900

Oxford
The Ashmolean Museum.
The Ashmolean Museum contains the oldest public collection in Great Britain; it was designed to serve the purposes of teaching. It is a very large and all embracing collection and like Cambridge, very important for serious students.

The curator is
Nick Mayhew,
The Ashmolean Museum,
Heberden Coin Room,
University of Oxford,
Oxford, OX1 2PH.
Tel: 01865 278058

York
Yorkshire Museum
The Yorkshire Museum holds one of the most important coin collections in the United Kingdom, being particularly strong in the fields of Roman coinage, Northumbrian stycas, English hammered silver and trade tokens. Hoards and single finds from Yorkshire are particularly well represented.

Many of the finest coins in the collection are featured in bright, modern displays, and the museum also stages regular temporary exhibitions of coins and medals.

The Keeper of Numismatics is:
Craig Barclay,
Yorkshire Museum,
Museum Gardens,
York YO1 7FR.
Tel: 01904 629745
E-mail: craig.barclay@york.gov.uk

Belfast
Ulster Museum.
The Ulster Museum has some very interesting display techniques and certainly makes the most of a relatively small collection. The museum acquired many of its important Irish pieces from the Carlyon-Britton collection and the enthusiastic directorship of Bill Seaby in the 1970s put it on the map numismatically.

The curator of coins is:
Mr Robert Heslip,
Ulster Museum,
Botanic Gardens,
Belfast,
Northern Ireland,
BT9 5AB.
Tel: 01232 381251

Dublin
National Museum of Ireland.
The National Museum has the most important collection of Irish coins and houses the former collection of the Royal Irish Academy. The museum is

currently undergoing reorganisation and there is now a small exhibition at Collins Barracks in Benburb Street; however coins can also be seen if an appointment is made.

The curator of coins is:
Mr Michael Kenny,
National Museum of Ireland,
Kildare Street,
Dublin 2,
Eire.
Tel: 003531 6618811

Other important museums

There are many other museums up and down the country which have excellent collections of British coins. The following are well worth a visit:

Blackburn Museum, Museum Street, **Blackburn**, Lancashire (01254 867170) has a good reputation for numismatics.

City Museum, Queen's Road, **Bristol** BS8 1RL (01179 223571). Especially good on coins of the Bristol mint.

Royal Albert Memorial Museum, Queen Street, **Exeter** EX4 3RX (01392 265858) has a very good collection of Exeter mint coins.

Manx Museum, Douglas, Isle of Man (01624 675522). Particularly excellent for students of Viking and Hiberno-Norse.

A view of the Yorkshire Museum.

City Museum, Municipal Buildings, The Headrow, **Leed**s, West Yorkshire (01132 478279). An excellent all round collection.

Manchester Museum, The University, **Manchester** M13 (0161 275634). Another excellent all round collection.

Reading Museum and Art Gallery, Blagrave Street, **Reading**, Berkshire (01735 399809). Good medieval and interesting local finds.

Many of our museums have co-operated with the British Academy to produce a wonderful series of books under the heading of *Sylloge of coins of the British Isles* which now runs to 50 volumes. Some of these volumes refer to coins held in Museums overseas, but we list here the ones which deal with coins in these islands, and this will give students a better idea of some of the material they have for study.

1. Fitzwilliam Museum, Cambridge. Ancient British and Anglo-Saxon Coins by P. Grierson.
2. Hunterian Museum, Glasgow. Anglo-Saxon Coins, by A.S. Robertson.
5. Grosvenor Museum, Chester. Coins with the Chester Mint-Signature, by E.J.E. Pirie.
6. National Museum of Antiquities of Scotland, Edinburgh. Anglo-Saxon Coins, by R.B.K. Stevenson.
8. British Museum. Hiberno-Norse Coins, by R.H.M. Dolley.
9. Ashmolean Museum, Oxford, Part I, Anglo-Irish Coins, John-Edward III, by M. Dolley and W. Seaby.
10. Ulster Museum. Belfast. Part I, Anglo-Irish Coins, John Edward III by M. Dolley and W. Seaby.
11. Reading University, Anglo-Saxon and Norman Coins, by C.E. Blunt and M. Dolley.
12. Ashmolean Museum, Oxford, Part II. English Coins

1066-1279, by D.M. Metcalf.
17. Midland Museums, Ancient British Coins, and Coins of the British and Gloucestershire Mints, by L.V. Grinsell, C.E. Blunt and M. Dolley.
21. Yorkshire Collections. Coins from Northumbrian Mints c.895-1279; Ancient British and Later Coins from other Mints to 1279, by E.J.E.Pirie.
23. Ashmolean Museum, Oxford, Part III. Coins of Henry VII, by D.M. Metcalf.
24. West Country Museums. Ancient British, Anglo-Saxon and Anglo-Norman Coins, by A.J.H. Gunstone.
26. Museums in East Anglia. Morley St Peter Hoard, and Anglo-Saxon, Norman and Angevin Coins, and Later

Medal of Matthew Boulton (courtesy of Birmingham Museum and Art Gallery).

Coins of the Norwich Mint by T.H. McK. Clough.
27. Lincolnshire Collections. Coins from Lincolnshire Mints and Ancient British and Later Coins to 1272, by A.J.H. Gunstone.
29. Mersey Country Museums. Ancient British and Later Coins to 1279, by M. Warhurst.
32. Ulster Museum, Belfast, Part II. Hiberno-Norse Coins, by W. Seaby.
34. British Museum, Anglo-Saxon Coins, Part V. Athelstan to Edgar's Reform, by M.M. Archibald and C.E. Blunt.
35. Ashmolean and Hunterian Museums. Scottish Coins, by J.D. Bateson and N.J. Mayhew.
42. South-Eastern Museums. Ancient British, Anglo-Saxon and Later Coins to 1279, by A.J.H. Gunstone, with V. Smart and others.
43. Thompson, R.H. and Dickinson, M. Part 3. Hampshire to Lincolnshire. 1992. liv, 216(2) including 51 plates with descriptive text (Sylloge of Coins of the British Isles. Volume 43.) Cloth. £25.
* - - Part 4. Norfolk to Somerset. 1993. Including 50 plates, with text. Cloth. In preparation. Prices to be announced.
44. Stockholm Part V. Forthcoming.
46. Tokens 1575-1750. Part V. Staffordshire to Westmorland by R.H. Thompson and M.J. Dickinson.
47. Schneider Collection. Part 1. English Gold Coins 1257-1603 by Peter Woodhead.
48. Northern Museums - Ancient British, Anglo-Saxon, Norman and Plantagenet Coins to 1279 by J. Booth. 1997.

Useful Books

HERE is a small selection of books dealing with the coins that are covered in COINS MARKET VALUES. Books are the tools of the trade and an investment in a small library will be money well spent. The more you can teach yourself the better.

We have included the prices you can expect to pay, but since some of the books are long out of print they can only be obtained second-hand (indicated in the list by SH).

Bateson, J.D. *Coinage in Scotland*. 1997. 175pp. and well illustrated. £20. The most up to date narrative account of the coins, and the only currently in print.

Bateson, J.D. *Scottish Coins*. 1987. Shire Publications no.189. 32pp. and illustrated. £2. A useful little 'taster' to the subject. The Shire Publications are always good value.

Besly, E. *Coins and Medals of the English Civil War*. 1990. 121pp. and beautifully illustrated. (SH)

Besly, E. *Loose Change, a guide to common coins and medals*. Cardiff 1997. 57pp, beautifully illustrated. £6.95.

Blunt, C.E. Stewart, B.H.I.H., Lyon, C.S.S. *Coinage in Tenth Century England*. 1989. 372pp. 27 plates. £60.

Byatt, D. *Promises to Pay. The First Three Hundred Years of Bank of England Notes*. 1994. 246pp., beautifully illustrated. £35.

British Academy (publisher) *Sylloge of Coins of the British Isles* 48 volumes many still in print available individually. (See list under Museums.)

Brooke, G.C. *English Coins*, Reprint Edition. London 1966. 300pp., 72 plates. (SH). An important one volume account of English coinage.

Challis, C. *A new History of the Royal Mint*. 1992. 806pp., 70 figures and maps. £95. A very substantial volume.

Coincraft's Standard Catalogue of English and UK Coins, 1999. 741pp., 5000+ photographs. £19.50.

Coincraft's Standard Catalogue of the coins of Scotland, Ireland, Channel Islands and Isle of Man 1999. 439pp., fully illustrated. A new volume £34.50.

Cooper, D. *Coins and Minting*. 1996. Shire Publications 106. 32pp. and illustrated. £2.25. An excellent account of minting through the ages.

Cooper, D. *The Art and Craft of Coinmaking*. 1988. 264pp. fully illustrated. £2.25. An excellent account of minting through the ages.

Dolley, M. *Viking Coins in the Danelaw and Dublin*. 1965. 32pp., 16 plates. (SH). This and the next two are excellent little introductory handbooks.

Dolley, M. *Anglo-Saxon Pennies* - Reprint, 1970. 32pp., 16 plates. (SH).

Dolley, M. *The Norman Conquest and English Coinage*. 1966. 40pp., illustrated. (SH).

Dowle, A. and Finn, P. *The Guide Book to the Coinage of Ireland*. 1969. (SH). The first standard catalogue of Irish, useful still for information on patterns and proofs and good bibliography.

Dyer, G.P. (Editor). *Royal Sovereign 1489-1989*. 1989. 99pp., fully illustrated. £30. An attractive book published by the Royal Mint to coincide with the 500 anniversary of the Sovereign.

Elias, E.R.D. *The Anglo-Gallic coins*. 1984. 262pp., fully illustrated. £20. Essential for collectors of this series.

Freeman, A. *The Moneyer and Mint in the Reign of Edward the Confessor 1042-1066*. 2 parts, 1985. £40. A complete survey of the coinage of one reign.

Frey, A.R. *Dictionary of Numismatic Names*. Reprinted 1973. 311pp., and an additional 94pp. of glossary of numismatic terms. (SH). The best numismatic dictionary, well worth searching for a second hand copy.

Grinsell, L.V. *The history and Coinage of the Bristol Mint*. Bristol Museum and Art Gallery publication. 1986. 60pp., fully illustrated. £5.

Grueber, H.A. *Handbook of the Coins of Great Britain and Ireland*, revised edition London 1970. 272pp., 64 plates. (SH). A superb book, full of information, and well worth searching for.

Hobbs, Richard. *British Iron Age Coins in the British Museum*. 1996. 246pp., 137 plates. £40. Invaluable. The British Museum Catalogue listing over 4,500 pieces.

Holmes, Richard. *Scottish Coins, a history of small change in Scotland*. An invaluable guide to the identification of 'historic' small change. Edinburgh 1998. 112pp, many illustrations. £5.99.

de Jersey, P. *Celtic Coinage in Britain*. Shire Publications 1996. 56pp., illustrated. £4.99.

Linecar, H.W.A. *British Coin Designs and Designers*. 1977. 146pp., fully illustrated. (SH).

Linecar, H.W.A. *The Crown Pieces of Great Britain and the Commonwealth of Nations*. 1969. 102pp., fully illustrated. (SH). The only book dealing solely with all British crowns.

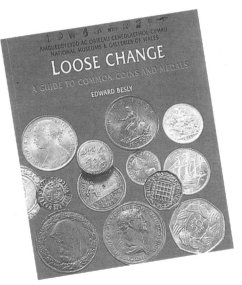

Lincecar, H.W.A. and Stone, A.G. *English proof and pattern crown-size pieces, 1658-1960.* 1968. 116pp., fully illustrated. (SH). An important book, full of useful information.

Manville, H.E. and Robertson, T.J. *Encyclopaedia of British Numismatics:* Vol.1 — British Numismatic Auction Catalogues from 1710 to the Present. 1986. 420pp., illustrated. £25.

Manville, H.E. Vol.2.1. *Numismatic Guide to British and Irish Periodicals 1731-1991.* 1993. 570pp., illustrated £60.

Manville, H.E. Vol.2.2. *Numismatic Guide to British and Irish Periodicals 1836-1995.* 1997. 634pp., 31 illustrations. £60. A highly important reference series.

McCammon, A.L.T. *Currencies of the Anglo-Norman Isles.* 1984. 358pp., 1000+ illustrations. £25. Essential for students and collectors.

North, J.J. *English Hammered Coins.* Volume 1. Early Anglo-Saxon to Henry III c.A.D.600-1272, 1994. 320pp., 20 plates. £35; Volume 2. Edward I to

Charles II 1272-1662, 1993. 224pp., 11 plates. £30. Essential. The first point of reference for all serious collectors.

North, J.J. and Preston-Morley, P.J. *The John G. Brooker Collection - Coins of Charles 1.* (Sylloge of Coins of the British Isles, Number 33) £19.50.

O'Sullivan, W. *The Earliest Irish Coinage.* 1981. 47pp., 4 plates. (SH) Deals with the Hiberno-Norse Coinage.

O'Sullivan, W. *The earliest Anglo-Irish Coinage.* 1964. 88pp., 10 plates. (SH). Deals with the coinage from 1185-1216. (There is a reprint available at £5.)

Peck, C.W. *English Copper, Tin and Bronze Coins in the British Museum 1558-1958.* 1960. 648pp., 50 plates. (SH). Essential. The seminal work on the subject.

Rayner, P.A. *English Silver Coins Since 1649.* 254pp., illustrated, 3rd edition 1992. £19.95. Essential. 3000 coins listed, 400 illustrated. Deals with varieties, rarities, patterns and proofs and mintage figures.

Robinson, B. *Silver Pennies and Linden Towels: The Story of the Royal Maundy.* 1992. 274pp., 118 illustrations. £29.95. A very important work, entertainingly presented.

Seaby. *Standard Catalogue of British Coins,* 33rd edition, 1998. 411pp., fully illustrated. £15. After half a century still the first point of reference for most collectors of English coins. Now produced by Spink and Son Ltd.

Spink and Son (publishers, but edited by H.A. Linecar). *The Milled Coinage of England 1662-1946.* Reprinted 1976. 146pp., illustrated. (SH). A useful volume dealing with the gold and silver coinage and giving degrees of rarity; superseded on the silver by Rayner, but important for the gold.

Stewart, I.H. *The Scottish Coinage,* Second edition, 1967. 215pp., 22 plates. (SH). Long out of print but still essential for the serious collector.

Sutherland, C.H.V. *English Coinage 600-1900.* 1973. 232pp., 108 plates. (SH). Beautifully written and probably the best narrative account of coinage, worth a search.

Thompson, J.D.A. *Inventory of British Coin Hoards AD 600-1500.* 1956. 165pp., 24 plates. (SH)

Van Arsdell, R.D. *Celtic Coinage of Britain.* 1989. 584pp., 54 plates, 80 maps. SH. A pioneering work which sparked much debate; important for the number of illustrations alone.

Withers, P. and B. *British Coin Weights.* A corpus of the coin-weights made for use in England, Scotland and

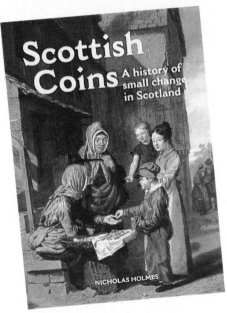

Ireland. 1993. 366pp., fully illustrated and with a price guide. £95. A labour of love for the authors; an essential volume for the serious student.

Woodhead, P. *The Herbert Schneider Collection of English Gold Coins.* Part 1. Henry III-Elizabeth I. 1996. 466pp., 83 plates each with descriptive text. £60. A wonderful catalogue of the finest collection in private hands. This first volume describes and illustrated 890 coins, most in superb condition.

Wren, C.R. *The Voided Long Cross Coinage 1247-1279.* 1993. 80pp., illustrated. £9.

Wren, C.R. *The Short Cross Coinage 1180-1247.* 1992. 90pp., illustrated. £8.75. Two very good guides to identification with excellent line drawings of the coins and lettering.

Williams, J. *Money, a history.* 1997. 256pp., fully illustrated. £25. A beautiful volume published to accompany the British Museum's HSBC Money Gallery opened in January 1997.

The Millennium Crown

The name of Jeffery Matthews may not be familiar to most coin collectors. For stamp collectors it is a far different story; Jeffery has been designing for the British Post Office for forty years.

Jeffery's education at the Brixton School of Building included a general grounding in design, plus a three-year training course in interior design. The curriculum included heraldry and lettering, which he thought strange at the time, but was soon to discover it produced an appreciation of space and composition.

He developed a liking for drawing, for plant form and architecture; at the same time he came to realise that heraldry is subject to personal interpretation. He discovered the versatility of graphic design, from book covers to bus tickets.

Leaving school, he joined a small studio, at which he undertook a variety of general graphic design work. That was until he decided to set himself up in business with a long-time friend, Alan Harmer. Alan had attended the Royal College of Art, where he and Jeffery would often meet up to discuss design.

Jeffery Matthews, and the Royal Mint presentation folder with the Millennium Crown.

At around the same time Jeffery was to meet his future wife, Christine.

Alan and Jeffery worked well together. Alan was the more entrepreneurial, seeking work in many areas, but mainly with publishers and architects. Jeffery developed his skills, especially for hand lettering, which was in vogue at the time

The Coronation in 1953 brought much work, most notably the text 'God Save the Queen' for the cover of Picture Post.

Unfortunately tragedy was to strike. Alan was drowned during a boating holiday.

Jeffery might well have sought work elsewhere, but Christine's determination persuaded him to continue the business, with she being the 'business manager'. It proved to be an arrangement which was to serve them both extremely well, until Chris sadly died in 1994. Even today, Chris's strength behind the partnership

The special, and attractive, folder from Royal Mint.

Jeffery Matthews' drawing for the medal to mark the Tercentenary of the Revival of the Order of the Thistle.

While not successful on that occasion, his designs were used in 1965 for two stamps to mark the 20th anniversary of the United Nations. From thence came a highly successful, and continuing, stamp design career, his work often being chosen when a distinguished and notable result is required. He has thus designed the stamps for several 'Royal' occasions such as the Silver Wedding in 1972, the 25th anniversary of the Coronation in 1978, the wedding of Prince Charles and Lady Diana Spencer in 1981, the wedding of Prince Andrew and Sarah Ferguson in 1986, the 80th birthday of Queen Elizabeth The Queen Mother in 1980, and the 60th birthday of The Queen in 1986.

remains ever present.

Jeffery's work has been used by many famous names, not least the British Post Office. Jeffery's details were on the records of the Council of Industrial Design (now the Design Council). Seeking designs for a set of stamps to be issued in 1960 to mark the 300th anniversary of the Charles II Act which established the 'General Letter Office', the Post Office approached Jeffery to submit ideas. Even though this was his first Post Office commission, his designs went to essay stage.

Jeffery's three ideas for the £2 coin.

The cast of the design by Jeffery for the £2 coin which was almost selected.

His early introduction to heraldry led to designs for the Quincentenary of the College of Arms in 1984, the tercentenary of the Revival of the Order of the Thistle in 1987, and the Queen's Beasts in 1998.

He designed the font for the numerals of the current British permanent stamps, and determined the colours of these stamps. He has also been involved with the designs of separate stamps for Northern Ireland, Scotland and Wales, and with stamps produced in 1990 to mark the 150th anniversary of the Penny Black.

His work in other areas is equally extensive: From the title banner for *The Sunday Times*, to the cover design for the official programme for The Royal Wedding in 1981. Clients have ranged from Reader's Digest to the Metal Box Company.

Jeffery first came into contact with the Royal Mint when the design was sought for a medal to mark the Tercentenary of the Revival of the Order of the Thistle in 1987. The Mint had launched a medal in 1986 to mark 1,000 years of Minting: this was part of a continuing series.

Jeffery produced his design as a detailed line drawing: one of the Mint's own modellers translated this as a cast. The work is still vividly remembered, so intricate was the design. Indeed, the drawing, cast, and final medal are still on display in the Royal Mint.

The story takes a pause until the Mint announced an open competition for the design for a new £2 coin. There were 1,200 entries. Jeffery submitted three ideas; his daughter, Sarah Jane, also, quite independently, submitted one (both Jeffery's son, Rory, and daughter, are in design).

The original drawing for the design of the Millennium Crown, and the cast made from the drawing.

Jeffery's designs featured Britannia, the four national emblems, and a maritime theme. This latter depicted the compass rose, acknowledging the fact that the British gave longitude and the Greenwich meridian to the world, with the meridian passing through a map of the British Isles, ingeniously linking the 'O' of TWO and POUNDS.

Both Jeffery and Sarah Jane were on the short-list of 29. In the end, Jeffery's design featuring the meridian was runner-up, but it was a close decision with the selected design.

The Royal Mint regarded Jeffery's design in very high esteem, so when ideas were sought for the reverse of a Millennium crown, he was one of nine artists, in addition to the Royal Mint's own engraving department, invited to submit ideas.

Since Greenwich will be the centre for Millennium celebrations, it seemed clear that he should develop the main theme of his design for the £2 coin.

The idea was developed to feature the meridian, and the theme of time. The coin would resemble a clock dial, with the hands at midnight, the hands being pivoted on Greenwich.

He allowed for variations of including the denomination £5, while the Royal Mint Advisory Committee felt that the words ANNO DOMINI should be added.

The design was drawn in pencil: tracing paper was used to develop the design through the use of overlays.

Again a modeller at the Royal Mint was assigned to the coin, this time Robert Evans. He worked with Jeffery to produce the desired effect: the lettering and map in relief; the central area having a textured look (a number of textures were tried, but the stippled look was preferred).

Jeffery found that the Mint, and in particular Robert Evans, were very sensitive and deferential to his wishes, not wishing to upset the concept. When slight modifications were need-

*Drawings which incorporate
ANNO DOMINI or A.D.*

ed, for example, technically it is not possible for the lettering actually to touch the central area, but a small gap is essential, these were handled with tact and understanding.

Jeffery's design was chosen.

It is fitting that someone with such a long and distinguished career, someone who has never compromised in his goal of producing the most fitting, effective and dignified designs, should be honoured by being the designer of the most significant coin for many years, that which leads us to the new Millennium.

The issued coin.

An Invitation

TO JOIN THE ROYAL MINT COIN CLUB

In order to satisfy the demands of the modern collector, the
Royal Mint has established its own Coin Club to provide its members
with the latest information on new coins from both home and abroad.
Recognised as the supreme examples of the minter's art, Royal Mint
collector coins form a tangible record of our heritage.

Some of the benefits of becoming a Coin Club member are:

FREE
Coin Club Membership.
No COMMITMENT
TO PURCHASE
whatsoever.
ROYAL MINT GUARANTEE
return your coins within 30 days
for an immediate refund.
FREE
Quarterly
Coin Club Magazine.
FREE
Postage & Packing
on all purchases.
INTEREST-FREE
Payments on selected
high-value products.

**ROYAL
MINT**

ADVANCE NOTIFICATION
of rare and
limited-edition issues.
OPPORTUNITY
to purchase products
which are NOT offered
to the general public.
SPECIAL PRE-ISSUE PRICES
(subject to status).
The **confidence** that
you are dealing with
one of the most
prestigious and reputable
numismatic organisations
in the world with
a history spanning
over 1100 years.

A TRADITION OF EXCELLENCE

Coin Grading

IT IS MOST important that newcomers to collecting should get to know the various grades of condition before attempting to buy or sell coins.

The system of grading most commonly used in Britain recognises the following main classes in descending order of quality: Brilliant Uncirculated (B.Unc,BU), Uncirculated (Unc), Extremely Fine (EF), Very Fine (VF), Fine (F), Fair, Poor.

It is not surprising that beginners get confused at their first encounter with these grades. The word 'FINE' implies a coin of high quality, yet this grade turns out to be very near the bottom of the scale and is in fact about the lowest grade acceptable to most collectors of modern coinage in Britain.

American grading

It is not really necessary to go into the details of American grading here, since it is only on a very few occasions that a British collector will order the coins he wants directly from an American dealer. However, across the Atlantic their grading system is quite different from ours, and whilst it purports to be a lot more accurate, it is actually much more prone, in our opinion, to be abused, and we prefer the English dealers' more conservative methods of grading. American dealers use many more terms than we do, ranging from Mint State to About Good. The latter could be described as 'very heavily worn, with portions of lettering, date and legend worn smooth. The date may be partly legible'. In England we would simply say 'Poor'.

Numerical method

The other area which British collectors will find difficult to evaluate is the American numerical method of describing coins as, for example, MS 70, MS 65. The MS simply stands for Mint State and an MS 65 would be described as 'an above average Uncirculated coin which may be brilliant or lightly toned but has some surface marks'. The MS system seemed to be acceptable at first but there now appear to be two schools of thought in America and you will quite frequently see coins graded in the more traditional manner as well as the MS style in sale catalogues. Fortunately American grades have not come into use in this country, although dealers have followed the American manner of embellishing coin descriptions to make them more desirable, which is understandable and in many ways can be an improvement on the old method of saying simply that the coin is 'Fine', which, of course, might not do justice to it.

Full mint lustre

There are two schools of thought on the use of the terms Brilliant Uncirculated and Uncirculated. The former is often considered to be the most useful and descriptive term for coins of copper, bronze, nickel-brass or other base metals, which display what is known as 'full mint lustre'. When this term is being used it is often necessary in the same context to employ the grade Uncirculated to describe coins which have never been in circulation but have lost the original lustre of a newly minted coin. However, some dealers and collectors tend to classify as Uncirculated all coins which have not circulated, whether they are brilliant or toned, and do not use the term Brilliant Uncirculated.

Fleur de coin

Sometimes FDC (fleur de coin) is used to define top grade coins, but this really only applies to pieces in perfect mint state, having no flaws or surface scratches. With modern methods of minting, slight damage to the surface is inevitable, except in the case of proofs, and therefore Brilliant Uncirculated or Uncirculated best describe the highest grade of modern coins.

The word 'proof' should not be used to denote a coin's condition. Proofs are pieces struck on specially prepared blanks from highly polished dies and usually have a mirror-like finish.

Opinions differ

In all this matter of condition it might be said that the grade 'is in the eye of the beholder', and there are always likely to be differences of opinion as to the exact grade of a coin. Some collectors and dealers have tried to make the existing scale of definitions more exact by adding letters such as N (Nearly), G (Good, meaning slightly better than the grade to which the letter is added), A (About or Almost) and so on. To be still more accurate, in cases where a coin wears more on one side than the other, two grades are shown, the first for the obverse, the second for the reverse thus: GVF/EF.

Additional description

Any major faults not apparent from the use of a particular grade are often described separately. These include dents and noticeable scratches, discoloration, areas of corrosion, edge knocks, holes, on otherwise good quality pieces, and the like.

Middle range of grades

One should always look for wear on the highest points of the design, of course, but these vary from coin to coin. To present a comprehensive guide to exact grading one would have to illustrate every grade of every coin type in a given series, on the lines of the famous *Guide to the Grading of United States Coins*, by Brown and Dunn. This is a complete book in itself (over 200 pages) and obviously such a mammoth task could not be attempted in the space available here. Therefore, on the following page we present representative examples from three different periods in the British series, to illustrate the 'middle' range of coin conditions.

Still in mint state

We have already dealt with the grades BU and Unc; they both describe coins which are still in the state in which they left the Mint, and which have never passed into general circulation. They are likely to show minor scratches and edge knocks due to the mass handling processes of modern minting.

Fair and Poor

At the other end of the scale we have Fair, a grade that is applied to very worn coins which still have the main parts of the design distinguishable, and Poor which denotes a grade in which the design and rim are worn almost flat and few details are discernible.

Here we show (enlarged) examples of the grades EF, VF and F. On the left are hammered long cross pennies of Aethelred II; in the centre, from the later hammered series, are groats of Henry VIII; on the right are shillings of William IV.

Extremely Fine. This describes coins which have been put into circulation, but have received only the minimum of damage since. There may be a few slight marks or minute scratches in the field (flat area around the main design), but otherwise the coin should show very little sign of having been in circulation.

Very Fine. Coins in this condition show some amount of wear on the raised surfaces, but all other detail is still very clear. Here, all three coins have had a little wear as can be seen in the details of the hair and face. However, they are still in attractive condition from the collector's viewpoint.

Fine. In this grade coins show noticeable wear on the raised parts of the design; most other details should still be clear. The penny and the groat show a lot of wear over the whole surface. On the shilling the hair above the ear has worn flat.

Extremely Fine (EF)

Very Fine (VF)

Fine (F)

Abbreviations and Terms
used in the Market Price Guide Section

* – Asterisks against some dates indicate that no firm prices were available at the time of going to press.

2mm – P of PENNY is 2mm from trident. On other 1895 pennies the space between is only 1mm.

AE – numismatic symbol for copper or copper alloys.

Arabic 1, Roman I – varieties of the 1 in 1887.

Arcs – decorative border of arcs which vary in number.

B (on William III coins) – minted at Bristol.

1866 shilling lettered BBITANNIAR in error

BBITANNIAR – lettering error.

Bank of England – this issued overstruck Spanish dollars for currency use in Britain 1804-1811.

black – farthings 1897-1918, artificially darkened to avoid confusion with half sovereigns.

briit – lettering error.

B. Unc, BU – Brilliant Uncirculated condition.

C (on milled gold coins) – minted at Ottawa (Canada).

C (on William III coins) – minted at Chester.

close colon – colon close to DEF.

crosslet 4 – having upper and lower serifs to horizontal bar of 4 (see plain 4).

cu-ni – cupro-nickel.

dashes (thus –) following dates in the price list indicate that some particular characteristic of a coin is the same as that last described. Two dashes mean that two characters are repeated, and so on.

debased – in 1920 the silver fineness in British coins was debased from .925 to .500.

diag – diagonal.

'Dorrien and Magens' – issue of shillings by a group of bankers. Suppressed on the day of issue.

DRITANNIAR – lettering error.

E (on William III coins) – minted at Exeter.

E, E* (on Queen Anne coins) – minted at Edinburgh.

Edin – Edinburgh.

EEC – European Economic Community.

EF (over price column) – Extremely Fine condition.

E.I.C. – East India Co (supplier of metal).

Elephant and castle

eleph, eleph & castle – elephant or elephant and castle provenance mark (below the bust) taken from the badge of the African ('Guinea') Company, which imported the metal for the coins.

Eng – English shilling. In 1937, English and Scottish versions of the shilling were introduced. English versions: lion standing on crown (1937-1951); three leopards on a shield (1953-66).

exergue – segment below main design, usually containing the date.

On this penny the exergue is the area containing the date

ext – extremely.

F – face value only.

F (over price column) – Fine condition.

(F) – forgeries exist of these pieces. In some cases the forgeries are complete fakes, in others where the date is rare the date of a common coin has been altered. Collectors are advised to be very cautious when buying any of these coins.

Fair – rather worn condition.

Fantasies – non-currency items, often just produced for the benefit of collectors.

far colon – colon father from DEF than in close colon variety.

FDC – Fleur de coin. A term used to describe coins in perfect mint condition, with no flaws, scratches or other marks.

fig(s) – figure(s).

fillet – hair band.

flan – blank for a coin or medal.

GEOE – lettering error.

Florin of Victoria with the design in the Gothic style

Gothic – Victorian coins featuring Gothic-style portrait and lettering.

guinea-head – die used for obverse of guinea.

H – mintmark of The Mint, Birmingham, Ltd.

hd – head.

hp, harp (early, ord etc.) – varieties of the Irish harp on reverse.

hearts – motif in top RH corner of Hanoverian shield on reverse.

illust – illustration, or illustrated.

im – initial mark.

inc, incuse – incised, sunk in.

inv – inverted.

JH – Jubilee Head.

The Jubilee Head was introduced on the coinage in 1887 to mark Victoria's Golden Jubilee

KN – mintmark of the Kings Norton Metal Co Ltd.

L.C.W. – Initials of Leonard Charles Wyon, engraver.

lge – large.

LIMA – coins bearing this word were struck from bullion captured by British ships from foreign vessels carrying South American treasure, some of which may have come from Peru (capital Lima).

1902 pennies showing the low horizon variety (A) and the normal horizon (B)

low horizon – on normal coins the horizon meets the point where Britannia's left leg crosses behind the right. On this variety the horizon is lower.

LVIII etc – regnal year in Roman numerals on the edge.

matt – type of proof without mirror-like finish.

M (on gold coins) – minted at Melbourne (Australia).

'military' – popular name for the 1813 guinea struck for the payment of troops fighting in the Napoleonic Wars.

mm – mintmark.

Mod eff – modified effigy of George V.

mule – coin struck from wrongly paired dies.

N (on William III coins) – minted at Norwich.

William III shilling with N (for Norwich mint) below the bust

no. – number.

obv – obverse, usually the 'head' side of a coin.

OH – Old Head.

ord – ordinary.

OT – ornamental trident.

P (on gold coins) – minted at Perth (Australia).

pattern – trial piece not issued for currency.

piedfort – a coin which has been specially struck on a thicker than normal blank. In France, whence the term originates, the Kings seem to have issued them as presentation pieces from the 12th century onwards. In Britain medieval and Tudor examples are known, and their issue has now been reintroduced by the Royal Mint, starting with the 20 pence piedfort of 1982.

plain (on silver coins) – no provenance marks in angles between shields on reverse.

plain 4 – with upper serif only to horizontal bar of 4 (see crosslet 4).

pln edge prf – plain edge proof.

plume(s) ⊤ symbol denoting Welsh mines as source of metal.

proof, prf – coin specially struck from highly polished dies. Usually has a mirror-like surface.

prov, provenance – a provenance mark on a coin (e.g. rose, plume, elephant) indicates the supplier of the bullion from which the coin was struck.

PT – plain trident.

raised – in relief, not incuse.

RB – round beads in border.

rev – reverse, 'tail' side of coin.

r – right.

r & p – roses and plumes.

Roses and plumes provenance marks

rose – symbol denoting west of England mines as source of metal.

RRITANNIAR – lettering error.

rsd – raised.

S (on gold coins) – minted at Sydney (Australia).

SA (on gold coins) – minted at Pretoria (South Africa).

Scottish shilling 1953-66

Scot – Scottish shilling. Lion seated on crown, holding sword and sceptre (1937-51); lion rampant, on shield (1953-66).

SS C – South Sea Company (source of metal).

1723 shilling bearing the South Sea Company's initials

SEC – SECUNDO, regnal year (on edge).

sh – shield(s).

sm – small.

'spade' – refers to spadelike shape of shield on George III gold coins.

'Spade' guinea, reverse

TB – toothed beads in border.

TER – TERTIO, regnal year (on edge).

trnctn, truncation – base of head or bust where the neck or shoulders terminate.

Unc – Uncirculated condition.

var – variety.

VF – Very Fine condition.

VIGO – struck from bullion captured in Vigo Bay.

VIP – 'very important person'. The so-called VIP crowns were the true proofs for the years of issue. Probably most of the limited number struck would have been presented to high ranking officials.

W.C.C. – Welsh Copper Co (supplier of metal).

wire type – figure of value in thin wire-like script.

W.W. – initials of William Wyon, engraver.

xxri – lettering error.

y, Y (on William III coins) – minted at York.

YH – Young Head.

Victoria Young Head Maundy fourpence

Treasure

ON September 24, 1997 the Treasure Act 1996 came into being, replacing the old medieval law of treasure trove. This widened the definition of finds that are treasure, and under the new procedures which are set out in the Code of Practice on the Act, the new Treasure Valuation Committee assists the Secretary of State for Culture to submit an annual report.

In the past, before an object could be declared treasure and therefore be the property of the Crown, it had to pass three tests: it had to be made substantially of gold or silver; it had to have been deliberately hidden with the intention of recovery; and its owner or the heirs had to be unknown. If then a museum wanted to keep the coins (or artefacts) the lawful finder normally received the full market value; if not the coins were returned to the finder.

The new Act removes the need to establish that objects were hidden with intention of being recovered; it also sets out the precise metal content required for a find to qualify as treasure; and it extends the definition of treasure.

'All coins that contain at least 10 per cent of gold or silver by weight of metal and that come from the same find, provided a find consists of at least two coins with gold or silver content of at least 10 per cent. The coins must be at least 300 years old at the time of discovery. In the case of finds consisting of coins that contain less than 10 per cent gold or silver there must be at least ten such coins ... Single coins will not be treasure, unless they are found in association with objects that are treasure, or unless there is exceptionally strong evidence that they were buried with the intention of recovery (for example, a single coin found in plough soil without any sign of a container would not provide such evidence).'

As far as more modern coins are concerned, such as finds of guineas or sovereigns, the Act reads as follows: 'Only objects that are less than 300 years old, that are made substantially of gold or silver, that have been deliberately hidden with the intention of recovery and whose owners or heirs are unknown will come into this category. In practice such finds are rare and the only such discoveries that have been made within recent years have been hoards of gold and silver coins of the 18th, 19th or 20th centuries. Single coins found on their own will not qualify under this provi-

Cover of the latest report from the Treasure Trove Reviewing Committee.

Front cover of the current 'The Treasure Act'.

sion unless there is exceptionally strong evidence to show that they were buried with the intention of recovery: for example, a single coin found in plough soil without any sign of a container would provide such. Therefore gold and silver objects that are clearly less than 300 years old need not be reported unless the finder has reason to believe that they may have been deliberately hidden with the intention of recovery.'

All this simplifies the task of coroners in determining whether or not a find is treasure, and it includes a new offence of non-declaration of treasure. Finally it states that lawful occupiers and landowners will have the right to be informed of finds of treasure from their land and they will be eligible for reward.

The Committee

The Treasure Trove Reviewing Committee was established in 1977 as an independent body to advise Ministers on the valuation of treasure trove finds. Under the new Act that body has been replaced by the Treasure Valuation Committee.

Under the new arrangements the national museums will no longer submit valuations to the Treasure Valuation Committee but instead the committee itself will commission valuation reports from expert advisers. All the interested parties (the finder, the landowner and the museum that intends to acquire the find) will be given the chance to comment on these valuations or indeed commission independent valuations of their own.

These reports are now delivered very quickly and there is no doubt that the new procedures are as transparently fair as it is possible to be. There is an annual report of the committee's findings published and available from the Department of National Heritage at £2.95. (A very interesting publication which is also available from the Book Department of Spink and Son Ltd.) The latest published report for the period

1996-1997 deals with 35 finds and is attractively illustrated throughout in colour.

At present the committee is chaired by Lord Stewartby, who is well known to coin collectors as the author of the standard work on Scottish coins and many learned articles on a wide area of early coins.

The current committee consists of:
Rt Hon Lord Stewartby (Chairman)
Mr John Casey, university lecturer and expert on Roman coins
Mr Patrick Finn, coin dealer
Mr Dennis Jordan, President of the National Council for Metal Detecting
Dr Jack Ogden, National Association of Goldsmiths
Professor Norman Palmer, a leading authority on the law of treasure trove

Information for finders and metal detectorists:

Copies of The Treasure Act 1966, Code of Practice (England Wales) 1997, can be obtained from the Department of National Heritage. This gives much useful information including a current list of coroners in the UK, and a list of coins commonly found that contain less than 10 per cent of gold or silver. It also gives advice on the care of finds, identification and storage, etc.

There is also a very useful leaflet entitled 'The Treasure Act, information for finds of treasure' which deals with everything in a question and answer way, for example:
What should I do if I find something that may be treasure?;
How do I report a find of treasure?;
What if I do not report a find of treasure?;
How do I know that I will receive a fair price for my find?
Note: both these publications can presently be obtained free of charge from:
Department of National Heritage,
2-4 Cockspur Street,
London SW1Y 5DH.
Tel: 0171 211 6200

Forgeries

MOST collectors know that there have been forgeries since the earliest days of coin production, so it is only to be expected that some new forgeries appear on the scene every year. It seems that there is always someone willing to deceive the collector and the dealer. However, nowadays very few forgers end up making much money. As a result of the actions of the British Numismatic Trade Association, the trade is much more tightly knit than ever before, and anxious to stamp out new forgeries before they have a chance to become a serious menace.

They were last a matter of serious concern in the late 1960s and early 1970s, when an enormous number of 1887 £5 pieces and United States $20 manufactured in Beruit came on to the market. Also in the early 1970s the group of Dennington forgeries could have made a serious impact on the English hammered gold market, but for lucky early detection. (Unfortunately we have noticed a number of these are still in circulation, and so we will deal with them later in this article.)

In the late 1970s a crop of forgeries of Ancient British coins came to light causing a panic in academic and trade circles. This caused a lack of confidence in the trade and it has taken a number of years for everyone to feel happy that there was no further problem. The BNTA firmly pursues any mention of forgeries and one hopes that a new spate of copies of Anglo-Saxon coins from the West Country are not allowed to develop. They are being sold as replicas, but they are still deceptive in the wrong hands. Bob Forrest compiled a list of these and it was published by the IAPN Bulletin of Forgeries in 1995/6 Vol.20 No.2. He has now done an update of this which will be available at the end of the year.

The worrying forgeries

We mentioned earlier the 'Dennington' forgeries. It is now many years since the trial of Anthony Dennington at the Central Criminal Court, where he was found guilty of six charges of 'causing persons to pay money by falsely pretending that they were buying genuine antique coins' *The Times*, July 10, 1969). There are a small number of these pieces still circulating in the trade, and since they have deceived some collectors and dealers, we thought we should record them more fully here. The following is a list of the pieces which appeared in the IBSCC Bulletin in August 1976.

1 Henry III gold penny
2 Edward III Treaty period noble
3 Another, with saltire before King's name
4 Henry IV heavy coinage noble
5 Henry V noble, Class C (mullet at King's sword arm)
6 Henry V/VI mule noble
7 Henry VI noble, annulet issue, London
8 Edward IV ryal, Norwich
9 Another, York
10 Elizabeth I Angel

Dennington forgeries: Edward III noble (top) and Mary Fine Sovereign

11 Mary Fine Sovereign 1553
12 James I unite, mintmark mullet
13 James I rose ryal, 3rd coinage,
    mint mark lis
14 James I 3rd coinage laurel
15 Commonwealth unite 1651
16 Commonwealth half unite 1651
17 Charles II touch piece

One can only reiterate that these copies are generally very good and you must beware of them. The following points may be useful.

1 The coins are usually slightly 'shiny' in appearance, and the edges are not good, since they have been filed down and polished.

2 They are usually very 'hard' to touch, whereas there is a certain amount of 'spring' in the genuine articles.

3 They usually feel slightly thick, but not always, not quite like an electrotype but certainly thicker than normal.

4 Although the Mary Fine sovereign reproduction is heavy, at 16.1986 gr, these pieces are usually lighter in weight than the originals.

As far as forgeries of modern coins are concerned, the most worrying aspects has been the enormous increase in well produced forgeries in the last 25 years.

They are so well produced that it is often impossible for the naked eye to detect the difference, and it has therefore become the job of the scientist and metallurgist. Many of these pieces have deceived dealers and collectors, although they do not seem to have caused too great a crisis of confidence. This increase in the number of modern counterfeits has been due to the enormous rise in coin values since the 1960s.

It is well known that the vast majority of these modern forgeries has emanated from the Middle East, as we have suggested earlier, where it is *not* illegal to produce counterfeits of other countries' coins. It has proved to be very good business for a lot of these small forgers in Beruit, and one can only

rely on the alertness of the coin trade so that reports are circulated quickly whenever a new forgery is spotted.

Unfortunately, the main problem is still that the forger has every encouragement to continue production of copies, when one thinks of the profit involved. At the time of writing, it only takes about £290 worth of gold to make an 1887-dated five pound piece of correct composition, valued at around £650. We cannot, therefore, be complacent.

There is not enough space here to tell you in detail what to look for, and anyway detecting forgeries requires specialist knowledge, so a list of faults would not help. If you turn to the catalogue section of COINS MARKET VALUES you will find that as far as British coins are concerned we have placed **(F)** beside a number of coins which we know have been counterfeited, and which frequently turn up. However, you should watch out for sovereigns, in particular, of which there are forgeries of every date from 1900 to 1932 and even recent dates such as 1957 and 1976.

A list follows of the pieces you should be particularly careful about, especially if you notice that they are being offered below the normal catalogue value. Most modern forgeries of, say, Gothic crowns, seem to be offered at prices which are 10 per cent or 20 per cent below the current market price. The moral is, do not automatically think you have a bargain if the price is low – it could be a forgery!

Modern cast copies of Anglo-Saxon pennies: Ceolwulf 1st above, and Ceonwulf below

1738, 1739 two guineas
1793, 1798 guineas (there could also
  be other dates)
1820 pattern two pounds
1839 five pounds (in particular the
  plain edge variety)
1887 five pounds
1887 (two pounds (there seem to be
  many forgeries of these)
1893 five pounds, two pounds
1902 five pounds, two pounds
1911 five pounds, two pounds
  1817, 1819, 1822, 1825, 1827,
  1887, 1889, 1892, 1892M,
  1908C, 1913C sovereigns;
  also every date from 1900 to
  1932 inclusive, plus 1957,
  1959, 1963, 1966, 1967,
  1974, 1976
1847 Gothic crowns
1905 halfcrowns

A 'Behra' counterfeit of the 1950s. The last of a series bearing the dates 1902 to 1920, where the original pattern piece was a genuine South African sovereign of unknown date but post 1924. An attempt was made to remove the SA mint mark on the tool used to prepare the dies but traces still remained and were transferred to all the dies.

Other safeguards against forgery
(a) The best method of protection against purchasing forgeries is to buy your coins from a reputable dealer who is a member of the British Numismatic Trade Association or the International Association of Professional Numismatists, or one who will unconditionally guarantee that all his coins are genuine.
(b) Legal tender coins, which include five and two pound pieces, sovereigns, half sovereigns and crowns, are protected by the Forgery and Counterfeiting Act, and it is the responsibility of the police to prosecute in cases where this Act has been contravened.
(c) If your dealer is unhelpful over a non legal tender item which you have purchased and which you think has been falsely described, you can take legal action under the Trades Description Act 1968. However, we should warn you that it can be a tedious and long-winded business, but if you want to proceed in this you should contact your local Trading Standards Office or Consumer Protection department.

The different types of forgery
There are many different forgeries, but essentially they can be divided into two main groups. First of all there are contemporary forgeries intended to be used as face-value money (as in the cases, some years ago, of the counterfeit 50p pieces, which even worked in slot machines), and secondly forgeries intended to deceive collectors.

Contemporary forgeries, those pieces struck in imitation of currency coins, are obviously not a serious problem to numismatists. The recent ones cause more trouble to bank clerks, anyway, and are not of sufficiently good standard to deceive numismatic experts. In general, those produced in the Middle Ages were base (which was how the forger made a profit), consisting wholly of base metal or occasionally having a thin coating of the proper metal on the outside. Sometimes they were struck, but more often they were cast. Whatever the problems they caused at the time of issue, they are now often as interesting as the regular coins of the period.

However, one can be less light-hearted about copies which are made to deceive collectors. The following five methods of reproduction have been used.

1. Electrotyping. These copies would normally deceive an expert.

2. Casting. Old casts are easily recognisable, having marks made by air bubbles on the surface, and showing a generally 'fuzzy' effect. Much more of a problem are the modern cast copies, produced by sophisticated 'pressure-casting', which can be extremely difficult for all but most expert to distinguish from the originals (more of this later).

3. The fabrication of false dies. With hammered coins counterfeits are not difficult for an expert to detect. However, the sophisticated die production techniques used in Beirut have resulted in the worrying features of modern gold and silver coins described later.

4. The use of genuine dies put to some illegal use such as restriking (a mintmaster in West Germany was convicted in 1975 of that very issue).

5. Alteration of a genuine coin. (Ask your dealer how many George V pennies he has seen with the date altered to 1933 – it does happen!)

Counterfeit Coin Club
There is now a Counterfeit Coin Club which produces a small journal four times a year. If you are interested in joining, write to its President: Ken Peters, 2 Kings Road, Biggin Hill, Kent TN16 3XU.

Literature on forgery
The back numbers of Spink's *Numismatic Circulars* and Seaby's *Coin and Medal Bulletins* are useful sources of information on the forgeries that have been recorded over the years. The ISBCC (set up by an IAPN in 1975 by the late Vincent Newman) also produced a series of important forgery bulletins, mainly on modern coins, and are very useful if you can find them on the second-hand shelves. The IAPN themselves still produce very good reports on forgeries for their own members.

As far as hammered coins are concerned, still the most useful work is that by L.A. Lawrence in the *British Numismatic Journal* as long ago as 1905! ('Forgery in relation to Numismatics'. BNJ 1905-1907, a series of articles; occasionally it can be found bound as one volume).

British Coin Prices

CELTIC COINAGE

The distribution of the tribes in Britain based on the map in 'The coinage of Ancient Britain', *by R.P. Mack, published by Spink and Son Ltd and B.A. Seaby Ltd.*

Key to towns:
1. Calleva Atrebatum (Silchester)
2. Verulamium (St Albans)
3. Camulodunum (Colchester)

It is always difficult to produce a priced catalogue of coins, but none is more difficult than the early British series. The market has developed considerably since the publication of R.D. Van Arsdell's *Celtic Coinage of Britain,* which is an essential book for collectors (584 pages, 54 plates and many other illustrations, maps and diagrams).

A word of caution, though; quite a number of forgeries exist, some of relatively recent production, and unfortunately also numerous items from undeclared hoards are on the market, which makes it essential to buy from a reputable dealer.

We are very grateful for the help of Robert Van Arsdell since he produced the synopsis of the material which we have used. We have kept this very basic, and simply linked it up for easy reference with *The Coinage of Ancient Britain* by R. P. Mack, third edition, London 1975 (now out of print), and with the *British Museum Catalogue of British Iron Age Coins* by R. Hobbs, where it is possible. In the following lists Mack types are indicated by 'M' and BMC types by 'B'. The V numbers relate to the Van Arsdell catalogue. The existence of forgeries is indicated by **(F).**

CELTIC COINAGE

Gold staters without legends

AMBIANI	F	VF
Large flan type M1, 3, V10, 12	£600	£1900

Ambiani large flan type

	F	VF
Defaced die type M5, 7, V30, 33 ...	£300	£900
Abstract type M26, 30, V44, 46	£200	£400
Gallic War type M27, a, V50, 52 (F) ...	£130	£240

Gallic War gold stater

SUESSIONES		
Abstract type M34a, V85	£250	£400

VE MONOGRAM		
M82, a, b, V87 (F)	£275	£600

WESTERHAM		
M28, 29, V200, 202 , B1-24	£220	£400

Chute Gold Starter, V1205

CHUTE		
M32, V1205, B35-76 (F)	£130	£220

CLACTON		
Type I M47, V1458, B137-144	£275	£500
Type II M46, a, V30, 1455, B145-179	£260	£480

CORIELTAUVI		
Scyphate type M—, V—, B3187-93	£250	£600

CORIELTAUVI (N.E. COAST TYPE)		
Type I M50-51a, V800, B182-191 ...	£180	£375
Type II M52-57, S27, V804	£175	£325

Norfolk Wolf stater VA610-3

NORFOLK	F	VF
Wolf type M49, a, b, V610, B212-278	£230	£475

CORIELTAUVI		
South Ferriby Kite & Domino type, M449-450a, V.811, B3146-3186	£200	£400

Coritani (South Ferriby)

WHADDON CHASE		
M133-138, V1470-1478, B279-350 (F)	£175	£350
Middle , Late Whaddon Chase V1485-1509	£220	£450

Whaddon Chase stater

WONERSH		
M147, 148, V1522, B351-56	£250	£600

WEALD		
M84, 229, V144, 150, B2466-68	£350	£750

ICENI		
Freckenham Type I M397-399, 403b, V620, B3384-95	£200	£450
Freckenham Type II M401, 2, 3a, 3c, V626, B3396-3419	£200	£450
Snettisham Type M—, V—, B3353-83	£220	£500

Iceni gold stater

ATREBATIC		
M58-61, V210-216, B445-76	£275	£475

Atrebatic stater

Verica gold stater

SAVERNAKE FOREST
M62, V1526, B359-64 ... ...   £200   £450

DOBUNNIC
M374, V1005, B2937-40 ... ...   £275   £600

	F	VF
EPATICCUS		
M262, V575, B2021-23	£600	£1850
DUBNOVELLAUNUS		
In Kent M283, V176, B2492-98	£400	£800
In Essex M275, V1650, B2425-40 ...	£200	£475
EPPILLUS		
In Kent M300-1, V430, B1125-28 ...	£600	£2000
ADDEDOMAROS (THREE TYPES)		
M266, 7, V1605, B2390-94 **(F)**	£200	£500
TASCIOVANUS		
Bucranium M149, V1680,		
B1591-1607 **(F)**	£250	£600

Gold quarter staters without legends

	F	VF
AMBIANI		
Large flan type M2, 4, V15, 20 **(F)**	£250	£650
Defaced die type M6, 8, V35, 37	£200	£500
GEOMETRIC		
M37, 39, 41, 41A, 42, V65, 146, 69,		
67	£60	£125
SUSSEX		
M40, 43-45, V143, 1225-1229	£70	£160
VE MONOGRAM		
M83, V87 **(F)**	£160	£350

VOLISIOS DUMNOCOVEROS

	F	VF
Equestrian M154-7, V1730-1736,		
B1608-13	£250	£400
TASCIO/RICON M184, V1780,		
B1625-36	£475	£1250
SEGO		
M194, V1845, B1625-27	£600	£2000
ANDOCO		
M197, V1860, B2011-14	£500	£1250

Atrebatic quarter stater, Bognor Cog Wheel

ATREBATIC
M63-67, 69-75, V220-256, B478-546   £100   £270

Caesar's trophy, quarter stater VA145

KENTISH
Caesar's Trophy type V145 ... ...   £100   £200

Tasciovanus Celtic Warrior

Gold staters with legends

	F	VF
COMMIUS		
M92, V350, B724-730	£450	£1350
TINCOMARUS		
M93, 93, V362, 363, B761-74	£600	£1600
VERICA		
Equestrian type M121, V500,		
B1143-58	£350	£700
Vine leaf type M125, V520, B1159-76	£500	£950

Cunobeline Gold Stater, V1910

CELTIC COINAGE

	F	VF
CUNOBELINE		
Two horses M201, V1910, B1769-71	£650	£1500
Corn ear M203 etc. V2010,		
B1772-1835 (F)	£240	£500

ANDOCO Stater

	F	VF
ANTED of the Dobunni		
M385-6, V1062-1066, B3023-27 (F)	£450	£900
EISU		
M388, V1105, B3039-42 (F)	£475	£1100
INAM		
M390, V1140, B3056 (F)	extremely rare	
CATTI		
M391, V1130, B3057-60 (F)	£250	£525
COMUX		
M392, V1092, B3061-63 (F)	£650	£1450
CORIO		
M393, V1035, B3064-3133 ... ... ·	£375	£675
BODVOC		
M395, V1052, B3135-42 (F)	£650	£1350

Bodvoc

	F	VF
VEP CORF		
M459-460, V940, 930, B3296-3300 (F)	£350	£950
DUMNOC TIGIR SENO		
M461, V972, B3325-27 (F)	£700	£1500
VOLISIOS DUMNOCOVEROS		
M463, V978, B3330-36	£400	£850

Cunobeline quarter stater V.1913-1

Gold quarter staters with legends

	F	VF
TINCOMARUS		
Abstract type M95, V365	£185	£450
Medusa head type M97, V387,		
B811-24	£300	£600
Tablet type M101-4, V387-390,		
B825-79	£170	£350

Tincommius Medusa head gold quarter stater

	F	VF
EPPILLUS		
CALLEVA M107, V407, B986-1015 ...	£180	£400

Eppillus CALLEVA type

	F	VF
VERICA		
Horse type M111-114, V465-468,		
B1143-46	£120	£250
TASCIOVANUS		
Horse type M152-3, V1690,1692,		
B1641-1650	£130	£275
CUNOBELINE		
Various types, B1836-55 from	£150	£350

Silver coins without legends

	F	VF
DUROTRIGES		
Silver stater M317, V1235,		
B2525-2731 (F)	£35	£110
Geometric type M319, V1242,		
B2734-79	£40	£120
Starfish type M320, V1270,		
B2780-81	£60	£130

Starfish Unit

	F	VF
DOBUNNIC		
Face M374a, b, 5, 6, 8, V1020,		
B2950-3000	£25	£60
Abstract M378a-384d, V1042,		
B3012-22	£15	£45

Corieltauvi, showing boar and horse

	F	VF
CORIELTAUVI		
Boar type M405a, V855, B3194-3250	£75	£160
South Ferriby M410 etc, V875	£50	£100

Iceni Unit, V730

ICENI	F	VF
Boar type M407-9, V655-659, B3440-3511	£25	£60
Wreath type M414, 5, 440, V679, 675, B3763-74	£20	£45
Face type M412-413e, V665, B3536-55	£50	£125

QUEEN BOUDICA

	F	VF
Face type M413, 413D, V790, 792, B3556-3759	£35	£125

Silver coins of Boudica (left) and Commius (right)

COMMIUS		
Head left M446b, V355, 357, B731-58	£35	£100

Silver coins with legends

EPPILLUS	F	VF
CALLEVA type M108, V415, B1016-1115	£55	£120

EPATICCUS		
Eagle type M263, V580, B2024-2289	£25	£60
Victory type M263a, V581, B2294-2328	£35	£85

Verica, Lion type unit V505

VERICA		
Lim type M123, V505, B1332-59 ...	£40	£120

Silver unit, Epaticcus

CARATACUS		
Eagle Type M265, V593, B2376-2384 (F)	£125	£265

TASCIOVANUS		
Equestrian M158, V1745, B1667-68	£70	£225
VER type M161, V1699, B1670-73 ...	£75	£225

CUNOBELINE		
Equestrian M216-8, 6, V1951, 1953, 2047, B1862	£70	£210
Bust right M236, VA2055, B1871-73	£70	£225

ANTED of the Dobunni		
M387, V1082, B3032-38	£80	£175

EISU		
M389, V1110, B3043-55	£65	£150

CELTIC COINAGE

BODVOC
M396, V1057, B3143-45 **(F)** £125 £300

ANTED of the Iceni
M419-421, V710, 711, 715,
B3791-4009 ... ... £25 £60

ECEN
M424, V730, B4033-4215 ... ... £20 £50

EDNAM
M423, 425b, V740, 734, B4219-4281 £40 £80

ECE
M425a, 426, 7, 8, V761, 764,
762, 766, B4348-4538 ... ... £20 £40

AESU
M432, V775, B4558-72 ... ... £70 £150

PRASUTAGUS
King of the Iceni (husband of Boudica),
B4577-4580 ... ... £600 £1200

ESUP ASU
M4566, VA924, B3272 ... ... £80 £175

VEP CORF
M460b, 464, V394, 950, B3277-3382,
B3305-3314 ... ... £60 £125

DUMNOC TIGIR SENO
M462, V974 B3328-3329 ... ... £175 £400

VOLISIOS DUMNOCOVEROS
M463a, V978, 980, B3339 ... ... £150 £350

ALE SCA
M469, V996 ... ... £300 *

Bronze, base metal coins without legends

	F	VF
POTIN		
Experimental type M22a, V104	£60	£100

Potin coin class II

Class I M9-22, V122-131	£20	£65
Class II M23-25, V136-139	£35	£95
Thurrock Types V1402-1442	£25	£50

	F	VF
ARMORICAN		
Billon stater	£30	£75
Billon quarter stater	£40	£100
DUROTRIGES		
Bronze stater M318, V1290	£25	£50
Cast type M332-370, V1322-1370 ...	£30	£75
NORTH THAMES		
M273, 274, 281, V1646 1615, 1669	£45	£120
NORTH KENT		
M295, 296, V154	£80	£170

Bronze coins with legends

DUBNOVELLAUNUS in Essex		
M277, 8, V1665, 1667	£50	£200
TASCIOVANUS		
Head, beard M168, 9, V1707	£50	£200
VERLAMIO M172, V1808	£50	£200
Head, VER M177, V1816	£70	£250
Boar, VER M179, V1713	£80	£250
Equestrian M190, V1892	£125	£270
Centaur M192, V1882	£100	£270
ANDOCO		
M200, V1871	£65	£175
CUNOBELINE		
Victory, TASC M221, V1971	£40	£120
Victory, CUN M22, a, V1973	£35	£140
Winged animal, M225, V2081	£35	£150

Cunobeline bronze with Centaur reverse

Head, beard, M226, 9, V2131, 2085	£35	£140
Panel, sphinx, M230, V1977	£35	£150
Winged beast, M231, V1979	£40	£140
Centaur, M242, V2089	£30	£120
Sow, M243, V2091	£40	£120
Warrior, M244, V2093	£30	£110
Boar, TASC, M245, V1983	£50	£180
Bull, TASC M246, V2095	£40	£120
Metal worker, M248, V2097	£35	£140
Pegasus, M249, V2099	£30	£100
Horse, CAMV, M250, V2101	£35	£140
Jupiter, horse, M251, V2103	£40	£170
Janus head, M252, V2105	£55	£175
Jupiter, lion, M253, V1207	£45	£140
Sphinx, fig, M260, a, V2109	£40	£170

ENGLISH HAMMERED
Gold from 1344 and Silver from *circa* 600

Prices in this section are approximately what collectors can expect to pay for the commonest types of the coins listed; for most other types prices will range upwards from these amounts. Precise valuations cannot be given since they vary from dealer to dealer and, in any case, have to be determined by consideration of a number of factors eg, the coin's condition (which is of prime importance in deciding its value).

For more detailed information refer to *English Hammered Coins,* Volumes 1 and 2, by J.J. North and published by Spink and Son Ltd. Any serious collectors should also obtain a copy of the important new volume, *The Herbert Schneider Collection, Volume One, English Gold Coins 1257-1603,* published by Spink and Son, 1996.

GOLD COINS
The Plantagenet Kings

Henry III gold penny

HENRY III 1216-1272   F   VF
Gold Penny
This specimen sold for £159,500 (including buyers premium) at a Spink auction on 9 July 1996.

Edward III quarter noble

EDWARD III 1327-77
Third coinage
		F	VF
Florins or Double leopard		ext. rare	
Half florins or leopard...		ext. rare	
Quarter florins or helms		ext. rare	
Nobles	from £1000	*	
Half nobles	from £1500	*	
Quarter nobles		£300	£750

Fourth coinage
Pre-treaty with France (i.e. before 1315) with French title
Nobles	£350	£650
Half nobles	£225	£475
Quarter nobles	£130	£300

Transitional treaty period, 1361. Aquitaine title added
Nobles	£390	£700
Half nobles	£200	£450
Quarter nobles	£140	£300

Edward III 1327-1377, Half noble, Transitional Treaty

Treaty period 1361-9 omit FRANC   F   VF
Nobles, London	£320	£600
Nobles, Calais		
(C in centre of rev.)	£350	£750
Half nobles, London	£220	£400
Half nobles, Calais	£320	£750
Quarter nobles, London	£130	£275
Quarter nobles, Calais	£170	£350

Post-treaty period 1369-77 French title resumed
Nobles, London	£450	£750
Nobles, Calais		
(flag at stern or C in centre)	£375	£800
Half nobles, London	ext. rare	
Half nobles, Calais	£500	£1000

There are many other issues and varieties in this reign. These prices relate to the commoner pieces.

Richard II London half noble

RICHARD II 1377-99
Nobles, London	£600	£1200
Nobles, Calais		
(flag at stern)	£650	£1350
Half nobles, London	£600	£1400

HAMMERED GOLD

	F	VF
Half nobles, Calais		
(flag at stern)	£900	£2000
Quarter nobles, London	£325	£650

There are many different varieties and different styles of lettering.

HENRY IV 1399-1413
Heavy coinage
	F	VF
Nobles (120grs) London	£3500	£8000
Nobles, Calais (flag at stern)	£4500	*
Half nobles, London	£2900	*
Half nobles, Calais	£3500	*
Quarter nobles, London	£950	£2000
Quarter nobles, Calais	£1000	£2500

Light coinage
	F	VF
Nobles (108grs)	£850	£1800
Half nobles	£2500	*
Quarter nobles	£450	£950

Henry V noble

HENRY V 1413-22
	F	VF
Nobles, many varieties, from	£375	£700
Half nobles	£400	£800
Quarter nobles	£220	£400

This reign sees an increase in the use of privy marks to differentiate issues.

Henry VI noble, Annulet issue

HENRY VI 1422-61
Annulet issue (1422-27)
	F	VF
Nobles, London	£350	£650
Nobles, Calais (flag at stern)	£450	£900
Nobles, York	£475	£950
Half nobles, London	£250	£500
Half nobles, Calais	£475	£950
Half nobles, York	£475	£950
Quarter nobles, London	£170	£300
Quarter nobles, Calais	£200	£450
Quarter nobles, York	£250	£500

Henry VI, Quarter-Noble, Annulet issue

Rosette-mascle issue 1427-30 ... ...
	F	VF
Nobles, London	£650	£1350
Nobles, Calais	£800	£1500
Half nobles, London	£850	£1600
Half nobles, Calais	£950	£2000
Quarter nobles, London	£350	£700
Quarter nobles, Calais	£400	£800

Pinecone-mascle issue 1430-4
	F	VF
Nobles, London	£650	£1300
Half nobles, London	£1000	*
Quarter noble	£700	*

Henry VI quarter noble, leaf-mascle

Leaf-mascle issue 1434-5
	F	VF
Nobles	£1500	£3000
Half nobles	£2000	*
Quarter nobles	£1250	*

Leaf-trefoil issue 1435-8
	F	VF
Nobles	£2000	*
Quarter noble	£2500	*

Trefoil issue 1438-43
	F	VF
Nobles	£1500	£3500

Henry VI Gold Noble, Pinecone-mascle, London

Leaf-pellet issue 1445-54
Nobles	£1500	£3500

Cross-pellet issue 1454-60
Nobles	£2000	*

EDWARD IV 1st reign 1461-70
Heavy coinage 1461-64/5
Nobles (108grs)	£3500	*
Quarter noble	ext. rare	

Edward IV noble, heavy coinage

Light coinage 1464-70

	F	VF
Ryals or rose nobles (120grs), London	£350	£650
Flemish copy	£275	£475

Edward IV Light Coinage 1464-70, Ryal, York

	F	VF
Ryals, Bristol (B in waves)	£450	£850
Ryals, Coventry (C in waves))	£700	£1600
Ryals, Norwich (N in waves)	£850	£1800
Ryals, York (E in waves)	£450	£900
Half ryals, London	£300	£600
Half ryals, Bristol (B in waves) ...	£450	£900
Half ryals, Coventry (C in waves) ...	£1750	*
Half ryals Norwich (N in waves) ...	£1500	*
Half ryals, York (E in waves)	£350	£700
Quarter ryals	£200	£450
Angels	£3750	*

Edward IV angel, first reign

HAMMERED GOLD

	F	VF
HENRY VI (restored) 1470-71		
Angels, London	£650	£1400
Angels, Bristol (B in waves)	£1000	£2250
Half angels, London	£1500	£3500
Half angels, Bristol (B in waves) ...	£2000	*
EDWARD IV 2nd reign 1471-83		
Angels, London	£250	£500
Angels, Bristol (B in waves)	£1000	£2500
Half angels, some varieties	£250	£500
EDWARD IV or V		
mm halved sun and rose		
Angels	£1000	£2500
EDWARD V 1483		
mm boar's head on obverse, halved sun and rose on reverse.		
Angels	£7000	*
Half angel	ext. rare	
RICHARD III 1483-5		
Angel, reading EDWARD, with R over E by mast	ext. rare	
Angels, as before, but *mm* boar's head	ext. rare	
Angels, reading RICARD or RICAD	£800	£1600
Half angels	£3500	*

Gold Angel, mm boar's head on obverse, and halved sun and rose on reverse

The Tudor Monarchs

Henry VII sovereign

HENRY VII 1485-1509	F	VF
Sovereigns of 20 shillings (all ext. rare) from	£7000	£14000
Ryals	£8000	£16000
Angels, varieties, different *mm* from	£290	£550
Half angels	£200	£450

HAMMERED GOLD

Henry VII 1485-1509, Angel with Mint Mark pheon

HENRY VIII 1509-47

First coinage 1509-26

	F	VF
Sovereigns of 20 shillings *mm* crowned portcullis only	£3500	*
Angels (6s 8d) ... ... from	£275	£550
Half angels	£200	£475

Second coinage 1526-44

	F	VF
Sovereigns of 22s 6d, various *mm* ...	£2750	£6000
Angels (7s 6d)	£400	£750
Half angels *mm* lis	£500	£1000
George-nobles *mm* rose	£3000	£6500
Half-George noble	ext. rare	
Crowns of the rose *mm* rose	ext. rare	
Crowns of the double-rose		
HK (Henry and Katherine of Aragon)	£275	£500
HA (Henry and Anne Boleyn) ...	£450	£800
HI (Henry and Jane Seymour) ...	£350	£650
HR (HENRICUS REX)	£250	£500
Halfcrowns of the double-rose		
HK	£250	£650
HI	£275	£650
HR	£400	£800

Third coinage 1544-47

	F	VF
Sovereigns of 20s, London ... from	£1800	£5000
Sovereigns of 20s, Southwark	£1600	£3750
Sovereigns of 20s, Bristol	£2750	£6000
Half sovereigns, London	£300	£600
Half sovereigns, Southwark	£350	£700
Half sovereigns, Bristol	£450	£1000

Henry VIII Angel, 3rd coinage with mint mark lis (shown slightly enlarged)

	F	VF
Angels	£250	£500
Half angels	£250	£475
Quarter angels	£250	£500
Crowns, HENRIC 8, London	£250	£500
Crowns, Southwark	£300	£600
Crowns, Bristol	£300	£600

	F	VF
Halfcrowns, London	£200	£450
Halfcrowns, Southwark	£300	£600
Halfcrowns, Bristol	£300	£650

EDWARD VI 1547-53
Posthumous coinage in name of Henry VIII (1547-51)

	F	VF
Sovereigns, London	£2000	£4750
Sovereigns, Bristol	£2500	£5500
Half sovereigns, London	£300	£650
Half sovereigns, Southwark	£300	£650
Crowns, London	£350	£700
Crowns, Southwark	£450	£900
Halfcrowns, London	£300	£650
Halfcrowns, Southwark	£300	£650

Coinage in Edward's own name
First period 1547-49

	F	VF
Half sovereigns, Tower, read EDWARD 6	£600	£1250

Edward VI sovereign, posthumous coinage (not actual size)

	F	VF
Half sovereigns, Southwark	£550	£1200
Crown	£2000	*
Halfcrowns	£1500	*

Second period 1549-50

	F	VF
Sovereigns	£1800	£4500
Half sovereigns, uncrowned bust London	£1500	*
Half sovereigns, SCUTUM on obv. ...	£500	£1250
Half sovereigns, Durham House MDXL VII	£3000	*
Half sovereigns, crowned bust, London	£500	£1250
Half sovereigns, half-length bust, Durham House	£3000	*
Crowns, uncrowned bust	£800	£1500
Crowns, crowned bust	£650	£1350
Halfcrowns, uncrowned bust	£650	£1300
Halfcrowns, crowned bust	£600	£1200

Edward VI fine sovereign of 30s third period with mint mark ostrich head

COIN MARKET VALUES

Edward VI Sovereign of
20 Shillings. Third Period

Third period 1550-53
'Fine' sovereigns of 30s, king
enthroned £7500 £20000
Sovereigns of 20s, half-length figure ... £950 £2500
Half sovereigns, similar to last £600 £1400
Crowns, similar but SCUTUM on rev ... £700 £1600
Halfcrowns, similar £750 £1800
Angels £4000 £9000
Half angel ... ... ext. rare

MARY 1553-4
Sovereigns, different dates, some
undated, some *mms* £2000 £4500
Ryals, dated MDUI (1553) £7500 £15000
Angels, *mm* pomegranate £650 £1400
Half angels £2000 £6500

Mary Gold Sovereign of 1553

HAMMERED GOLD

	F	VF
PHILIP AND MARY 1554-8		
Angels, *mm* lis	£1700	£4000
Half angels	£4000	*

Philip and Mary angel

Elizabeth I 1558-1603
Hammered issues
'Fine' sovereigns of 30s, different
issues from £1700 £4000
Ryals £3500 £9000
Angels, different issues £350 £350
Half angels £300 £600
Quarter angels £275 £550

Elizabeth I quarter angel

	F	VF
Pounds of 20 shillings, different mint marks from	£700	£1600
Half pounds, different issues	£450	£900
Crowns —	£400	£800
Halfcrowns —	£400	£800

Elizabeth I hammered halfcrown

Milled issues
Half pounds, one issue but different
marks £800 £2000
Crowns — £800 £2000
Halfcrowns — £1200 £3000

The Stuart Kings

James I gold Spur-ryal

James I Thistle crown

3rd coinage 1619-25

			F	VF
Rose-ryals, varieties	... ...		£950	£2500
Spur-ryals	... ...		£2200	£4500
Angels	... ...		£700	£1500
Laurels, different busts	... ...		£225	£450
Half Laurels	... ...		£170	£350
Quarter laurels	... ...		£130	£250

JAMES I 1603-25
1st coinage 1603-4

	F	VF
Sovereigns of 20 shillings two bust	£800	£1800
Half sovereigns	£2000	£4000
Crowns	£900	£2500
Halfcrowns	£350	£750

2nd coinage 1604-19

		F	VF
Rose-ryals of 30 shillings	... ...	£750	£2000
Spur-ryals of 15 shillings	... ...	£2000	£4000
Angels		£600	£1350
Half angels		£1500	£4000
Unites, different busts		£250	£500
Double crowns —		£200	£450
Britain crowns —		£150	£300

James I laurel

CHARLES I 1625-49
Tower Mint 1625-42
Initial marks: lis, cross calvary, negro's head, castle, anchor, heart, plume, rose, harp, portcullis, bell, crown, tun, triangle, star, triangle in circle

James I
Rose-ryal of
30 shillings

Charles I Unite, Tower Mint, 1625-43

		F	VF
Angels, varieties		£800	£2500
Angels, pierced as touchpieces		£400	£850
Unites –		£230	£475
Double Crowns –		£200	£400
Crowns –		£140	£275

			F	VF
Halfcrowns —			£140	£260
Thistle crowns, varieties	... ...		£150	£300

Charles I Double Crown, Tower Mint with mint mark heart

Tower Mint under Parliament 1642-9 F VF
Initial marks: (P), (R), eye, sun, sceptre

		F	VF
Unites, varieties	... ...	£400	£850
Double crowns –	... ...	£450	£950
Crowns –	... ...	£250	£475

Briot's milled issues 1631-2
Initial marks: anemone and **B**, daisy and **B, B**

Angels	... ...	£4000	*
Unites	... ...	£900	£2000
Double crowns	... ...	£700	£1600
Crowns	... ...	£1000	*

Coins of provincial mints
Bristol 1645

Unites	... ...	£5000	*
Half unites	... ...		ext. rare

Chester 1644

Unites	... ...	£8000	*

Exeter 1643-44

Unites	... ...	£8000	*

Oxford 1642-46

Triple unites, from	... ...	£2500	£5000
Unites from	... ...	£700	£1400
Half unites from	... ...	£700	£1400

Truro 1642-43

Half unites	... ...		ext. rare

Shrewsbury 1644

Triple unites and unites	... ...		ext. rare

Worcester 1643-44

Unites	... ...		ext. rare

Charles I Oxford triple unite, 1643

HAMMERED GOLD

Siege pieces 1645-49		F	VF
Pontefract besieged 1648-49			
Unites **(F)**	... ...		ext. rare

Commonwealth 1650 gold unite

COMMONWEALTH 1649-60

Unites *im* sun	... ...	£450	£900
– *im* anchor	... ...	£1250	£3000
Double crowns *im* sun	... ...	£350	£750
– *im* anchor	... ...	£1000	£2500
Crowns *im* sun	... ...	£300	£600
– *im* anchor	... ...	£1250	*

Commonwealth crown

CHARLES II 1660-85
Hammered Coinage 1660-62

Charles II gold unite

Unites, two issues from	... ...	£600	£1400
Double crowns –	... ...	£500	£1200
Crowns –	... ...	£475	£1000

SILVER COINS

In this section column headings are mainly F (Fine) and VF (Very Fine), but for pennies of the early Plantagenets – a series in which higher-grade coins are seldom available – prices are shown under the headings Fair and F. Again it should be noted that throughout the section prices are approximate, for the commonest types only, and are the amounts collectors can expect to pay – not dealers' buying prices. Descriptions of some early Anglo-Saxon coins are, of necessity, brief because of pressure on space. Descriptions such as 'cross/moneyer's name' indicate that a cross appears on the obverse and the moneyer's name on the reverse. For more details see Standard Catalogue of British Coins – Volume 1 published by Spink & Son Ltd, and English Hammered Coins, Volumes 1 and 2, by J. J. North, published by Spink and Son Ltd. (A new edition of Volume 2 was published in 1991 and a new edition of Volume 1 was published in 1994).

Anglo-Saxon Sceats and Stycas

Examples of Sceats

EARLY PERIOD c 600-750	F	VF
Silver sceats ... ...from	£65	£150

A fascinating series with great variation of styles of early art. Large numbers of types and varieties.

NORTHUMBRIAN KINGS c 737-867	F	VF
Silver sceats c 737-796 ...from	£150	£350
Copper stycas c 810-867 ...from	£15	£35

Struck for many kings. Numerous moneyers and different varieties. The copper styca is the commonest coin in the Anglo-Saxon series.

ARCHBISHOPS OF YORK c 732-900	F	VF
Silver sceats ... ...from	£75	£160
Copper stycas ... ...from	£35	£75

From here onwards until the reign of Edward I all coins are silver pennies unless otherwise stated

Kings of Kent

HEABERHT c 764	F	VF
Monogram/cross		ext. rare
One moneyer (EOBA).		

ECGBERHT c 765-780		
Monogram/cross	£950	£2000
Two moneyers (BABBA and UDD)		

EADBERHT PRAEN 797-798		
EADBERHT REX/moneyer	£1000	£2000
Three moneyers		

Penny of Eadberht Praen

CUTHRED 789-807	F	VF
Non-portrait, various designs from	£400	£850
Bust right	£475	£1250
Different moneyers, varieties etc.		

BALDRED c 825		
Bust right	£800	£2000
Cross/cross	£600	£1500
different types and moneyers		

Baldred penny, bust right

ANONYMOUS c 823		
Bust right	£550	£1400
Different varieties and moneyers.		

Archbishops of Canterbury

JAENBERHT 766-792	F	VF
Various types (non-portrait) from	£1000	£2500

AETHELHEARD 793-805		
Various types (non-portrait) from	£800	£1750

WULFRED 805-832		
Various groups (portrait types) from	£500	£1000

CEOLNOTH 833-870		
Various groups (portrait types) from	£375	£800

Ceolnoth penny

AETHERED 870-889	F	VF
Various types (portrait, non-portrait)	£1200	*
PLEGMUND 890-914		
Various types (all non-portrait) from	£375	£900

Kings of Mercia

Offa portrait penny

OFFA 757-796	F	VF
Non-portrait from	*	*
Portrait from	£650	£1250
Many types and varieties		

Cynethryth (wife of Offa) portrait penny

CYNETHRYTH (wife of Offa)		
Portraits	£2000	£4500
Non-portrait	£1500	£3000

COENWULF 796-821		
Various types (portrait, non-portrait)from	£275	£550

Coenwulf portrait penny

CEOLWULF 1821-823		
Various types (portrait)	£750	£1500

BEORNWULF 823-825		
Various types (portrait)	£850	£2000

Beornwulf penny

LUDICA 825-827		
Two types (portrait) (F)	£2500	*

WIGLAF 827-829, 830-840		
Two groups (portrait, non-portrait)	£1800	£4000

BERHTWULF 840-852		
Two groups (portrait, non-portrait)	£750	£1500

HAMMERED SILVER

Berhtwulf penny

BURGRED 852-874	F	VF
One type (portrait), five variants	£95	£200

CEOLWULF II 874-c 877		
Two types (portrait))	£2500	£5000

Kings of East Anglia

BEONNA c 758	F	VF
Silver sceat	£450	£950

AETHELBERHT LUL (died 794)		
Portrait type (F)		ext. rare

Eadwald penny

EADWALD c 796	F	VF
Non-portrait types	£950	£2750
AETHELSTAN I c 850		
Various types (portrait, non-portrait)	£350	£700
AETHELWEARD c 850		
Non-portrait types	£500	£1250
EADMUND 855-870		
Non-portrait types	£200	£450

Viking Invaders 878-954

ALFRED	F	VF
Imitations of Alfred pennies and halfpennies from	£350	£700
(Many different types, portrait and non portrait)		
ANGLIA		
AETHELSTAN II 878-890		
Cross/moneyer	£1000	*
OSWALD (Unknown in history except from coins)		
A/cross	£1250	*
ST EADMUND		
Memorial coinage, various legends etc.	£80	£170
Many moneyers.		
Halfpenny, similar	£400	£950

HAMMERED SILVER

St Eadmund memorial penny

	F	VF
ST MARTIN OF LINCOLN c 925		
Sword/cross	£2000	*
AETHELRED c 870		
Temple/cross	£1000	*
YORK		
SIEVERT-SIEFRED-CNUT c 897		
Crosslet/small cross	£120	£200
Many different groups and varieties		
Halfpenny, similar	£450	£950
EARL SIHTRIC (unknown)		
Non-portrait	£1500	*
REGNALD c 919-921		
Various types, some blundered	£1200	*
SIHTRIC I 921-927		
Sword/cross	£1250	*
ANLAF GUTHFRITHSSON 939-941		
Raven/cross	£1500	£3000
Cross/cross	£1500	*
Flower/cross	£1500	*
ANLAF SIHTRICSSON 941-944, 948-952		
Various types	£1500	*
SIHTRIC II c 942-943		
Shield/standard	£1750	*
REGNALD II c 941-943		
Cross/cross	£2000	*
Shield/standard	£2000	*
ERIC BLOODAXE 948, 952-954		
Cross/moneyer	£1500	*
Sword/cross	£2000	*

St Peter of York halfpenny

	F	VF
ST PETER OF YORK c 905-927		
Various types ... ...from	£200	£450
Halfpenny, similar	£750	*

Kings of Wessex

	F	VF
BEORHTRIC 786-802		
Two types (non-portrait)	ext. rare	
ECGBERHT 802-839		
FOUR GROUPS (portrait, non-portrait)	£800	£2000
Mints of Canterbury, London, Rochester, Winchester		

Aethelwulf Portrait Penny, Canterbury

	F	VF
AETHELWULF 839-858		
Four phases (portrait, non-portrait)	£200	£450
from Mints of Canterbury, Rochester (?)		
AETHELBERHT 858-866		
Two types (portrait) ... ...from	£200	£450
Many moneyers.		
AETHELRED I 865-871		
Portrait types ... ...from	£250	£700
Many moneyers.		
ALFRED THE GREAT 871-899		
Portrait in style of Aethelred I ...	£275	£700
Four other portrait types commonest being those		
with the London monogram reverse	£650	£1400
Halfpennies	£400	£975

Alfred the Great Penny, London monogram on reverse

	F	VF
Non-portrait types ... ...from	£250	£450
Many different styles of lettering etc.		
Halfpennies	£350	£800
EDWARD THE ELDER 899-924		
Non-portrait types:		
Cross/moneyer's name in two lines	£140	£350
Halfpennies as previous	£700	£1500

Rare penny of Edward the Elder with building on reverse

	F	VF
Portrait types:		
Bust/moneyer's name	£400	£975
Many types, varieties and moneyers.		
Types featuring buildings, floral		
designs, etc	£800	£2500
Many types, varieties and moneyers.		

Kings of all England

AETHELSTAN 924-39 ... ... F VF

Aethelstan 924-939, Penny, building type reverse

Non-portrait types:

Cross/moneyer's name in two lines	£175	£450
Cross/cross	£200	£500

Portrait types:

bust/moneyer's name in two lines	£550	£1500
Bust/small cross	£375	£950

Many other issues, some featuring buildings as illustrated above. There are also different mints and moneyer's names.

Aethelstan portrait penny with small cross on reverse

EADMUND 939-46
Non-portrait types:

Cross or rosette/moneyer's name in two lines	£180	£500
Silver halfpenny, similar	£750	£1700

Eadmund penny, two-line type

Portrait types:

Crowned bust/small cross	£400	£950
Helmeted bust/cross crosslet ...	£750	£1800

Many other issues and varieties; also different mint names and moneyers.

EADRED 946-55
Non-portrait types:

Cross/moneyer's name in two lines	£130	£300
Silver halfpenny similar	£600	£1200
Rosette/moneyer's name	£200	£450

HAMMERED SILVER

Eadred penny, portrait type

Portrait types: F VF

Crowned bust/small cross	£300	£700

Again many variations and mint names and moneyers.

HOWEL DDA (King of Wales), died c948
Small cross/moneyer's name in two lines (GILLYS) ... ... ext. rare

EADWIG 955-59
Non-portrait types:

Cross/moneyer's name ... from	£175	£375

Many variations, some rare.

Silver halfpennies, similar . from	£1200	*

Portrait types:

Bust/cross ... ... from	£2000	*

EADGAR 959-75
Non-portrait types:

Cross/moneyer's name ... from	£110	£220
Cross/cross ... ... from	£110	£200
Rosette/rosette ... ... from	£150	£300
Halfpennies ... ... from	£1200	*

Eadgar, 959-957, Non Portrait Penny, Winchester

Portrait types

Pre-Reform	£500	£1250
Halfpenny, diademed bust/London monogram ... ... from	£1200	*
Reform (c.972)	£600	£1250

Many other varieties.

EDWARD THE MARTYR 975-78
Portrait types:

Bust left/small cross	£750	£1600

Many different mints and moneyers.

AETHELRED II 978-1016

Aethelred II 978-1016, Penny, Last small cross type

First small cross ... ... from	£400	£975
First hand ... ... from	£85	£160
Second hand ... ... from	£80	£150
Benediction hand ... ... from	£500	£1400

HAMMERED SILVER

	F	VF
CRUX ... ... from	£80	£140

Aethelred II CRUX type penny

Aethelred II , Long Cross penny

	F	VF
Long Cross	£80	£130
Helmet	£85	£150
Agnus Dei	£3000	*

Other issues and varieties, many mint names and moneyers.

Aethelred II long cross penny

CNUT 1016-35

	F	VF
Quatrefoil ... ... from	£70	£130

Cnut quatrefoil type penny

	F	VF
Pointed helmet ... ... from	£70	£130

Cnut pointed helmet type penny

	F	VF
Small cross ... ... from	£65	£110
Jewel cross ... ... from	£450	*

Other types, and many different mint names and moneyers.

HAROLD I 1035-40

	F	VF
Jewel cross ... ... from	£180	£400

	F	VF
Long cross with trefoils ... from	£180	£400
Long cross with fleurs-de-lis from	£175	£375

Many different mint names and moneyers.

HARTHACNUT 1035-42

	F	VF
Jewel cross, bust left	£800	£2000
– bust right	£700	£1700
Arm and sceptre types	£600	£1400

Different mint names and moneyers.

	F	VF
Scandinavian types struck at Lund	£200	£400

EDWARD THE CONFESSOR 1042-66

	F	VF
PACX type ... ... from	£150	£350
Radiate crown/small cross from	£80	£140
Trefoil quadrilateral	£80	£150
Small flan ... ... from	£80	£130
Expanding cross types ... from	£85	£150

Edward the Confessor Penny, Expanding Cross Type

	F	VF
Helmet types	£80	£150
Sovereign/eagles	£100	£200
Hammer cross	£80	£135

Edward the Confessor Hammer Cross Penny

	F	VF
Bust facing	£80	£135
Cross and piles	£95	£150
Large bust, facing, with sceptre	£1000	£2500

Other issues, including a unique gold penny; many different mint names and moneyers.

HAROLD II 1066

	F	VF
Crowned head left with sceptre	£400	£800

Harold II Penny, bust left with sceptre

	F	VF
Similar but no sceptre	£450	£900

Harold II, bust left, without sceptre

	F	VF
Crowned head right with sceptre	£750	£1400

The Norman Kings

WILLIAM I 1066-87

		F	VF
Profile/cross fleury	... ...from	£160	£370
Bonnet	... ...from	£120	£240
Canopy	... ...from	£210	£500
Two sceptres	... ...from	£170	£450
Two stars	... ...from	£130	£250
Sword	... ...from	£200	£450

William I profile/cross fleury penny

		F	VF
Profile/cross and trefoils	...from	£300	£650
PAXS	... ...from	£100	£160

WILLIAM II 1087-1100

William II, cross voided type penny

		F	VF
Profile	... ...from	£300	£700
Cross in quatrefoil	... ...from	£275	£550
Cross voided	... ...from	£250	£550
Cross pattee over fleury	...from	£350	£700
Cross fleury and piles	... ...from	£400	£850

Henry I penny; small bust/cross and annulets

HENRY I 1100-1135

		F	VF
Annulets	... ...from	£275	£650
Profile/cross fleury	... ...from	£220	£450
PAX	... ...from	£250	£475
Annulets and piles	... ...from	£300	£600
Voided cross and fleurs	... ...from	£500	£1000
Pointing bust and stars	... ...from	£650	£1250
Quatrefoil and piles	... ...from	£275	£500
Profile/cross and annulets	from	£700	£1600
Cross in quatrefoil	... ...from	£470	£900

Henry I, full face/cross fleury penny

HAMMERED SILVER

	F	VF
Full face/cross fleury	£170	£350
Double inscription	£325	£750
Small bust/cross and annulets	£275	£600
Star in lozenge fleury	£275	£550
Pellets in quatrefoil	£130	£300
Quadrilateral on cross fleury ...	£110	£250
Halfpennies	£1200	*

STEPHEN 1135-54

	F	VF
Cross moline (Watford) ...from	£95	£200

Stephen 'Watford' Penny

	F	VF
Cross moline PERERIC	£350	£750
Voided cross and mullets	£170	£400

Stephen Penny, voided cross pattée with mullets

	F	VF
Profile/cross fleury	£300	£750
Voided cross pommée (Awbridge)	£200	£420

There are also a number of irregular issues produced during the Civil War, all of which are very rare. These include several extremely rare and attractive pieces bearing the names of Empress Matilda and barons, such as Eustace Fitzjohn and Robert de Stuteville.

The Plantagenet Kings

HENRY II 1154-89 Fair F

Henry II Cross and Crosslets (Tealby) Penny

	Fair	F
Cross and crosslets ('Tealby' coinage)	£25	£50

The issue is classified by bust variants into six groups, struck at 32 mints.

Henry II Short Cross Penny 1b

HAMMERED SILVER

	F	VF
Short cross pennies	£30	£75

The 'short cross' coinage was introduced in 1180 and continued through successive reigns until Henry III brought about a change in 1247. HENRICVS REX appears on all these coins but they can be classified into reigns by the styles of the busts and lettering. We recommend a copy of C.R. Wren's illustrated guide The Short Cross Coinage 1180-1247, *as the best guide to identification.*

Richard I, 1189-1199, Short Cross Penny

RICHARD I 1189-99

Short cross pennies	£40	£95

JOHN 1199-1216

Short cross pennies	£35	£70

John Short Cross Penny

HENRY III 1216-72

Short cross pennies	£20	£35
Long cross pennies no sceptre	£15	£35
Long cross pennies with sceptre	£15	£35

Henry III, Long Cross Penny, no sceptre

Henry III, Long Cross Penny with sceptre

The 'long cross' pennies, first introduced in 1247, are divided into two groups: those with sceptre and those without. They also fall into five basic classes, with many varieties. We recommend C.R. Wren's, The Voided Long Cross Coinage, 1247-79 *as the best guide to identification.*

Edward I, 1st coinage, Long Cross penny

	F	VF

EDWARD I 1272-1307
1st coinage 1272-78

Long cross pennies ... ...from	£25	£70

similar in style to those of Henry III but with more realistic beard.

Edward I Penny, London

New coinage 1278-1307

Groats	£1000	£2750
Pennies, various classes, mints from	£10	£30
Halfpennies – ... ...from	£25	£65
Farthings – ... ...from	£65	£160

Edward I Farthing, London

Any new collector wishing to become serious about this area should obtain a copy of Edwardian English Silver Coins 1279-1351. Sylloge of coins of the British Isles 39 (The JJ North collection)

EDWARD II 1307-27

Pennies, various classes, mints from	£12	£50
Halfpennies ... ...from	£50	£125
Farthings ... ...from	£65	£160

EDWARD III 1327-77
1st and 2nd coinages 1327-43

Pennies (only 1st coinage) various types and mints	£250	£450
Halfpennies, different types and mints	£20	£45
Farthings	£50	£130

3rd coinage 1344-51 (Florin Coinage)

Pennies, various types and mints	£15	£65
Halfpennies –	£15	£45
Farthings	£50	£120

Edward III 1327-77, Groat Treaty Period

4th coinage 1351-77

	F	VF
Groats, many types and mints from	£35	£95

Edward III halfgroat Post-Treaty

		F	VF
Halfgroats –	... ...	£20	£55
Pennies –	... ...	£18	£50
Halfpennies, different types	...	£100	£200
Farthings, a few types	... ...	£120	£250

Henry IV halfpenny

RICHARD II 1377-99

	F	VF
Groats, four types from	£250	£550

Henry VI Annulet issue halfgroat

	F	VF
Halfgroats	£190	£450
Pennies, various types, London	£250	£550
Pennies, various types, York ...	£50	£120
Pennies, Durham	£190	£450
Halfpennies, three main types ...	£30	£80
Farthings, some varieties	£150	£375

HENRY IV 1399-1413

	F	VF
Groats, varieties ... ...from	£1500	£4000
Halfgroats –	£600	£1600
Pennies –	£250	£750
Halfpennies	£170	£400
Farthings –	£500	*

Henry V Groat

HAMMERED SILVER

HENRY V 1413-22

	F	VF
Groats, varieties ... ...from	£80	£200
Halfgroats	£75	£180
Pennies	£35	£90
Halfpennies	£30	£75
Farthings	£160	£375

HENRY VI 1422-61
Annulet issue 1422-1427

	F	VF
Groats	£30	£70
Halfgroats	£25	£60
Pennies	£20	£50
Halfpennies	£20	£50
Farthings	£160	£350

Rosette-Mascle issue 1427-1430

	F	VF
Groats	£40	£120
Halfgroats	£30	£70
Pennies	£30	£70
Halfpennies	£20	£50
Farthings	£120	£250

Pinecone-Mascle 1430-1434

	F	VF
Groats	£35	£90
Halfgroats	£30	£70
Pennies	£30	£70
Halfpennies	£25	£50
Farthings	£120	£250

Leaf-Mascle issue 1434-1435

	F	VF
Groats	£60	£160
Halfgroats	£60	£150
Pennies	£50	£120
Halfpennies	£30	£70

Leaf-Trefoil 1435-1438

	F	VF
Groats	£50	£120
Halfgroats	£35	£100
Pennies	£50	£100
Halfpennies	£25	£60
Farthings	£135	£300

Trefoil 1438-1443

	F	VF
Groats	£60	£140
Halfgroats	£200	£400
Halfpennies	£40	£90

Trefoil-Pellet 1443-1445

	F	VF
Groats	£75	£200

Henry VI Groat, Leaf-Pellet issue

Leaf-Pellet 1445-1454

	F	VF
Groats	£45	£130
Halfgroats	£40	£100
Pennies	£40	£90
Halfpennies	£30	£65
Farthings	£150	£300

HAMMERED SILVER

Unmarked 1445-1454   F   VF

	F	VF
Groats	£275	£650
Halfgroats	£200	£450

Cross-Pellet 1454-1460

	F	VF
Groats	£90	£200
Halfgroats	£200	£450
Pennies	£60	£120
Halfpennies	£60	£120
Farthings	£150	*

Lis-Pellet 1454-1460

	F	VF
Groats	£175	£450

These are many different varieties, mintmarks and mints in this reign. These prices are for commonest prices in each issue.

EDWARD IV 1st Reign 1461-1470
Heavy coinage 1461-4

	F	VF
Groats, many classes, all London	£90	£200
Halfgroats, many classes, all London	£250	£550
Pennies, different classes. London, York and Durham	£150	£300
Halfpennies, different classes, all London	£60	£130
Farthings. London	£350	£600

Edward IV Groat. Light Coinage

Light coinage 1464-70

	F	VF
Groats, many different issues, varieties, *mms* and mints from	£35	£90
Halfgroats, ditto	£35	£70
Pennies, ditto	£30	£65
Halfpennies, ditto	£30	£70
Farthings Two issues	£300	£600

Henry VI (restored), Groat, London

HENRY VI (restored) 1470-71

	F	VF
Groats, different mints, *mms* from	£130	£290
Halfgroats – from	£250	£500
Pennies – from	£240	£500
Halfpennies – from	£125	£300

EDWARD IV 2nd reign 1471-83

	F	VF
Groats, different varieties, mints etc	£35	£90
Halfgroats	£30	£70
Pennies	£30	£75
Halfpennies	£25	£70

EDWARD V 1483
(The coins read EDWARD but are now considered to be attributable to Richard III)
(Mintmark boar's head)

Groats	£2500	*
Halfgroats		ext. rare
Penny		ext. rare

Richard III Groat, London Mint

RICHARD III 1483-85

	F	VF
Groats, London and York mints, various combinations of *mms*	£270	£500
Halfgroats	£700	£1400
Pennies, York and Durham (London mint unique)	£160	£350
Halfpennies	£130	£260
Farthing	*	*

PERKIN WARBECK, PRETENDER'

Groat, 1494 [cf. BNJ XXVI, p. 125]	£700	£2000

The Tudor Monarchs

HENRY VII 1485-1509
Facing bust issues:

Henry VII Groat London open crown type

Groats, all London

	F	VF
Open crown without arches ...	£75	£250
Crown with two arches unjewelled	£60	£140
Crown with two jewelled arches	£55	£120
Similar but only one arch jewelled	£40	£100
Similar but tall thin lettering ...	£40	£120
Similar but single arch, tall thin lettering	£40	£100

Halfgroats, London

	F	VF
Open crown without arches, tressure unbroken	£300	£700
Double arched crown	£50	£150

	F	VF
Unarched crown	£35	£70
Some varieties and different *mms*.		
Halfgroats, Canterbury		
Open crown, without arches ...	£35	£80
Double arched crown	£30	£70
Some varieties and different *mms*.		
Halfgroats, York		
Double arched crown	£35	£80
Unarched crown with tressure		
broken	£30	£70
Double arched crown with keys		
at side of bust	£25	£70
Many varieties and different mms.		
Pennies, facing bust type		
London	£200	£400
Canterbury, open crown	£200	£450
– arched crown	£45	£120
Durham, Bishop Sherwood		
(S on breast)	£60	£160
York	£40	£90
Many varieties and mms.		
Pennies, 'sovereign enthroned' type		
London, many varieties	£35	£80
Durham –	£45	£100
York –	£35	£80
Halfpennies, London		
Open crown	£50	£130
Arched crown	£35	£100
Crown with lower arch	£25	£80
Some varieties and mms.		
Halfpennies, Canterbury		
Open crown	£150	*
Arched crown	£100	£200
Halfpennies, York		
Arched crown and key below bus	£90	£200
Farthings, all London	£150	*
Profile issues:		
Testoons im lis, three different		
legends	£4000	£8000

Henry VII profile issue testoon

Groats, all London		
Tentative issue (double band to		
crown)	£140	£400

Henry VII Groat, Tentative issue

HAMMERED SILVER

	F	VF
Regular issue (triple band to		
crown)	£60	£150
Some varieties, and *mms*		
Halfgroats		
London	£50	£150
– no numeral after king's name	£400	*
Canterbury	£30	£80
York, two keys below shield ...	£30	£80
– XB by shield	£400	*

HENRY VIII 1509-47
With portrait of Henry VII
1st coinage 1509-26

Groats, London	£80	£200
Groats, Tournai	£350	£975
Groats, Tournai, without portrait	£2000	*
Halfgroats, London	£60	£175
Halfgroats, Canterbury, varieties	£40	£120
Halfgroats, York, varieties	£35	£120
Halfgroats, Tournai	£1500	*
Pennies, 'sovereign enthroned'		
type, London	£35	£90
Pennies, Canterbury, varieties ...	£75	£150
Pennies, Durham, varieties ...	£30	£70
Halfpennies, facing bust type,		
London	£35	£80
Canterbury	£70	£150
Farthings, portcullis type, London	£350	£800

*Henry VIII second coinage groat,
with Irish title HIB REX*

With young portrait of Henry VIII
2nd coinage 1526-44

Groats, London, varieties, *mms*	£40	£120
Groats, Irish title, HIB REX	£350	£850
Groats, York *mms*	£80	£220
Halfgroats, London *mms*	£35	£100
Halfgroats, Canterbury *mms* ...	£30	£90
Halfgroats, York *mms*	£30	£90
Pennies 'sovereign enthroned' type		
London, varieties, *mms*	£30	£90
Canterbury, varieties, *mms* ...	£70	£160
Durham –	£30	£90
York	£90	£200

Henry VIII, Halfpenny, 2nd Coingage, London

Halfpennies, facing bust type		
London, varieties, *mms*	£35	£90
Canterbury	£60	£150
York	£70	£140
Farthings, portcullis type	£400	*

HAMMERED SILVER

With old bearded portrait 3rd coinage 1544-47 Posthumous issues 1547-51	F	VF
Testoons (or shillings)		
London (Tower mint), varieties,		
mms	£500	£1400
Southwark, varieties, mms ...	£500	£1500
Bristol, varieties, mms	£600	£1600
Groats, six different busts,		
varieties, mms		
London (Tower mint)	£50	£170
Southwark	£50	£170
Bristol	£65	£180
Canterbury	£65	£190
London (Durham House)	£170	£500

Henry VIII third coinage groat

Halfgroats, only one style of bust (except York which has two), varieties, mms		
London (Tower mint)	£45	£140
Southwark	£70	£250
Bristol	£65	£180
Canterbury	£35	£130
York	£60	£160
London (Durham House)	£300	£600

Henry VIII Penny, 3rd Coinage Tower

Henry VIII Penny, 3rd Coinage, Bristol

Pennies (facing bust) varieties, mms		
London (Tower mint)	£40	£120
Southwark	£75	£175
London (Durham House)	£250	£600
Bristol	£50	£160
Canterbury	£40	£140
York	£45	£140
Halfpennies (facing bust) varieties, mms		
London (Tower mint)	£50	£150
Bristol	£90	£200
Canterbury	£50	£120
York	£40	£120

EDWARD VI 1547-53 1st period 1547-49	F	VF
Shillings, London (Durham House),		
mm bow, patterns (?)		ext. rare
Groats, London (Tower),		
mm arrow	£475	£1200
Groats, London (Southwark),		
mm E, none	£500	£1400
Halfgroats, London (Tower),		
mm arrow	£400	£900
Halfgroats, London (Southwark),		
mm arrow, E	£400	£800
Halfgroats, Canterbury, mm none	£250	£600
Pennies, London (Tower),		
mm	£300	£650
Pennies, London (Southwark),		
mm E	£350	£750
Pennies, Bristol,		
mm none	£225	£600
Halfpennies, London (Tower),		
mm uncertain	£375	£900
Halfpennies, Bristol, mm none	£300	£800

Edward VI 2nd period shilling. Tower mint with mintmark Y.

Edward VI, Shilling, 2nd period Canterbury with mintmark t.

2nd period 1549-50	F	VF
Shillings, London (Tower) various		
mms	£100	£300
Shillings, Bristol, mm TC	£650	£1500
Shillings, Canterbury, mm T or t	£150	£450
Shillings, London (Durham House),		
mm bow, varieties	£250	£650

3rd period £550-53		
Base silver (similar to issues of 2nd period)		
Shillings, London (Tower),		
mm lis, lion, rose	£150	£400
Pennies, London (Tower),		
mm escallop	£90	£200
Pennies, York, mm mullet	£60	£160
Halfpennies, London (Tower) ...	£200	*

Fine Silver	F	VF
Crown 1551 mm Y, 1551-53		
mm tun	£275	£650

Edward VI Halfcrown 1551, walking horse

	F	VF
Halfcrown, walking horse, 1551, mm Y	£200	£500
Halfcrowns, galloping horse, 1551-52, mm tun	£300	£800

Edward VI 1552 halfcrown galloping horse

	F	VF
Halfcrowns, walking horse, 1553, mm tun	£650	£1500
Shillings, mm Y, tun	£60	£190
Sixpences, London (Tower), mm y, tun	£65	£190
Sixpences, York, mm mullet ...	£120	£375
Threepences, London (Tower), mm tun	£130	£450
Threepences, York mm mullet ...	£270	£650
Pennies, sovereign type	£750	£1500
Farthings, portcullis type	£700	*

Mary Groat

Mary Portrait Penny

MARY 1553-54

	F	VF
Groats, mm pomegranate	£60	£200
Halfgroats, similar	£550	*
Pennies, rev VERITAS TEMP FILIA ...	£400	*
Pennies, rev CIVITAS LONDON	£400	*

PHILIP AND MARY 1554-58

	F	VF
Shillings, full titles, without date	£170	£550
– also without XII	£175	£600
– dated 1554	£175	£550
– dated 1554, English titles ...	£200	£600
– dated 1555, English titles only	£200	£550
– dated 1554, English titles only also without XII	£350	*
– 1555, as last	£500	*
– 1554 but date below bust ...	£600	*
– 1555 but date below bust ...	£600	*
– 1555 similar to previous but without ANG	£700	*
Sixpences, full titles, 1554	£150	£550
– full titles, undated	*	*
– English titles, 1555	£200	£600
– similar but date below bust, 1554	£500	*
– English titles, 1557	£220	£650
– similar, but date below bust, 1557	£750	*
Groats, mm lis	£80	£250
Halfgroats, mm lis	£450	£1250

Philip and Mary Shilling, 1554 and full titles

	F	VF
Pennies, mm lis	£350	£700
Base pennies, without portrait	£50	£160

HAMMERED SILVER

ELIZABETH I 1558-1603   F   VF
Hammered coinage, 1st issue 1558-61
Shillings ELIZABETH

	F	VF
Wire-line circles	£250	£750
Beaded inner circles	£125	£350
ET for Z	£50	£180

Edward VI shilling greyhound countermark (reign of Elizabeth), and Elizabeth I hammered groat

Groats

	F	VF
Wire-line inner circles	£120	£400
Beaded inner circles	£45	£170
ET for Z	£30	£150

Halfgroats

	F	VF
Wire-line inner circles	£150	£375
Beaded inner circles	£30	£80

Elizabeth I Penny, wire-line inner circle

Pennies

	F	VF
Wire-line inner circles	£175	£450
Beaded inner circles	£20	£70
Countermarked shillings of Edward VI, 1560-61		
With portcullis mark (Current for 4½d) **(F)**	£1250	*
With greyhound mark (current for 2½d) **(F)**	1400	*

Hammered coinage, 2nd issue 1561-82

	F	VF
Sixpences, dated 1561-82	£30	£120
Threepences, 1561-82	£20	£75
Halfgroats, undated	£35	£90
Threehalfpences, 1561-62, 1564-70, 1572-79, 1581-82	£25	£90
Pennies, undated	£25	£70
Threefarthings, 1561-62, 1568, 1572-78, 1581-82	£60	£150

Elizabeth I Halfcrown, 1601

Hammered coinage, 3rd issue 1583-1603

	F	VF
Crowns, im **1**	£450	£950
Crowns, im **2**	£600	£1500
Halfcrowns, im **1**	£300	£700
Halfcrowns, im **2 (F)**	£900	£2500
Shillings ELIZAB	£50	£170
Sixpences, 1582-1602	£35	£130
Halfgroats, E D G ROSA etc	£15	£75
Pennies	£18	£70
Halfpennies, portcullis type ...	£25	£75

There are many different mintmarks, such as lis, bell, lion etc., featured on the hammered coins of Elizabeth I, and these marks enable one to date those coins which are not themselves dated. For more details see J.J. North's English Hammered Coinage, *Volume 2.*

Elizabeth I Miled Coinage, Sixpence, 1562

Milled Coinage
Shillings

	F	VF
large size	£275	£750
Intermediate	£130	£400
Small	£110	£350
Sixpences		
1561	£35	£140
1562	£30	£120
1563-64, 1566	£55	£200
1567-68	£55	£200
1570-71	£100	£350
Groats, undated	£120	£375
Threepences, 1561, 1562-64 ...	£90	£275
Halfgroats	£90	£300
Threefarthings		ext rare

The Stuart Kings

JAMES I 1603-25	F	VF
1st coinage 1603-04		
Crowns, rev EXURGAT etc	£425	£950
Halfcrowns –	£475	£1400
Shillings, varieties	£50	£200
Sixpences, dated 1603-04,		
varieties	£35	£150
Halfgroats, undated	£25	£75
Pennies –	£30	£80

James I Sixpence, 1603

2nd coinage 1604-19		
Crowns rev QVAE DEVS etc ...	£400	£800
Halfcrowns –	£600	£1400

James I 2nd coinage shilling

	F	VF
Shillings, varieties	£35	£150
Sixpences, dated 1604-15,		
varieties etc.	£30	£100
Halfgroats, varieties	£15	£60
Pennies	£15	£40
Halfpennies	£15	£45

James I Shilling, 3rd Coinage

3rd coinage 1619-25		
Crowns	£250	£550
– Plume over reverse shield ...	£300	£650
Halfcrowns	£100	£300
– Plume over reverse shield ...	£170	£450

HAMMERED SILVER

	F	VF

James I halfcrown with plume over shield on reverse

	F	VF
Shillings	£35	£150
– Plume over reverse shield ...	£90	£250
Sixpences dated 1621-24	£30	£130
Halfgroats	£15	£35
Pennies	£15	£30
Halfpennies	£15	£40

James I sixpence of 1622

CHARLES I 1625-1649	F	VF
Tower Mint 1625-1643		
Crowns		
(Obv. King on horseback. Rev. shield)		
1st horseman/square shield		
im lis, cross calvary	£250	£600
As last/plume above shield		
im lis, cross calvary, castle ...	£550	£1250
2nd horseman/oval shield		
im plume, rose harp.		
Some varieties, from	£220	£550
3rd horseman/round shield		
im bell, crown, tun, anchor,		
triangle, star, portcullis, triangle		
in circle. Some varieties, from	£250	£600
Halfcrowns		
(Obv. King on horseback. Rev. shield)		

*Charles I
Tower halfcrown:
first horseman*

HAMMERED SILVER

	F	VF
1st horseman/square shield		
im lis, cross calvary, negro's head, castle, anchor.		
Many varieties, from	£100	£300
2nd horseman/oval shield		
im plume, rose, harp, portcullis.		
Many varieties, from	£80	£200
3rd horseman/round shield		
im bell, crown, tun, portcullis, anchor, triangle, star		
Many varieties, from	£60	£150
4th horseman/round shield		
im star, triangle in circle	£35	£120

*Charles I
Tower Halfcrown,
mintmark
triangle*

Shillings

	F	VF
1st bust/square shield		
***im* lis, cross calvary**		
Some varieties	£50	£160
2nd bust/square shield		
im cross calvary, negro's head, castle, anchor, heart, plume		
Many varieties, from	£45	£150
3rd bust/oval shield		
im plume, rose	£35	£130
4th bust/oval or round shield		
im harp, portcullis, bell, crown, tun		
Many varieties, from	£40	£150
5th bust/square shield		
im tun, anchor, triangle		
Many varieties, from	£35	£130
6th bust/square shield		
im anchor, triangle, star, triangle in circle		
Some varieties, from	£35	£130

Sixpences
(early ones are dated)

	F	VF
1st bust/square shield, date above		
1625 *im* lis, cross calvary		
1626 *im* cross calvary	£50	£170
2nd bust/square shield, date above		
1625, 1626 *im* cross calvary		
1626, 1627 *im* negro's head		
1626, 1628 *im* castle		
1628, 1629 *im* anchor		
1629 *im* heart		
1630 *im* heart, plume	£95	£250

	F	VF
3rd bust/oval shield		
im plume, rose	£45	£170
4th bust/oval or round shield		
im harp, portcullis, bell, crown, tun	£35	£130

Charles I Tower sixpence mm bell

	F	VF
5th bust/square shield		
im tun, anchor, triangle		
Many varieties, from	£35	£130
6th bust/square shield		
im triangle, star	£30	£130
Halfgroats		
Crowned rose both sides		
im lis, cross calvary, blackamoor's head	£15	£50
2nd bust/oval shield		
im plume, rose	£18	£60
3rd bust/oval shield		
im rose, plume	£15	£60
4th bust/oval or round shield,		
im harp, crown, portcullis, bell, tun, anchor, triangle, star		
Many varieties from	£15	£60
5th bust/round shield		
im anchor	£25	£100
Pennies		
Uncrowned rose both sides		
im one or two pellets, lis, negro's head	£15	£40
2nd bust/oval shield		
im plume	£18	£60
3rd bust/oval shield		
im plume, rose	£15	£60
4th bust/oval shield		
im harp, one or two pellets, portcullis, bell, triangle	£15	£60
5th bust/oval shield		
im one or two pellets, none	£15	£45
Halfpennies		
Uncrowned rose both sides		
im none	£15	£45

Tower Mint, under Parliament 1643-48

Crowns
(Obv. King on horseback, Rev. shield)

	F	VF
4th horseman/round shield		
im (**P**), (**R**), eye sun	£290	£650
5th horseman/round shield		
im sun, sceptre	£350	£750

Halfcrowns
(Obv. King on horseback, Rev. shield)

	F	VF
3rd horseman/round shield		
im (**P**), (**R**), eye sun	£70	£275
im (**P**), foreshortened horse	£150	£375
5th horseman (tall)/round shield		
im sun, sceptre	£75	£300

Sixpence of Broit's 2nd milled issue

Charles I Parliament shilling, mm eye

Shillings (revs. all square shield)
6th bust (crude)

	F	VF
im (**P**), (**R**), eye, sun	£45	£200
7th bust (tall, slim)		
im sun, sceptre	£45	£200
8th bust (shorter, older)		
im sceptre	£45	£250

Sixpences (revs. all square shield)
6th bust

	F	VF
im (**P**), (**R**), eye sun	£80	£200
7th bust		
im (**R**), eye, sun, sceptre ...	£75	£200
8th bust, (crude style)		
im eye, sun	£90	£250

Halfgroats
4th bust/round shield

	F	VF
im (**P**), (**R**), eye sceptre ...	£30	£80
7th bust (old/round shield)		
im eye, sun, sceptre	£25	£70

Pennies
7th bust/oval shield

	F	VF
im one or two pellets	£20	£60

Briot's hammered issues 1638-39
im: anchor, triangle over anchor

	F	VF
Halfcrowns	£600	£1250
Shillings	£350	£900

*Charles I
Crown
of Exeter*

PROVINCIAL MINTS
York 1642-44
im: lion

	F	VF
Halfcrowns, varieties from	£90	£250
Shillings –	£80	£200
Sixpences –	£150	£375
Threepences	£40	£95

Aberystwyth 1638-42
im: open book

	F	VF
Halfcrowns, varieties from	£400	£1000
Shillings –	£180	£450
Sixpences –	£180	£500
Groats –	£35	£80

Charles I Briot's crown

Briot's 1st milled issued 1631-32
im: flower and **B**

	F	VF
Crowns	£300	£800
Halfcrowns...	£190	£480
Shillings	£130	£350
Sixpences	£70	£200
Halfgroats	£35	£70
Pennies	£30	£70

Briot's 2nd milled issue 1638-39
im: anchor, anchor and B, anchor and mullet

	F	VF
Halfcrowns	£160	£400
Shillings	£80	£200
Sixpences	£40	£100

Aberystwyth groat

	F	VF
Threepences –	£30	£60
Halfgroats –	£40	£90
Pennies –	£70	£200
Halfpennies	£150	£350

Aberystwyth – Furnace 1647-48
im: crown

	F	VF
Halfcrowns from	£1000	£2500
Shillings		ext. rare

HAMMERED SILVER

	F	VF
Sixpences		ext. rare
Groats	£200	£450
Threepences	£250	£600
Halfgroats	£250	£600
Pennies	£600	£1250

Shrewsbury 1642
mm: plume without band

	F	VF
Pounds, varieties from	£950	£3000
Halfpounds –	£450	£950
Crowns –	£400	£900
Halfcrowns –	£250	£600
Shillings –	£600	£1350

Oxford 1642-46
mm: plume with band

	F	VF
Pounds, varieties from	£950	£3000
Halfpounds –	£350	£700
Crowns –	£350	£700
Halfcrowns –	£90	£250
Shillings –	£100	£275
Sixpences –	£140	£300
Groats –	£50	£160
Threepences –	£40	£150
Halfgroats –	£80	£200
Pennies –	£100	£250

Bristol 1643-45
im: Bristol monogram, acorn, plumelet

	F	VF
Halfcrowns, varieties from	£130	£350

Charles I halfcrown of York with mm lion

	F	VF
Shillings –	£130	£300
Sixpences –	£150	£400
Groats –	£120	£280
Threepences –	£140	£400
Halfgroats –	£200	£450
Pennies –	£320	£650

Charles I sixpence, Bristol 1644

A, B, and plumes issues
Associated with Thomas Bushell; previously assigned to Lundy

	F	VF
Halfcrowns, varieties from	£450	£1250

	F	VF
Shillings –	£250	£650
Sixpences –	£150	£400
Groats –	£90	£200
Threepences –	£90	£170
Halfgroats –	£300	£700

Truro 1642-43
im: rose, bugle

	F	VF
Crowns, varieties	£200	£450
Halfcrowns –	£475	£950
Shillings –		ext. rare

Bristol shilling 1644

Exeter 1643-46
im Ex, rose, castle

	F	VF
Halfpounds		ext. rare
Crowns, varieties	£170	£400
Halfcrowns	£100	£300
Shillings	£170	£400
Sixpences	£170	£400
Groats	£60	£150
Threepences	£80	£180
Halfgroats –	£120	£350
Pennies	£250	£475

Worcester 1643-4
im: castle, helmet, leopard's head, lion, two lions, lis, rose, star

	F	VF
Halfcrowns, many varieties ...	£450	£950

Salopia (Shrewsbury) 1644
im: helmet, lis, rose (in legend)

	F	VF
Halfcrowns, many varieties ...	£550	£2000

Worcester or Salopia (Shrewsbury)
im: bird, boar's head, lis, castle, cross, and annulets, helmet, lion, lis, pear, rose, scroll

	F	VF
Shillings, varieties	£650	£1800
Sixpences	£800	£1750
Groats	£400	£1250
Threepences	£350	£850
Halfgroats	£400	£900

'HC' mint (probably Hartlebury Castle, Worcester 1646)
im: pear, three pears

	F	VF
Halfcrowns	£1250	£3000

Chester 1644
im: cinquefoil, plume, prostrate gerb, three gerbs

	F	VF
Halfcrowns, varieties	£550	£1250
Shillings		ext. rare
Threepences		very rare

Welsh Marches mint? 1644	F	VF
Halfcrowns...	£450	£900

Welsh Marches mint, halfcrown

SIEGE PIECES
Carlisle besieged 1644-45

	F	VF
Three shillings	£2500	£6000
Shillings (**F**)	£1700	£3500

Newark besieged many times
(surrendered May 6, 1646)

	F	VF
Halfcrowns, 1645-46 (**F**)	£350	£750

Newark Besieged, Shilling, dated 1645

	F	VF
Shillings, 1645-46, varieties (**F**)	£250	£600
Ninepences, 1645-46	£250	£550
Sixpences	£200	£600

Pontefract besieged 1648-49

Two shillings		ext. rare
Shillings, 1648, varieties	£600	£1250

Ponefract Besieged 1648, Siege Shilling

Scarborough besieged 1644-45
Many odd values issued here, all of which are extremely rare. The coin's value was decided by the intrinsic value of the piece of metal from which it was made.

HAMMERED SILVER

F   VF

Examples: 5s 8d, 2s 4d, 1s 9d, 1s 3d, 7d etc. (**F**).
Collectors could expect to pay at least £2000 or more in F and £4000 in VF for any of these.

COMMONWEALTH 1649-60

	F	VF
Crowns, *im* sun 1649,51-54, 56 ...	£350	£650
Halfcrowns, *im* sun 1649, 1651-6	£130	£350
—*im* anchor 1658-60	£450	£950

Commonwealth Shilling, 1651

	F	VF
Shillings, *im* sun 1649, 1661-87	£70	£170
—*im* anchor 1658-60	£350	£700

A superb 1651 sixpence

	F	VF
Sixpences, *im* sun 1649, 1651-7	£80	£170
—*im* anchor 1658-6	£350	£700
Halfgroats undated	£25	£70
Pennies undated	£25	£60
Halfpennies undated	£25	£60

CHARLES II 1660-85
Hammered coinage 1660-62

	F	VF
Halfcrowns, three issues ... from	£200	£500
Shillings— ... ... from	£80	£350

Charles II hammered issue shilling

	F	VF
Sixpences—	£60	£200
Fourpences, third issue only ...	£20	£70
Threepences— ... ... from	£25	£65
Twopences, three issues from	£15	£50
Pennies— ... ... from	£25	£60

'ROYAL' AND 'ROSE' BASE METAL FARTHINGS

Until 1613 English coins were struck only in gold or silver — the monarchy considered that base metal issues would be discreditable to the royal prerogative of coining. However, silver coins had become far too small, farthings so tiny that they had to be discontinued. So to meet demands for small change James I authorised Lord Harington to issue copper farthing tokens. Subsequently this authority passed in turn to the Duke of Lennox, the Duchess of Richmond and Lord Maltravers. It ceased by order of Parliament in 1644.

	Fair	F	VF	EF
JAMES I				
Royal farthing tokens				
Type 1 Harington (circa 1613). Small copper flan with tin-washed surface, mint-mark between sceptres below crown	£10	£35	£120	*
Type 2 Harington (circa 1613). Larger flan, no tin wash	£12	£25	£75	*
Type 3 Lennox (1614-25). IACO starts at 1 o'clock position	£8	£20	£50	*
Type 4 Lennox (1622-25). Oval flan, IACO starts at 7 o'clock	£12	£30	£75	*
CHARLES I				
Royal farthing tokens				
Type 1 Richmond (1625-34). Single arched crown	£8	£15	£40	*
Type 2 Transitional (circa 1634). Double arched crown	£8	£20	£60	*
Type 3 Maltravers (1634-36). Inner circles	£8	£20	£45	£95
Type 4 Richmond (1625-34). As Type 1 but oval	£8	£30	*	*
Type 5 Maltravers (1634-36). Double arched crown	£15	£50	*	*
Rose farthing tokens (rose on reverse)				
Type 1 Small thick flan	£7	£15	£35	*
Type 2 Same, but single arched crown	£7	£15	£40	*
Type 3 Same, but sceptres below crown	£15	£50	*	*

James I Harington farthings, types 1, 2 and 3 (left to right)

Charles I Richmond, Maltravers and Rose farthings (left to right)

COINS MARKET VALUES

MILLED COINAGE from 1656

Again it must be stressed that the prices shown in this guide are the approximate amounts collectors can expect to pay for coins — they are not dealers' buying prices. Information for this guide is drawn from auction results and dealers' lists, with the aim of determining firm valuations. Prices still vary enormously from sale to sale and from one dealer's list to another. Allowance must also be made for the variance in the standards of grading. The prices given here aim at a reasonable assessment of the market at the time of compilation, but they are not the product of computers, which would, in any case, provide only average (not necessarily accurate) prices. It is not possible to forecast such values because of the erratic fluctuations that can occur, not only in boom conditions but also during times of economic uncertainty, and an annual catalogue of this type cannot be up to date on the bullion prices of common sovereigns, for example. If you are buying or selling bullion gold coins, refer to current quotations from bullion dealers.

With some denominations in the silver and copper series, column headings indicating condition change at the beginning of the lists of George III coins. The condition (grade) of a coin is of great importance in determining its market value. Notes on grading and on abbreviations etc. used in these price guides appear elsewhere in this publication.

Cromwell gold patterns

These were struck by order of Cromwell, with the consent of the Council. The dies were made by Thomas Simon, and the coins were struck on Peter Blondeau's machine. The fifty shillings and the broad were struck from the same dies, but the fifty shillings has the edge inscription PROTECTOR LITERIS LITERAE NUMMIS CORONA ER SALUS, while the broad is not so thick and has a grained edge. No original strikings of the half broad are known, but some were struck from dies made by John Tanner in 1738. All three denominations are dated 1656.

Oliver Cromwell gold half broad 1656

	F	VF	EF	Unc
Fifty shillings	*	*	£15000	*
Broad	£2000	£3500	£6000	£7500
Half broad	*	*	£6500	£8500

Five guineas

CHARLES II	F	VF	EF	Unc
1668-78 pointed end to trnctn of bust ...	£1200	£2500	£6500	*
1668, 69, 75—eleph below bust	£1200	£2500	£6500	*
1675-8—eleph & castle below bust	£1200	£2500	£6500	*
1678-84 rounded end to trnctn	£1100	£2000	£5800	*
1680-4—eleph & castle	£1500	£2750	£7000	*
JAMES II				
1686 sceptres in wrong order on rev ...	£1200	£2250	£6000	£10000
1687-8 sceptres correct	£1200	£2250	£6000	£10000
1687-8 eleph & castle	£1250	£2500	£6500	£10000
WILLIAM AND MARY				
1691-4 no prov mark	£1200	£2000	£5250	£9500
1691-4 eleph & castle	£1350	£2500	£6000	£10000
WILLIAM III				
1699-1700 no prov mark	£1200	£2000	£4750	£8500
1699 eleph & castle	£1400	£2500	£5500	£9500
1701 new bust 'fine work'	£1350	£2250	£5250	£8500

Charles II 1676 five guineas, elephant and castle

FIVE GUINEAS

George II 1729 five guineas

*Charles II 1664 two guineas
elephant below bust*

James II 1687 two guineas

	F	VF	EF	Unc
ANNE				
Pre-Union with Scotland				
1703 VIGO below bust	*	*	£35000	*
1705-6 plain below	£1350	£2750	£6000	£9500
Post-Union with Scotland				
1706	£1250	£2500	£5500	£9000
1709 Larger lettering, wider shield and				
crowns	£1250	£2500	£5250	£8500
1711, 1713-4 broader bust	£1250	£2500	£5250	£8500

Pre-Union reverses have separate shields (top and right) for England and Scotland. Post-Union reverses have the English and Scottish arms side by side on the top and bottom shields.

GEORGE I				
1716, 17, 20, 26	£1750	£2750	£7000	£10000
GEORGE II				
1729, 31, 35, 38, 41 YH	£1350	£2250	£4000	£7000
1729 E,I,C, below head	£1350	£2500	£4500	£7500
1746 OH, lima below	£1350	£2750	£4750	£8000
1748, 53 plain below	£1350	£2750	£4750	£8000
GEORGE III				
1770, 73, 77 patterns only	*	*	£30000	£45000

Two guineas

CHARLES II	F	VF	EF	Unc
1664, 5, 9, 71 pointed end to trnctn	£650	£1100	£3500	£6500
1664 elephant below	£650	£1100	£3500	£6500
1675-84 rounded end to trnctn	£550	£1000	£3000	£6000
1676, 78, 82-84 eleph & castle below bust	£700	£1250	£4500	£7500
1678 elephant below				ext. rare
JAMES II				
1687	£800	£1950	£4500	£7500
1688/9	£850	£2000	£5000	£8000
WILLIAM AND MARY				
1691, 3, 4 eleph & castle	£800	£1650	£3750	£6000
1693, 4 no prov mark	£750	£1400	£3250	£5500
WILLIAM III				
1701	£1000	£1950	£3500	£6500
ANNE				
(none struck before Union)				
1709, 11, 13, 14	£650	£1200	£2500	£5000
GEORGE I				
1717,20,26	£650	£1250	£2500	£4000
GEORGE II				
1734, 5, 8, 9,YH (**F**)	£400	£650	£1500	£2250
1739, 40 intermediate head (**F**)	£450	£700	£1750	£2750
1748, 53 OH	£475	£750	£2000	£3000
GEORGE III				
1768, 73, 77 patterns only	*	*	£12500	£22500

Guineas

CHARLES II	F	VF	EF	Unc
1663 pointed trnctn	£450	£750	£3000	£5500
1663—eleph	£450	£750	£3500	*
1664 trnctn indented	£450	£750	£3000	*
1664—eleph	*	*	£6000	*

GUINEAS

*Charles II 1663 guinea
elephant below bust*

	F	VF	EF	Unc
1664-73 sloping pointed trncttn	£350	£600	£2750	£5500
1664, 5, 8 — eleph	£450	£1000	£3250	*
1672-84 rounded trncttn	£300	£500	£2500	*
1674-84 — eleph & castle	£450	£850	£4000	*
1677, 8 — eleph	*	£1750	*	*

JAMES II
1685, 6 1st bust	£250	£500	£1750	£3000
1685 — eleph & castle	£275	£550	£1900	*
1686-8 2nd bust	£275	£525	£1750	£3000
1686-8 — eleph & castle	£275	£550	£1850	*

WILLIAM AND MARY
1689-94 no prov mark	£300	£475	£1750	£3500
1689-94 eleph & castle	£325	£575	£2000	*
1692 eleph	£550	£1200	*	*

WILLIAM III
1695, 6 1st bust	£250	£400	£1500	£2500
1695, 7 — eleph & castle	*	*	*	*
1697-1701 2nd bust	£250	£400	£1500	*
1698-1701 — eleph & castle	£450	£1100	*	*
1701 3rd bust 'fine work'	£350	£600	£2500	*

ANNE
Pre-Union[1]
1702, 1705-7 plain below bust	£300	£600	£1500	£2750
1703 VIGO below	£500	*	*	*

Post Union[1]
1707, 8 1st bust	£200	£375	£950	£2000
1707 — eleph & castle	£400	£850	£2750	*
1707-9 2nd bust	£200	£375	£950	£2000
1708-9 — eleph & castle	£450	£1100	£3500	*
1710-1714 3rd bust	£200	£375	£900	£1400

[1]See note in prices of five guinea pieces for Anne.

Anne 1713 guinea

GEORGE I
1714 1st head PR. EL. (Prince Elector) in rev legend	£600	£1200	£2200	£3500
1715 2nd head, tie with two ends	£275	£450	£1250	£2500
1715 3rd head, hair not curling round trncttn	£225	£400	£1150	£2250
1716-23 4th head, tie with loop	£200	£350	£950	£2000
1721, 2 — eleph & castle	£500	*	*	*
1723-7 5th head, smaller, older bust	£225	£400	£1150	£2250
1726 — eleph & castle	£500	£1350	*	*

GEORGE II
1727 1st YH, small lettering	£450	£850	£2250	£3750
1727, 8 — larger lettering	£300	£500	£1800	*
1729-32 2nd YH (narrower)	£250	£500	£1500	*
1729, 31, 2 — E.I.C. below	£350	£800	£1900	£3000
1732-8 — larger lettering	£200	£500	£1350	£2000
1732 — E.I.C. below	£350	£600	£1750	*
1739, 40, 43 intermediate head	£200	£450	£1000	£1900
1739 — E.I.C. below	£350	£750	£2000	*
1745, 6 — larger lettering	£200	£600	£1350	*
1745 — LIMA below	£500	£1000	£2750	*
1747-53, 5, 6, 8, 9, 60, OH	£200	£300	£850	£1750

GEORGE III
1761, 1st head	£500	£1000	£2500	£3500
1763, 4, 2nd head	£200	£500	£1750	*
1765-73, 3rd head	£100	£250	£650	£1200
1774-9, 81-6, 4th head	£100	£180	£350	£700
1789-99, 5th head, 'spade' rev (F)	£100	£165	£275	£425
1813, 6th head, rev shield in Garter ('Military guinea')	£250	£500	£850	£1200

George III 1768 guinea

William and Mary 1691 half guinea

William III 1695 half guinea

George I 1719 half guinea

George I half guinea, 1725

George II 1756 half guinea

George III 1788 half guinea with 'spade' type shield on reverse

George I 1718 quarter guinea

Half Guineas

	F	VF	EF	Unc
CHARLES II				
1669-72 bust with pointed trnctn	£250	£450	£1750	*
1672-84 rounded trnctn...	£250	£450	£1750	*
1676-8, 80, 82-4 — eleph & castle	£300	£600	£2500	*
JAMES II				
1686-8 no prov mark	£300	£450	£1750	£2750
1686 eleph & castle	£650	*	*	*
WILLIAM AND MARY				
1689 1st busts	£250	£450	£1500	£2750
1690-4 2nd busts	£250	£400	£1500	*
1691-2 — eleph & castle	£300	£450	£1750	*
1692 — eleph			ext. rare	
WILLIAM III				
1695 no prov mark	£200	£350	£1250	£2250
1695, 6 eleph & castle	£350	£700	£2000	*
1697-1701 larger harp on rev	£250	£450	£1500	*
1698 — eleph & castle	£300	£500	£2000	*
ANNE				
Pre-Union[1]				
1702, 5 plain below bust	£250	£500	£1500	*
1703 VIGO below	£2500	£3500	*	*
Post-Union[1]				
1707-14 plain	£175	£275	£650	£1400
[1]See note in prices of five guineas for Anne.				
GEORGE I				
1715, 17-23, 1st head	£150	£250	£600	£1200
1721 eleph & castle	£300	£800	*	*
1724-7, smaller older head	£150	£250	£600	£1200
GEORGE II				
1728-39 YH	£150	£250	£850	£1750
1729-32, 9 — E.I.C. below	£175	£325	£1200	*
1740, 3, 5, 6, intermediate head	£150	£275	£750	*
1745 — LIMA below	£650	£1000	£2750	*
1747-53, 5, 6, 58-60 OH	£150	£225	£600	£1500
GEORGE III				
1762, 3, 1st head	£200	£375	£1000	*
1764-6, 8, 9, 72-5, 2nd head	£100	£150	£400	£750
1774, 5, 3rd head	£500	£900	£1800	*
1775-9, 81, 83-6, 4th head	£75	£100	£250	£450
1787-91, 93-8, 1800, 5th head	£60	£80	£175	£350
1801-3, 6th head	£60	£75	£165	£300
1804, 6, 8-11, 13, 7th head	£60	£75	£165	£300

Third guineas

	F	VF	EF	Unc
GEORGE III				
1797-1800 1st head	£40	£60	£100	£195
1801-3 — date close to crown on reverse	£40	£60	£100	£195
1804, 6, 8-11, 2nd head	£40	£70	£125	£200

Quarter guineas

	F	VF	EF	Unc
GEORGE I				
1718	£40	£75	£110	£195
GEORGE III	F	VF	EF	Unc
1762	£45	£75	£150	£250

COINS MARKET VALUES

Britannias

(See under Decimal Coinage)

Five pounds

	F	VF	EF	Unc
GEORGE III				
1820 pattern **(F)**	*	*	*	£35000
GEORGE IV				
1826 proof	*	*	£5000	£7000
VICTORIA				
1839 proof with 'Una and the Lion' rev **(F)**	*	£7500	£12500	£17500
1887 JH **(F)**	£350	£475	£600	£800
1887 proof	*	*	£1200	£2000
1893 OH **(F)**	£400	£750	£1000	£1400
1893 proof	*	*	£1250	£2250
EDWARD VII				
1902 **(F)**	£350	£450	£550	£700
1902 proof	*	*	£600	£750
GEORGE V				
1911 proof **(F)** ...	*	*	£950	£1250
GEORGE VI				
1937 proof	*	*	*	£600

ELIZABETH II

In 1984 the Royal Mint issued the first of an annual issue of Brilliant Uncirculated £5 coins. These bear the symbol 'U' in a circle to the left of the date on the reverse to indicate the standard of striking.

1981 proof	£400
1984	£400
1985	£425
1986	£425
1987 new effigy	£425
1988	£425
1989 500th anniversary of the sovereign, BU	£450
1990 Queen Mother's 90th birthday, proof	£575
1990	£435
1991	£450
1992	£450
1993 Coronation, proof	£700
1993	£475
1994	£500
1995	£535
1996 Queen's 70th Birthday, proof	£645
... ... BU	£575
1997 Golden Wedding, proof	£650
1997	£535
1998 Prince Charles 50th Birthday, proof	£600
1998 New Portrait	£535
1999 Diana Memorial	£600
1999 Millennium	£600

Reverse of the gold proof five pounds marking the Queen Mother's 90th birthday (for silver and cupro-nickel versions see Decimal Coinage)

Two pounds

	F	VF	EF	Unc
GEORGE III				
1820 pattern **(F)**	*	*	£9500	£12500

George III 1820 pattern two pounds

	F	VF	EF	Unc
GEORGE IV ...	F	VF	EF	Unc
1823 St George on reverse **(F)**	£250	£400	£650	£1200
1826 proof, shield reverse	*	*	£2000	£3000

William IV 1831 proof two pounds

	F	VF	EF	Unc
WILLIAM IV				
1831 proof	*	*	£3000	£4500
VICTORIA				
1887 JH **(F)** ...	£185	£220	£265	£300
1887 proof	*	*	£500	£800
1893 OH **(F)** ...	£220	£300	£400	£550
1893 proof	*	*	£500	£900
EDWARD VII				
1902 **(F)**	£175	£210	£265	£300
1902 proof	*	*	£275	£325
GEORGE V				
1911 proof **(F)**	*	*	*	£450

1937 proof two pounds

	F	VF	EF	Unc
GEORGE VI				
1937 proof ...	*	*	*	£375

TWO POUNDS

ELIZABETH II	F	VF	EF	Unc
1983 proof				£225
1986 Commonwealth Games, proof				£225
1987 proof				£250
1988 proof				£250
1989 500th anniversary of the sovereign, proof				£275
1990 proof				£250
1991 proof				£250
1993 proof				£250
1994 gold proof				£425
1994 gold proof 'mule'				£750
1995 VE day gold proof				£375
1995 50th Anniversary of UN, proof				£300
1996 European Football Championship				£350
1997 Bimetal proof				£350
1998 New portrait, proof				£300
1999 Rugby World Cup............				£300

Sovereigns

GEORGE III	F	VF	EF	Unc
1817 **(F)**	£110	£190	£450	£700
1818	£110	£220	£550	£800
1819 ....£12500	£25000	£55000		*
1820	£110	£200	£500	£750

GEORGE IV

Type Laureate head/St George

1821	£110	£190	£500	£700
1822 **(F)**	£110	£190	£500	£700
1823	£150	£250	£750	£950
1824	£110	£190	£500	£700
1825	£250	£500	£1250	*

George IV 1826 proof sovereign

Type bare head/shield

1825 **(F)**	£100	£175	£425	£700
1826	£100	£175	£450	£750
1826 proof	*		£950	£2000
1827 **(F)**	£100	£175	£450	£750
1828 **(F)**	£650	£2000	£4000	*
1829	£100	£175	£425	£700
1830	£100	£175	£425	£700

WILLIAM IV

1831	£125	£200	£550	£850
1831 proof	*	*	£1500	£2850

William IV 1831 proof sovereign

1832 **(F)**	£110	£180	£500	£700
1833	£110	£200	£550	£750
1835	£110	£180	£500	£700
1836	£110	£180	£500	£700
1837	£120	£200	£550	£750

VICTORIA

Type 1, YH obv, shield rev

1838	£85	£125	£275	£650

Victoria 1839 proof sovereign

	F	VF	EF	Unc
1839	£95	£175	£750	£1200
1839 proof	*	*	£1200	£2500
1841	£500	£900	£3000	*
1842	*	*	£100	£250
1843	*	*	£100	£200
1843 narrow shield	£650	£1200	£2000	*
1844	*	*	£100	£200
1845	*	*	£100	£200
1846	*	*	£100	£200
1847	*	*	£100	£200
1848	*	*	£100	£200
1849	*	*	£100	£200
1850	*	*	£100	£200
1851	*	*	£100	£200
1852	*	*	£100	£200
1853	*	*	£90	£200

Victoria 1853 sovereign, shield on reverse

1853 proof	*	*	£4000	£5500
1854	*	*	£100	£200
1855	*	*	£100	£200
1856	*	*	£100	£200
1857	*	*	£100	£200
1858	*	*	£125	£250
1859	*	*	£80	£175
1859 'Ansell' ...	£120	£400	£1250	*
1860	*	*	£100	£200
1861	*	*	£80	£175
1862	*	*	£80	£175
1863	*	*	£70	£150
1863 die number below wreath on rev	*	*	£70	£150
1863 '827' on truncation ...	£1500	£2250	£3750	*
1864 die no. ...	*	*	£70	£150
1865 die no. ...	*	*	£70	£150
1866 die no. ...	*	*	£70	£150
1868 die no. ...	*	*	£70	£150
1869 die no. ...	*	*	£70	£150
1870 die no. ...	*	*	£70	£150
1871 die no. ...	*	*	£70	£110
1871 S (Sydney mint) below wreath	*	*	£125	£250
1872	*	*	£70	£125
1872 die no. ...	*	*	£60	£100
1872 M (Melbourne mint) below wreath	*	*	£100	£250
1872 S	*	*	£100	£250
1873 die no. ...	*	*	£70	£150
1873 S	*	*	£100	£250
1874 die no. ...	£300	£850	£2500	*
1874 M	*	*	£100	£250
1875 S	*	*	£100	£250
1877 S	*	*	£80	£200

	F	VF	EF	Unc
1878 S	*	*	£100	£200
1879 S	*	*	£80	£200
1880 M	£200	£750	£1500	£2750
1880 S	*	*	£100	£250
1881 M	*	£80	£125	£250
1881 S	*	*	£100	£250
1882 M	*	*	£100	£250
1882 S	*	*	£75	£175
1883 M	*	£125	£300	£600
1883 S	*	*	£75	£150
1884 M	*	*	£100	£250
1884 S	*	*	£75	£175
1885 M	*	*	£100	£200
1885 S	*	*	£75	£175
1886 M	£250	£1000	£2000	£3000
1886 S	*	*	£80	£175
1887 M	£200	£500	£1250	£2000
1887 S	*	*	£80	£175

Type II. YH obv, St George and Dragon rev

	F	VF	EF	Unc
1871	*	*	£75	£120
1871 S below head	*	£75	£120	£200
1872	*	*	£90	£150
1872 M below head	*	£85	£150	£300
1872 S	*	*	£150	£250
1873	*	*	£75	£125
1873 M	*	£75	£150	£300
1873 S	*	*	£150	£250
1874	*	*	£75	£125
1874 M	*	*	£150	£300
1874 S	*	*	£100	£200
1875 M	*	*	£150	£300
1875 S	*	*	£100	£200
1876	*	*	£75	£175
1876 M	*	*	£150	£300
1876 S	*	*	£125	£250
1877 M	*	*	£125	£300
1878	*	*	£75	£125
1878 M	*	*	£125	£300
1879	*	£95	£450	£750
1879 M	*	*	£125	£250
1879 S	*	*	£250	£650
1880	*	*	£70	£125
1880 M	*	*	£125	£300
1880 S	*	*	£150	£300
1881 M	*	*	£150	£300
1881 S	*	*	£125	£300
1882 M	*	*	£80	£175
1882 S	*	*	£75	£125
1883 M	*	*	£75	£150
1883 S	*	*	£70	£100
1884	*	*	£70	£120
1884 M	*	*	£80	£120
1884 S	*	*	£70	£100
1885	*	*	£80	£120
1885 M	*	*	£80	£125
1885 S	*	*	£70	£110
1886 M	*	*	£80	£125
1886 S	*	*	£70	£100
1887 M	*	*	£80	£120
1887 S	*	*	£70	£110

Jubilee head coinage

	F	VF	EF	Unc
1887 (F)	*	*	£60	£85
1887 proof	*	*	£300	£450
1887 M on ground below dragon	*	*	£100	£250
1887 S on ground below dragon	*	*	£400	£750
1888	* -	*	*	£70
1888 M	*	*	*	£90
1888 S	*	*	*	£90
1889	*	*	*	£70
1889 M	*	*	*	£90

SOVEREIGNS

	F	VF	EF	Unc
1889 S	*	*	*	£80
1890	*	*	*	£70
1890	*	*	*	£80
1890 S	*	*	*	£80
1891	*	*	*	£70
1891 M	*	*	*	£80
1891 S	*	*	*	£80
1892	*	*	*	£70
1892 M	*	*	*	£80
1892 S	*	*	*	£80
1893 M	*	*	*	£80
1893 S	*	*	*	£80

Old head coinage

	F	VF	EF	Unc
1893	*	*	*	£65
1893 proof	*	*	£350	£500
1893 M	*	*	*	£65
1893 S	*	*	*	£65
1894	*	*	*	£65
1894 M	*	*	*	£65
1894 S	*	*	*	£65
1895	*	*	*	£65
1895 M	*	*	*	£65
1895 S	*	*	*	£65
1896	*	*	*	£65
1896 M	*	*	*	£65
1896 S	*	*	*	£65
1897 M	*	*	*	£65
1897 S	*	*	*	£65
1898	*	*	*	£65
1898 M	*	*	*	£65
1898 S	*	*	*	£65
1899	*	*	*	£65

1898 Victoria Old Head sovereign

	F	VF	EF	Unc
1899 M	*	*	*	£65
1899 P (Perth mint) on ground below dragon	*	*	*	£200
1899 S	*	*	*	£150
1900	*	*	*	£65
1900 M	*	*	*	£65
1900 P	*	*	*	£110
1900 S	*	*	*	£100
1901	*	*	*	£65
1901 M	*	*	*	£65
1901 P	*	*	*	£110
1901 S	*	*	*	£85

EDWARD VII

	F	VF	EF	Unc
1902	*	*	*	£65
1902 proof	*	*	£80	£125
1902 M	*	*	*	£65
1902 P	*	*	*	£65
1902 S	*	*	*	£65
1903	*	*	*	£65
1903 M	*	*	*	£65
1903 P	*	*	*	£65
1903 S	*	*	*	£65
1904	*	*	*	£65
1904 M	*	*	*	£65
1904 P	*	*	*	£65
1904 S	*	*	*	£65
1905	*	*	*	£65
1905 M	*	*	*	£65
1905 P	*	*	*	£65

SOVEREIGNS

	F	VF	EF	Unc
1905 S	*	*	*	£65
1906	*	*	*	£68
1906 M	*	*	*	£68
1906 P	*	*	*	£68
1906 S	*	*	*	£65
1907	*	*	*	£65
1907 M	*	*	*	£65
1907 P	*	*	*	£65
1907 S	*	*	*	£65
1908	*	*	*	£65
1908 C (Canada, Ottawa mint) on ground below dragon (F)	*	*	£1000	£2000
1908 M	*	*	*	£65
1908 P	*	*	*	£65
1908 S	*	*	*	£65
1909	*	*	*	£65
1909 C	*	*	£75	£150
1909 M	*	*	*	£65
1909 P	*	*	*	£65
1909 S	*	*	*	£65
1910	*	*	*	£65
1910 C	*	*	£75	£150
1910 M	*	*	*	£65
1910 P	*	*	*	£65
1910 S	*	*	*	£65

GEORGE V

	F	VF	EF	Unc
1911	*	*	*	£60
1911 proof	*	*	£150	£250
1911 C	*	*	*	£70
1911 M	*	*	*	£60
1911 P	*	*	*	£60
1911 S	*	*	*	£60
1912	*	*	*	£60
1912 M	*	*	*	£60
1912 P	*	*	*	£60
1912 S	*	*	*	£60
1913	*	*	*	£60
1913 C (F)	*	£100	£150	£300
1913 M	*	*	*	£60
1913 P	*	*	*	£60
1913 S	*	*	*	£60
1914	*	*	*	£60
1914 C	*	£60	£100	£150
1914 M	*	*	*	£60
1914 P	*	*	*	£60
1914 S	*	*	*	£60
1915	*	*	*	£60
1915 M	*	*	*	£60
1915 P	*	*	*	£60
1915 S	*	*	*	£60
1916	*	*	*	£60
1916 C	*	£2500	£6000	*
1916 M	*	*	*	£60
1916 P	*	*	*	£60
1916 S	*	*	*	£60
1917 (F)	*	£1750	£2500	*
1917 C	*	*	£60	£90
1917 M	*	*	*	£60
1917 P	*	*	*	£60
1917 S	*	*	*	£60
1918 C	*	*	£60	£90
1918 I (Indian mint, Bombay), on ground below dragon	*	*	*	£70
1918 M	*	*	*	£60
1918 P	*	*	*	£ 60
1918 S	*	*	*	£60
1919 C	*	*	£65	£100
1919 M	*	*	*	£60
1919 P	*	*	*	£60
1919 S	*	*	*	£60
1920 M	*	£850	£2500	*

	F	VF	EF	Unc
1920 P	*	*	*	£60
1920 S	*	*	highest	rarity
1921 M	*	£2000	£4000	£6000
1921 P	*	*	*	£70
1921 S	*	£500	£1200	£2500
1922 M	*	£1750	£3500	£6000
1922 P	*	*	*	£70
1922 S	*	£2750	£8500	£1350
1923 M	*	*	*	£70
1923 S	*	£2000	£4000	£6500
1923 SA (South Africa, Pretoria Mint) on ground below dragon	*	£1250	£1750	£2500
1924 M	*	*	£60	£90
1924 P	*	*	*	£75
1924 S	*	£500	£1000	£1500
1924 SA	*	*	£2000	£3000
1925	*	*	*	£70
1925 M	*	*	*	£70
1925 P	*	*	£120	£175
1925 S	*	*	*	£70
1925 SA	*	*	*	£60
1926 M	*	*	*	£70
1926 P	*	£200	£400	£750
1926 S	*	£4000	£10000	£17500
1926 SA	*	*	*	£60
1927 P	*	*	£125	£250
1927 SA	*	*	*	£60
1928 M	*	£800	£1750	£2500
1928 P	*	*	£85	£120
1928 SA	*	*	*	£60
1929 M	*	£400	£900	£1500
1929 P	*	*	*	£60
1929 SA	*	*	*	£60
1930 M	*	*	£150	£300
1930 P	*	*	*	£60
1930 SA	*	*	*	£60
1931 M	*	£125	£250	£500
1931 P	*	*	*	£60
1931 SA	*	*	*	£60
1932 SA	*	*	*	£60

GEORGE VI

	F	VF	EF	Unc
1937 proof only		*	*	£450

ELIZABETH II

	F	VF	EF	Unc
1957	*	*	*	£55
1958	*	*	*	£55
1959	*	*	*	£55
1962	*	*	*	£55
1963	*	*	*	£55
1964	*	*	*	£55
1965	*	*	*	£55
1966	*	*	*	£55
1967	*	*	*	£55
1968	*	*	*	£55
1974	*	*	*	£55
1976	*	*	*	£55
1978	*	*	*	£55
1979	*	*	*	£55
1979 proof	*	*	*	£85
1980	*	*	*	£55
1980 proof	*	*	*	£85
1981	*	*	*	£55
1981 proof	*	*	*	£85
1982	*	*	*	£55
1982 proof	*	*	*	£85
1983 proof	*	*	*	£100
1984 proof	*	*	*	£100
1985 proof	*	*	*	£105
1986 proof	*	*	*	£105
1987 proof	*	*	*	£105
1988 proof	*	*	*	£150
1989 500th anniversary of the sovereign, proof	*	*	*	£140

SOVEREIGNS

	F	VF	EF	Unc
1990 proof	*	*	*	£150
1991 proof	*	*	*	£160
1992 proof	*	*	*	£160
1993 proof	*	*	*	£160
1994 proof	*	*	*	£160
1995 proof	*	*	*	£160
1996 proof	*	*	*	£160
1997 proof	*	*	*	£160
1998 new portrait proof*	*	*	*	£160
1999 proof	*	*	*	£155

Half sovereigns

GEORGE III

	F	VF	EF	Unc
1817	£60	£90	£200	£400
1818	£50	£100	£175	£500
1820	£55	£100	£250	£500

GEORGE IV
Laureate head/ornate shield, date on rev

	F	VF	EF	Unc
1821	£250	£600	£1250	£2000
1823 plain shield	£70	£100	£350	£575
1824	£65	£100	£300	£550
1825	£65	£100	£300	£550

Bare head, date on obv/shield, full legend rev

1826	£65	£90	£300	£550
1827	£65	£90	£300	£600
1828	£65	£90	£325	£650

WILLIAM IV

1834 reduced size	£80	£125	£450	£750
1835 normal size	£80	£125	£400	£650
1836 sixpence obverse die				
... ...	£200	£500	£1950	£2750
1836	£100	£200	£500	£750
1837	£80	£100	£400	£650

Victoria 1839 proof half sovereign

VICTORIA
Young head/shield rev

	F	VF	EF	Unc
1838	*	£100	£200	£400
1839 proof only	*	*	*	£1250
1841	*	£100	£200	£400
1842	*	£100	£200	£425
1843	*	£100	£200	£475
1844	*	£100	£200	£425
1845	*	£150	£300	*
1846	*	£100	£200	£475
1847	*	£100	£200	£425
1848	*	£125	£250	£500
1849	*	£100	£200	£450
1850	£100	£225	£750	£1000
1851	*	£100	£200	£450
1852	*	£100	£200	£400
1853	*	£100	£200	£425
1854	£125	£200	*	*
1855	*	£100	£200	£400
1856	*	£100	£200	£400
1857	*	£75	£175	£350
1858	*	£75	£175	£350
1859	*	£75	£175	£350
1860	*	£75	£175	£350
1861	*	£100	£200	£425
1862	£300	£750	£1500	*
1863	*	£100	£200	£375
1863 die no.... ...	*	£75	£150	£325
1864 die no.... ...	*	£75	£150	£300
1865 die no.... ...	*	£75	£150	£325
1866 die no.	*	£75	£150	£325

	F	VF	EF	Unc
1867 die no.... ...	*	£75	£150	£325
1869 die no.... ...	*	£75	£150	£325
1870 die no.... ...	*	£75	£150	£325
1871 die no. ...	*	£75	£150	£325
1871 S below shield	*	£175	£650	£1500
1872 die no. ...	*	£75	£150	£325
1872 S	*	£175	£650	£1500
1873 die no. ...	*	£75	£150	£325
1873 M below shield	*	£175	£650	£1500

Victoria 1874 half sovereign

1874 die no. ...	*	*	£100	£325
1875 die no. ...	*	*	£100	£325
1875 S	*	*	£650	£1500
1876 die no. ...	*	*	£100	£300
1877 die no. ...	*	*	£90	£250
1877 M	£100	£200	£850	£1650
1878 die no. ...	*	*	£90	£250
1879 die no. ...	*	*	£90	£250
1879 S	£100	£200	£750	£1550
1880	*	*	£90	£225
1880 die no. ...	*	*	£90	£225
1880 S	£150	£250	£900	£2000
1881 S	£150	£250	£900	£2000
1881 M	£150	£300	£900	£2000
1882 S	£200	£650	£3500	£6500
1882 M	*	£175	£750	£1600
1883	*	*	£90	£200
1883 S	£80	£175	£650	£1500
1884	*	*	£90	£200
1884 M	£80	£175	£750	£1500
1885	*	*	£85	£200
1885 M	£150	£400	£1500	£3750
1886 S	£65	£150	£650	£1500
1886 M	£100	£250	£1000	£3250
1887 S	£80	£175	£900	£2500
1887 M	£125	£500	£2500	£4500

Jubilee head/shield rev

1887	*	*	£60	£80
1887 proof	*	*	£200	£375
1887 M	*	£150	£350	£750
1887 S	*	£150	£400	*
1889 S	*	£150	£350	*
1890	*	*	£50	£80
1891	*	*	£50	£80
1891 S	*	*	£400	£750
1892	*	*	£50	£85
1893	*	*	£50	£85
1893 M	*	*	£450	£1000

Old head/St George reverse

1893	*	*	£45	£60
1893 proof	*	*	£225	£450
1893 M	£750	*	*	*
1893 S	£60	£120	£300	£800
1894	*	*	£45	£60
1895	*	*	£45	£60
1896	*	*	£45	£60
1896 M	£70	£125	£450	£1000
1897	*	*	£40	£65
1897 S	*	£90	£250	£450
1898	*	*	£40	£65
1899	*	*	£40	£65
1899 M	£70	£125	£450	£1500
1899 P Proof only	*	*	*	£10000
1900	*	*	£40	£60
1900 M	£70	£125	£450	£1500
1900 P	£300	£500	£1200	£2500
1900 S	*	£80	£350	£1000
1901	*	*	£40	£65

COINS MARKET VALUES

	F	VF	EF	Unc
1901 P proof only	*	*	*	£6000

1902 matt proof half sovereign

EDWARD VII
	F	VF	EF	Unc
1902	*	*	*	£55
1902 proof	*	*	£75	£100
1902 S	*	*	£150	£450
1903	*	*	*	£60
1903 S	*	*	£90	£250
1904	*	*	*	£55
1904 P	£100	£200	£700	£1200
1905	*	*	*	£58
1906	*	*	*	£55
1906 M	*	*	£90	£350
1906 S	*	*	£85	£225
1907	*	*	*	£55
1907 M	*	*	£80	£200
1908	*	*	*	£55
1908 M	*	*	£80	£200
1908 P	*	£100	£600	*
1908 S	*	*	£80	£200
1909	*	*	*	£48
1909 M	*	*	£80	£275
1909 P	£70	£150	£500	£1500
1910	*	*	*	£48
1910 S	*	*	£80	£250

GEORGE V
	F	VF	EF	Unc
1911	*	*	*	£45
1911 proof	*	*	£100	£200
1911 P	*	*	£40	£80
1911 S	*	*	*	£50
1912	*	*	*	£45
1912 S	*	*	£40	£50
1913	*	*	*	£40
1914	*	*	*	£40
1914 S	*	*	*	£50
1915	*	*	*	£40
1915 M	*	*	£40	£50
1915 P	*	*	£40	£65
1915 S	*	*	*	£40
1916 S	*	*	*	£40
1918 P	*	£200	£500	£800
1923 SA proof...	*	*	*	£165
1925 SA	*	*	*	£40
1926 SA	*	*	*	£40

GEORGE VI
	F	VF	EF	Unc
1937 proof	*	*	*	£150

ELIZABETH II
	F	VF	EF	Unc
1980 proof	*	*	*	£55
1982	*	*	*	£38
1982 proof	*	*	*	£60
1983 proof	*	*	*	£60
1984 proof	*	*	*	£60
1985 proof	*	*	*	£65
1986 proof	*	*	*	£65
1987 proof	*	*	*	£65
1988 proof	*	*	*	£65
1989 500th anniversary of the sovereign, proof	*	*	*	£85
1990 proof	*	*	*	£80
1991 proof	*	*	*	£80
1992 proof	*	*	*	£90
1993 proof	*	*	*	£85
1994 proof	*	*	*	£85
1995 proof	*	*	*	£85
1996 proof	*	*	*	£85
1997 proof	*	*	*	£85
1998 new portrait proof	*	*	*	£85
1999 proof	*	*	*	£85

Crowns

CROMWELL	F	VF	EF
1658 ...	£700	£1200	£2250
1658 Dutch copy ...	*	£1750	£3500
1658 Tanner's copy ...	*	£2200	£4000

CHARLES II	F	VF	EF
1662 1st bust...	£95	£400	£2500
1663 –	£100	£500	£2750
1664 2nd bust	£100	£450	£3500
1665 –	£400	£1000	*
1666 –	£95	£500	£3500
1666 – eleph	£175	£650	£4000
1667 –	£75	£400	£2500
1668 –	£70	£400	£2000
1668/7 –	£100	£450	£3000
1669 –	£200	£750	*
1669/8 –	£200	£750	£4000
1670 –	£80	£400	£2250
1670/69 –	£120	£450	*
1671 –	£75	£450	£2500
1671 3rd bust	£75	£400	£2250
1672 –	£75	£400	£2200
1673 –	£75	£400	£2250
1673/2 –	£80	£350	£2250
1674 –	£4000	*	*
1675 –	£300	*	*
1675/4 –	£300	*	*
1676 –	£60	£300	£1500
1677 –	£70	£300	£1500
1677/6 –	£70	£300	£1500
1678/7 –	£120	£500	*
1679 –	£65	£300	£1500
1679 4th bust –	£90	£300	£1500
1680 3rd bust	£140	£500	£2000
1680/79 –	£70	£350	£1750
1680 4th bust –	£70	£300	£2000
1680/79 –	£125	£400	£2250
1681 – elephant & castle ...	£750	£2250	*
1681 –	£75	£400	£2250
1682 –	£100	£400	£2250
1682/1 –	£70	£400	£2250
1683 –	£175	£500	£2750
1684 –	£95	£450	£2250

JAMES II	F	VF	EF
1686 1st bust...	£125	£550	£1750
1687 2nd bust	£100	£400	£850
1688 –	£125	£450	£900
1688/7 –	£100	£425	£875

WILLIAM AND MARY	F	VF	EF
1691	£175	£500	£1400
1692	£195	£550	£1500
1692/2 inverted QVINTO...	£195	£550	£1500
1692/2 inverted QVARTO ...	£600	£1250	*

WILLIAM III	F	VF	EF
1695 1st bust...	£75	£275	£650
1696 –	£75	£275	£650
1696 – GEI error...	£150	£400	*
1696/5 –	£125	£375	£800
1696 2nd bust	*	*	*
1696 3rd bust	£75	£275	£650
1697	£600	£2000	£10000
1700 3rd bust variety ...	£75	£275	£600

ANNE	F	VF	EF
1703 1st bust VIGO	£200	£500	£2000
1705 –	£450	£850	£3000
1706 –	£125	£400	£800
1707 –	£100	£300	£700
1707 2nd bust	£85	£275	£600
1707 – E	£85	£275	£600
1708 –	£85	£300	£600

	F	VF	EF
1708 – E..	£80	£300	*
1708/7 –	£90	£325	*
1708 – plumes	£110	£300	£600
1713 3rd bust	£110	£300	£600

GEORGE I	F	VF	EF
1716	£175	£400	£1750
1718	£300	£600	£2200
1718/6	£200	£450	£1500
1720	£200	£450	£1500
1720/18	£175	£400	£1600
1723 SS C ...	£175	£450	£1500
1726 roses & plumes ...	£225	£550	£2200

GEORGE II	F	VF	EF
1732 YH	£140	£350	£750
1732 – proof	*	*	£2500
1734	£140	£350	£750
1735	£140	£350	£650
1736	£140	£350	£650
1739	£140	£350	£625
1741	£140	£350	£600
1743 OH	£125	£350	£600

1691 William & Mary Crown

	F	VF	EF
1746 – LIMA	£125	£350	£600
1746 – proof	*	*	£2250
1750	£150	£350	£700
1751	£200	£400	£850

GEORGE III	F	VF	EF	Unc
Oval counterstamp[1]	£75	£125	£250	£400
Octagonal Counterstamp[1]	£200	£350	£650	£950
1804 Bank of England dollar[1]	£50	£95	£225	£375
1818 LVIII	£10	£45	£175	£400
1818 – error edge	£250	*	*	*
1818 LIX	£10	£45	£150	£350

	F	VF	EF	Unc
1819 –	£10	£45	£175	£400
1819 – no edge stops	£50	£100	£350	*
1819/8 LIX	*	£100	£350	*
1819 LIX	£10	£35	£175	£400
1819 – no stop after TUTAMEN	£30	£50	£275	*
1820 lx	*	*	£175	£400
1820/19	£50	£150	£300	*

[1]Beware of contemporary forgeries. The counter-stamps are usually on Spanish-American dollars.

GEORGE IV

	F	VF	EF	Unc
1821 1st hd SEC ...	£35	£150	£400	£1000
1821 – prf	*	*	*	£1500
1821 – TER error edge	*	*	£1500	£2500
1822 – SEC	£60	£200	£500	£1250
1822 – – prf	*	*	*	*
1822 – TER	£50	£175	£450	£1100
1822 – – prf	*	*	*	£2500
1823 – prf	*	*	*	£11000
1826 2nd hd prf	*	*	£1250	£2250

WILLIAM IV

	F	VF	EF	Unc
1831 W.W.	*	*	£3750	£5000
1831 W.WYON	*	*	£4500	£6500
1834 W.W.	*	*	*	£10000

VICTORIA

	F	VF	EF	Unc
1839 proof	*	£750	£1500	£3000
1844 star stops	£25	£100	£750	£1750
1844 – prf	*	*	*	£5500
1844 cinquefoil stops	£25	£100	£750	£1750
1845	£25	£100	£750	£1750
1845 proof	*	*	*	£5000
1847	£25	£100	£850	£2000

Victoria 1847 Gothic crown

	F	VF	EF	Unc
1847 Gothic	£200	£400	£700	£1500
1847 – plain edge ...	*	£450	£800	£2000
1853 SEPTIMO	*	*	£2500	£4000
1853 plain	*	*	£3000	£5000
1887 JH	£12	£15	£25	£75
1887 – proof	*	*	£150	£350
1888 close date	£15	£25	£50	£85
1888 wide date	£45	£75	£120	£250
1889	£15	£25	£35	£75
1890	£15	£25	£35	£80
1891	£15	£25	£50	£100
1892	£15	£25	£50	£100
1893 LVI	£15	£25	£95	£200
1893 – proof	*	*	£150	£400
1893 LVII	£15	£65	£140	£275
1894 LVII	£15	£30	£95	£225
1894 LVIII...	£15	£30	£95	£240
1895 LVIII...	£15	£30	£95	£225
1895 LIX	£15	£30	£90	£200
1896 LIX	£15	£40	£175	£350
1896 LX	£15	£30	£90	£200
1897 LX	£15	£30	£90	£200
1897 LXI	£15	£30	£90	£220
1898 LXI	£15	£30	£125	£300
1898 LXII	£15	£30	£100	£225
1899 LXII	£15	£39	£85	£200
1899 LXIII...	£15	£30	£95	£225
1900 LXIII...	£15	£30	£95	£200
1900 LXIV...	£15	£30	£95	£225

EDWARD VII

	F	VF	EF	Unc
1902	£20	£35	£70	£100
1902 matt proof	*	*	£75	£100

GEORGE V

	F	VF	EF	Unc
1927 proof	*	*	£75	£125
1928	£50	£65	£100	£150
1929	£50	£70	£100	£175
1930	£50	£65	£110	£175
1931	£50	£65	£110	£175
1932	£70	£95	£185	£300
1933	£50	£65	£110	£175
1934	£250	£350	£600	£950
1935	£5	£7	£10	£18
1935 rsd edge prf ...	*	*	£125	£225
1935 gold proof	*	*	*	£10000
1935 prf in good silver (.925)	*	*	£650	£1250
1935 specimen	*	*	*	£40
1936	£50	£75	£165	£225

GEORGE VI

	F	VF	EF	Unc
1937	*	*	£8	£15
1937 proof	*	*	*	£30
1937 'VIP' proof	*	*	*	£350
1951	*	*	*	£5
1951 'VIP' proof	*	*	*	£200

ELIZABETH II

	F	VF	EF	Unc
1953	*	*	*	£7
1953 proof	*	*	*	£15
1953 'VIP' proof	*	*	*	£225
1960	*	*	*	£7
1960 'VIP' proof	*	*	*	£300
1960 polished dies ...	*	*	£4	£10
1965 Churchill	*	*	*	£1.50
1965 – 'satin' finish ...	*	*	*	£500

For issues 1972 onwards see under 25 pence in Decimal Coinage section.

George VI 1937
Crown (reverse)

Double florins

Victoria 1887 halfcrown

VICTORIA	F	VF	EF	Unc
1887 Roman 1	*	£10	£18	£35
1887 – proof	*	*	£125	£225
1887 Arabic 1	*	£12	£20	£45
1887 – proof	*	*	£90	£175
1888	*	£12	£28	£75
1888 inverted 1	£10	£20	£65	£150
1889	*	£10	£25	£60
1889 inverted 1	£10	£25	£65	£150
1890	*	£12	£25	£70

Three shilling bank tokens

Contemporary forgeries of these pieces, as well as of other George III coins, were produced in quite large numbers. Several varieties exist for the pieces dated 1811 and 1812. Prices given here are for the commonest types of these years.

GEORGE III	F	VF	EF	Unc
1811	*	£20	£50	£75
1812 draped bust ...	*	£20	£50	£75
1812 laureate head	*	£20	£50	£75
1813	*	£20	£50	£75
1814	*	£20	£50	£75
1815	*	£20	£50	£75
1816	£100	£250	£600	£1200

Halfcrowns

CROMWELL	F	VF	EF
1656	£800	£2000	£4000
1658	£450	£850	£1200

Cromwell 1658 halfcrown

	F	VF	EF
CHARLES II			
1663 1st bust	£70	£350	£1500
1664 2nd bust	£85	£200	£1650
1666/3 3rd bust	£750	*	*
1666/3 – elephant	£200	£750	£4500
1667/4 –	£1450	*	*
1668/4 –	£125	£275	*
1669 –	£225	£600	*
1669/4 –	£125	£375	*
1670 –	£50	£225	£1000
1671 3rd bust var	£50	£225	£1000
1671/0 –	£65	£275	£1100
1672 –	£70	£275	£1100
1672 4th bust	£100	£300	£1200
1673 –	£50	£225	£1250
1673 – plume below	£1000	*	*
1673 – plume both sides ...	£1750	*	*
1674 –	£95	£350	*
1674/3 –	£110	*	*
1675 –	£50	£225	£900
1676 –	£50	£225	£900
1677 –	£50	£225	£900
1678 –	£110	£450	*
1679 –	£50	£225	£900
1680 –	£125	£350	*
1681 –	£50	£225	£1000
1681/0 –	£50	£225	£1000
1681 – eleph & castle	£1250	*	*
1682 –	£100	£350	*
1682/1 –	£125	*	*
1682/79 –	£125	*	*
1683 –	£50	£275	£1250
1683 – plume below	£3000	*	*
1684/3 –	£150	£500	*

James III 1687 halfcrown

JAMES II	F	VF	EF
1685 1st bust	£75	£300	£750
1686 –	£75	£300	£750
1686/5 –	£125	£350	*
1687 –	£75	£300	£750

	F	VF	EF
1687/6 –	£85	£300	£850
1687 2nd bust	£100	£375	£950
1688 –	£75	£275	£750

WILLIAM AND MARY

	F	VF	EF
1689 1st busts 1st shield ...	£60	£200	£600
1689 – 2nd shield	£60	£200	£600
1690 – –	£75	£350	£700
1691 2nd busts 3rd shield ...	£65	£225	£650
1692 – –	£65	£225	£650
1693 – –	£60	£200	£600
1693 – – 3 inverted	£85	£300	£850
1693 3 over 3 inverted	£80	£250	£700

William and Mary 1693 Halfcrown

WILLIAM III

	F	VF	EF
1696 large shield early harp	£25	£70	£225
1696 – – B	£30	£125	£325
1696 – – C	£35	£125	£325
1696 – – E	£40	£150	£400
1696 – – N	£35	£125	£350
1696 – – Y	£30	£125	£325
1696 – – y/E	£65	£250	£650
1696 – ord harp	£75	£250	*
1696 – – C	£75	£250	*
1696 – – E	£85	£275	£500
1696 – – N	£85	£275	£500
1696 small shield	£20	£70	£225
1696 – B	£30	£125	£350
1696 – C	£55	£150	£400
1696 – E	£85	£225	£500
1696 – N	£30	£125	£350
1696 – y	£40	£125	£350
1696 2nd bust	*	*	*
1697 1st bust large shield ...	£20	£75	£175
1697 – – B	£30	£100	£275
1697 – – C	£35	£100	£300
1697 – – E	£35	£100	£300
1697 – – E/C	£80	£200	£500
1697 – – N	£30	£100	£400
1697 – – y	£30	£100	£300

1697 Halfcrown of NORWICH: N below bust

	F	VF	EF
1698 – –	£25	£80	£225
1699 – –	£40	£125	£400

HALFCROWNS

	F	VF	EF
1700 – –	£25	£65	£225
1701 – –	£30	£70	£275
1701 – eleph & castle	£500	*	*
1701 – plumes	£120	£375	£850
ANNE			
1703 plain	£300	£700	£1600
1703 VIGO	£50	£200	£450
1704 plumes	£125	£275	£750
1705 –	£75	£225	£550
1706 r & p	£35	£150	£300
1707 –	£30	£150	£300
1707 plain	£35	£85	£250
1707 E	£30	£90	£275
1708 plain	£20	£85	£250
1708 E	£30	£100	£350
1708 plumes	£40	£125	£375
1709 plain	£25	£80	£250
1709 E	£200	*	*
1710 r & p	£40	£125	£350
1712 –	£35	£85	£250
1713 plain	£50	£200	£500
1713 r & p	£30	£85	£300
1714 –	£30	£85	£350
1714/3	£100	*	*
GEORGE I			
1715 proof	*	*	£2500
1715 r & p	£90	£300	£600
1717 –	£100	£350	£700
1720 –	£150	£400	£800
1720/17 –	£85	£300	£650
1723 SS C	£75	£275	£450
1726 small r & p	£1250	£2500	£4000

Spanish Half Dollar with George III counterstamp (octagonal)

GEORGE II

	F	VF	EF
1731 YH proof	*	*	£1800
1731	£70	£250	£600
1732	£70	£250	£600
1734	£70	£250	£600
1735	£70	£250	£600
1736	£70	£250	£600
1739	£60	£200	£400
1741	£100	£275	£650
1743 OH	£60	£100	£300
1745	£60	£90	£225
1745 LIMA	£50	£100	£250
1746 –	£50	£100	£250
1746 plain, proof	*	*	£800
1750	£90	£250	£550
1751	£50	£275	£600
1741/39	£70	£200	£400

GEORGE III	F	VF	EF	Unc
Oval counterstamp usually on Spanish half dollar	£125	£250	£400	*

HALFCROWNS

	F	VF	EF	Unc
1816 large head	*	£50	£100	£200
1817 –	*	£50	£100	£200
1817 small head ...	*	£50	£100	£185
1818	*	£50	£100	£200
1819	*	£50	£100	£200
1819/8	*	*	*	*
1820	*	£60	£125	£225

George IV halfcrown of 1821

GEORGE IV

	F	VF	EF	Unc
1820 1st hd 1st rev ...	*	£50	£125	£250
1821 –	*	£50	£125	£250
1821 proof	*	*	£450	£750
1823	£350	£900	£3000	*
1823 – 2nd rev	*	£50	£125	£275
1824 – –	£25	£60	£175	£375
1824 2nd hd 3rd rev ...£1250	*	*	*	*
1825 – –	*	£70	£90	£200
1826 – –	*	£25	£90	£200
1826 – – proof	*	*	£200	£450
1828 – –	*	£35	£175	£300
1829 – –	*	£35	£125	£250

William IV 1831 halfcrown

WILLIAM IV

	F	VF	EF	Unc
1831	*	*	*	*
1831 proof	*	*	£250	£475
1834 ww	£30	£75	£200	£500
1834 ww in script ...	£12	£40	£95	£250
1835	£25	£75	£175	£400
1836	£12	£40	£95	£250
1836/5	£30	£85	£250	*
1837	£35	£90	£250	£600

VICTORIA

From time to time halfcrowns bearing dates ranging from 1861 to 1871 are found, but except for rare proofs: 1853, 1862 and 1864, no halfcrowns were struck between 1850 and 1874, so pieces dated for this period are now considered to be contemporary or later forgeries.

	F	VF	EF	Unc
1839 plain and ornate fillets, ww	*	£650	£2000	*
1839 – plain edge proof	*	*	£325	£650
1839 plain fillets, ww incuse	*	£900	£2000	£3000
1840	£15	£75	£185	£275
1841	£75	£225	£700	£1000
1842	£15	£40	£185	£300
1843	£50	£125	£300	£500
1844	£15	£40	£160	£300
1845	£15	£40	£225	£350
1846	£20	£50	£175	£300
1848	£75	£175	£450	£850
1848/6	£75	£200	£550	£950
1849 large date	£25	£75	£200	£450
1849 small date	£50	£175	£375	£750
1850	£25	£85	£275	£500
1853 proof	*	£350	£600	£1000
1862 proof	*	*	£1500	£2250
1864 proof	*	*	£1500	£2250
1874	*	£30	£95	£150
1875	*	£25	£75	£150
1876	*	£35	£120	£200
1876/5	*	*	*	*
1877	*	£25	£70	£150
1878	*	£25	£70	£150
1879	*	£35	£100	£200
1880	*	£25	£70	£150
1881	*	£25	£70	£150
1882	*	£25	£90	£170
1883	*	£25	£80	£140
1884	*	£25	£80	£150
1885	*	£25	£80	£150
1886	*	£25	£70	£140
1887 YH	*	£25	£70	£150
1887 JH	*	£15	£25	£40
1887 – proof	*	*	£70	£130
1888	*	£20	£35	£60
1889	*	£20	£35	£60
1890	*	£25	£40	£75
1891	*	£25	£40	£75
1892	*	£25	£40	£75
1893 OH	*	£20	£25	£60
1893 – proof	*	*	£80	£150
1894	*	£20	£40	£70
1895	*	£20	£35	£60
1896	*	£20	£30	£60
1897	*	£15	£35	£60
1898	*	£20	£35	£60
1899	*	£20	£35	£65
1900	*	£20	£35	£60
1901	*	£20	£30	£60

EDWARD VII

	F	VF	EF	Unc
1902	*	£15	£30	£60
1902 matt proof	*	*	*	£60
1903	£50	£120	£400	£800
1904	£35	£90	£300	£650
1905 (F)	£100	£250	£650	£1250
1906	*	£30	£100	£200
1907	*	£40	£100	£250
1908	*	£40	£200	£500
1909	*	£25	£100	£200
1910	*	£20	£60	£150

GEORGE V

	F	VF	EF	Unc
1911	*	£110	£30	£65
1911 proof	*	*	*	£85
1912	*	£14	£35	£80
1913	*	£14	£40	£90
1914	*	*	£15	£30
1915	*	*	£15	£20
1916	*	*	£15	£29

	F	VF	EF	Unc
1917	*	*	£20	£35
1918	*	*	£15	£30
1919	*	*	£20	£40
1920	*	*	£20	£40
1921	*	*	£25	£50
1922	*	*	£20	£50
1923	*	*	£12	£20
1924	*	*	£25	£55
1925	£12	£25	£200	£350

George V 1926 halfcrown

	F	VF	EF	Unc
1926	*	*	£30	£65
1926 mod eff	*	*	£35	£60
1927	*	*	£20	£40
1927 new rev, proof only	*	*	*	£35
1928	*	*	£10	£25
1929	*	*	£10	£20
1930	£7	£35	£125	£200
1931	*	*	£10	£20
1932	*	*	£15	£35
1933	*	*	£9	£20
1934	*	*	£20	£40
1935	*	*	£6	£14
1936	*	*	£6	£12

GEORGE VI

	F	VF	EF	Unc
1937	*	*	*	£9
1937 proof	*	*	*	£12
1938	*	*	£4	£20
1939	*	*	*	£14
1940	*	*	*	£8
1941	*	*	*	£7
1942	*	*	*	£7
1943	*	*	*	£7
1944	*	*	*	£7
1945	*	*	*	£7
1946	*	*	*	£5
1947	*	*	*	£5
1948	*	*	*	£5
1949	*	*	*	£8
1950	*	*	*	£8
1950 proof	*	*	*	£10
1951	*	*	*	£8
1951 proof	*	*	*	£10

ELIZABETH II

	F	VF	EF	Unc
1953	*	*	*	£3
1953 proof	*	*	*	£9
1954	*	*	£3	£20
1955	*	*	*	£4
1956	*	*	*	£4
1957	*	*	*	£3
1958	*	*	£3	£15
1959	*	*	£4	£35
1960	*	*	*	£3
1961	*	*	*	£1
1962	*	*	*	£1
1963	*	*	*	£1
1964	*	*	*	*
1965	*	*	*	*
1966	*	*	*	*
1967	*	*	*	*

Florins

The first florins produced in the reign of Victoria bore the legend VICTORIA REGINA and the date, omitting DEI GRATIA (By the Grace of God). They are therefore known as 'Godless' florins.

The date of a Victorian Gothic florin is shown in Roman numerals, in Gothic lettering on the obverse for example: mdccclvii (1857). Gothic florins were issued during the period 1851-1887.

VICTORIA	F	VF	EF	Unc
1848 'Godless' proof with milled edge	*	*	*	£1000
1848 'Godless' proof with plain edge	*	*	*	£500

Victoria 1849 'Godless' florin

	F	VF	EF	Unc
1849 – ww obliterated by circle	£25	£50	£100	£225
1849 – ww inside circle	£15	£40	£85	£150
1851 proof only	*	*	*	£4000
1852	£15	£40	£95	£180
1853	£15	£40	£95	£170
1853 no stop after date	£20	£50	£100	£200
1853 proof	*	*	*	£1000
1854	£250	£500	*	*
1855	*	£35	£100	£200
1856	*	£50	£140	£300
1857	*	£40	£125	£250
1858	*	£40	£125	£250
1859	*	£40	£125	£250
1859 no stop after date	*	£50	£130	£250
1860	*	£50	£140	£300
1862	£25	£100	£200	*
1863	£50	£170	£300	*
1864	*	£40	£125	£250
1865	*	£40	£125	£250
1865 colon after date	*	£50	£140	£300
1866	*	£50	£135	£275
1866 colon after date	*	£55	£160	£300
1867	£15	£70	£170	£325
1868	*	£50	£130	£250
1869	*	£45	£125	£250
1870	*	£40	£120	£225
1871	*	£40	£120	£225

Victoria 1859 Gothic florin

FLORINS

	F	VF	EF	Unc
1872	*	£35	£100	£200
1873	*	£35	£100	£200
1874	*	£35	£100	£200
1874 xxiv-/ (die 29) ...	£50	*	*	*
1875	*	£45	£100	£200
1876	*	£45	£100	£200
1877	*	£45	£100	*
1877 no ww	*	*	*	*
1877 42 arcs	*	*	*	*
1878	*	£40	£100	£200
1879 ww 48 arcs ...	*	£40	£100	£200
1879 die no.	£12	£40	£125	£250
1879 ww. 42 arcs ...	£12	£40	£60	£200
1879 no ww, 38 arcs	*	£45	£100	£200
1880	*	£40	£100	£200
1881	*	£40	£100	£200
1881 xxri	*	£40	£95	£175
1883	*	£40	£95	£175
1884	*	£40	£95	£175
1885	*	£40	£95	£175
1886	*	£40	£95	£175
1887 33 arcs	*	*	*	*
1887 46 arcs	*	£40	£135	£250
1887 JH	*	£10	£15	£25
1887 – proof	*	*	*	£75
1888	*	£10	£30	£60
1889	*	£10	£30	£60
1890	£8	£15	£45	£80
1891	£20	£50	£140	£250
1892	£20	£50	£100	£200
1893 OH	*	£10	£25	£50
1893 proof	*	*	*	£110
1894	*	£10	£40	£75
1895	*	£10	£35	£60
1896	*	£10	£25	£50
1897	*	£10	£25	£50
1898	*	£10	£25	£50
1899	*	£10	£25	£50
1900	*	£10	£25	£50
1901	*	£10	£25	£50

Edward VII 1902 florin

EDWARD VII

	F	VF	EF	Unc
1902	*	£8	£25	£50
1902 matt proof	*	*	*	£45
1903	*	£25	£50	£90
1904	*	£32	£100	£195
1905	£20	£75	£300	£600
1906	*	£20	£50	£90
1907	*	£25	£60	£100
1908	*	£30	£80	£150
1909	*	£25	£75	£170
1910	*	£15	£40	£80

GEORGE V

	F	VF	EF	Unc
1911	*	*	£25	£45
1911 proof	*	*	*	£50
1912	*	*	£30	£65

	F	VF	EF	Unc
1913	*	*	£35	£80
1914	*	*	£15	£30
1915	*	*	£12	£25
1916	*	*	£15	£30
1917	*	*	£18	£35
1918	*	*	£15	£30
1919	*	*	£18	£35
1920	*	*	£18	£35
1921	*	*	£18	£35
1922	*	*	£15	£30
1923	*	*	£15	£30
1924	*	*	£12	£35
1925	£15	£35	£125	£200
1926	*	*	£25	£60
1927 proof only	*	*	*	£40

George V 1928 florin

	F	VF	EF	Unc
1928	*	*	£7	£12
1929	*	*	£7	£12
1930	*	*	£10	£35
1931	*	*	£8	£20
1932	£15	£60	£150	£250
1933	*	*	£8	£15
1935	*	*	£8	£15
1936	*	*	£5	£10

GEORGE VI

	F	VF	EF	Unc
1937	*	*	*	£7
1937 proof	*	*	*	£12
1938	*	*	£4	£15
1939	*	*	*	£6
1940	*	*	*	£6
1941	*	*	*	£4
1942	*	*	*	£5
1943	*	*	*	£4
1944	*	*	*	£4
1945	*	*	*	£4
1946	*	*	*	£4
1947	*	*	*	£4
1948	*	*	*	£3
1949	*	*	*	£5
1950	*	*	*	£6
1950 proof	*	*	*	£8
1951	*	*	*	£5
1951 proof	*	*	*	£9

George VI 1949 florin

ELIZABETH II	F	VF	EF	Unc
1953	*	*	*	£2
1953 proof	*	*	*	£5
1954	*	*	*	£15
1955	*	*	*	£3
1956	*	*	*	£3
1957	*	*	*	£15
1958	*	*	*	£10
1959	*	*	*	£15
1960	*	*	*	£1
1961	*	*	*	£1
1962	*	*	*	*
1963	*	*	*	*
1964	*	*	*	*
1965	*	*	*	*
1966	*	*	*	*
1967	*	*	*	*

One and sixpence bank tokens

GEORGE III	F	VF	EF	Unc
1811	£5	£15	£30	£50
1812 laureate bust ...	£5	£15	£35	£60
1812 laureate head	£5	£15	£35	£60
1813	£5	£15	£35	£60
1814	£5	£15	£35	£60
1815	£5	£15	£35	£60
1816	£5	£15	£35	£60

Shillings

1658 shilling of Cromwell

CROMWELL	F	VF	EF
1658	£250	£550	£800
1658 Dutch copy	*	*	*

Charles II 1671 shilling, plumes below bust

CHARLES II	F	VF	EF
1663 1st bust	£50	£125	£400
1663 1st bust var	£50	£125	£400
1666 –	*	*	*
1666 – eleph	£200	£500	£2000
1666 guinea hd, eleph ...	£850	£1750	*

	F	VF	EF
1666 2nd bust	£500	£2000	£5000
1668 1st bust var	£250	£500	*
1668 2nd bust	£35	£125	£400
1668/7 –	£50	£140	£500
1669/6 1st bust var	£375	*	*
1669 2nd bust	*	*	*
1670 –	£50	£140	£450
1671 –	£55	£150	£500
1671 – plumes both sides	£175	£375	£950
1672 –	£40	£100	£400
1673 –	£45	£140	£500
1673/2 –	£50	£100	£425
1673 – plumes both sides	£250	£500	*
1674 –	£45	£125	£425
1674/3 –	£50	£150	£400
1674 – plumes both sides	£150	£400	£1000
1674 – plumes rev only ...	£150	£400	*
1674 3rd bust	£250	£550	*
1675 –	£300	£650	*
1675/3 –	£300	£650	*
1675 2nd bust	£200	£500	*
1675/4 –	£200	£500	*
1675 – plumes both sides	£200	£450	*
1676	£30	£100	£400
1676/5 –	£35	£125	£450
1676 – plumes both sides	£175	£450	£1200
1677 –	£35	£100	£400
1677 – plume obv only ...	£300	*	*
1678 –	£50	£125	£425
1678/7 –	£50	£140	£450
1679 –	£35	£100	£350
1679/7 –	£50	£125	£425
1679 plumes	£250	£550	*
1679 plumes obv only ...	£200	£500	*
1680 –	£500	£1000	*
1680 plumes	£175	£450	£1200
1680/79 –	*	*	*
1681 –	£100	£275	£500
1681/0	£100	£275	£500
1681/0 – eleph & castle ...	£850	*	*
1682/1	£175	£450	£1200
1683 –	*	*	*
1683 4th bust	£75	£175	£575
1684 –	£50	£150	£500

James II 1685 shilling

JAMES II	F	VF	EF
1685	£70	£200	£600
1685 no stops on rev ...	£125	*	*
1685 plume on rev	£3000	£6000	£10000
1686	£50	£150	£500
1686 V/S	£60	£175	£600
1687	£50	£150	£500
1687/6	£40	£125	£450
1688	£45	£150	£500
1688/7	£60	£175	£600
WILLIAM & MARY			
1692	£60	£200	£600
1693	£55	£150	£500

SHILLINGS

WILLIAM III

	F	VF	EF
1695	£15	£60	£175
1696	£15	£40	£125
1696 no stops on rev ...	£35	£100	£300
1669 in error	£500	*	*
1696 1st bust B	£20	£65	£200
1696 – C	£20	£65	£200
1696 – E	£20	£65	£200
1696 – N	£20	£65	£200
1696 – Y	£20	£65	£200
1696 – Y	£30	£80	£250
1696 2nd bust	highest rarity		
1696 3rd bust C	£70	£200	£450
1696 – E	£150	*	*
1697 1st bust	£15	£35	£100
1697 – no stops on rev ...	£35	£100	£300
1697 – B	£30	£65	£200
1697 – C	£20	£65	£200

1697 Shilling of BRISTOL: B below bust

1697 – E	£20	£75	£250
1697 – N	£20	£75	£250
1697 – Y	£20	£75	£250
1697 – Y	£25	£75	£750
1697 3rd bust	£15	£35	£100
1697 – B	£25	£80	£275
1697 – C	£15	£65	£200
1697 – E	£25	£75	£250
1697 – N	£20	£75	£250
1697 – Y	£20	£75	£250
1697 3rd bust var	£15	£35	£100
1697 – B	£20	£65	£200
1697 – C	£85	£150	£350
1698	£25	£75	£200
1698 – plumes	£85	£150	£400
1698 4th bust	£85	£150	£400
1699 –	£90	£175	£425
1699 5th bust	£50	£100	£325
1699 – plumes	£60	£200	£450
1699 – roses	£95	£250	£500
1700 –	£15	£40	£120
1700 – no stops on rev ...	£40	£85	£200
1700 – plume	£650	*	*
1701 –	£40	£125	£250
1701 – plumes	£20	£150	£350

Anne 1702 shilling, VIGO below bust

ANNE

1702 – 1st bust	£40	£100	£225
1702 – plumes	£50	£125	£350
1702 – VIGO	£40	£85	£200
1703 2nd bust VIGO	£40	£95	£250
1704 –	£225	£600	£1750
1704 – plumes	£60	£175	£350
1705 –	£60	£175	£350
1705 – plumes	£40	£95	£250
1705 – r&p	£40	£85	£225
1707 – r&p	£40	£85	£225
1707 – E	£40	£75	£175
1707 – E★	£75	£150	£350
1707 3rd bust	£20	£35	£100
1707 – plumes	£45	£85	£225
1707 – E	£20	£60	£175
1707 Edin bust E★	*	*	*
1708 2nd bust E	£75	£200	£500
1708 – E★	£50	£90	£300
1708/7 – E★	£60	£150	£400
1708 – r&p	£60	£175	£450
1708 3rd bust	£20	£45	£120
1708 – plumes	£40	£85	£225
1708 – r&p	£40	£35	£225
1708 – E	£60	£120	£325
1708 – E	£75	£125	£450
1708 – Edin bust E★	£40	£95	£300
1709 –	£45	£100	£325
1709 – E	£90	£175	£400
1709 3rd bust	£15	£35	£100
1710 – r&p	£30	£65	£200
1710 4th bust prf	*	*	*
1710 – r&p	£35	£80	£225
1711 3rd bust	£65	£120	£350
1711 4th bust	£20	£40	£100
1712 – r&p	£25	£45	£175
1713/2 –	£30	£50	£200
1714 –	£25	£50	£175

George I 1723 SS C shilling

GEORGE I

1715 1st bust r&p	£25	£65	£200
1716 –	£85	£250	£500
1717 –	£25	£65	£225
1718 –	£30	£75	£200
1719 –	£70	£200	£350
1720 –	£25	£65	£200
1720 – plain	£20	£55	£175
1720 – large 0	£20	£55	£175
1721 –	£175	£500	£850
1721 r&p	£20	£55	£175
1721/0 –	£20	£55	£175
1721/19 –	£25	£65	£200
1721/18 –	£25	£65	£200
1722 –	£20	£65	£200
1723 –	£20	£65	£200
1723 – SS C	£20	£45	£110
1723 – SSC French			
arms at date	£120	£275	£500
1723 2nd bust SS C	£25	£75	£150
1723 – r&p	£30	£85	£275
1723 – w.c.c.	£200	£400	£1000
1724 – r&p	£30	£85	£275
1724 – w.c.c.	£200	£450	£1200

	F	VF	EF
1725 – r & p	£25	£85	£275
1725 – no obv stops	£50	£150	£350
1725 – w.c.c.	£300	£500	£1400
1726 – r & p	£400	*	*
1726 – w.c.c.	£350	£600	£1500
1727 – r & p	£400	*	*
1727 – – no stops on obv	£350	£900	*

GEORGE II

	F	VF	EF
1727 YH plumes	£65	£175	£350
1727 – r & p	£50	£100	£250
1728 –	£65	£200	£450
1728 – r & p	£50	£100	£250
1729 – –	£50	£100	£250
1731 –	£25	£85	£225
1731 – plumes	£50	£150	£400
1732 – r & p	£40	£100	£225
1734 – –	£40	£90	£200
1735 –	£40	£90	£200
1736 – –	£40	£90	£200
1736/5 – –	£45	£95	£225
1737 – –	£25	£85	£175
1739 – roses	£15	£45	£150
1741 – roses	£15	£50	£150

1763 'Northumberland' Shilling

	F	VF	EF
1743 OH roses	£15	£45	£150
1745 –	£15	£45	£150
1745 – LIMA	£20	£45	£150
1746 – – LIMA	£65	£150	£450
1746/5 – LIMA	£65	£175	£500
1746 – proof	*	£300	£550
1747 – roses	£15	£40	£125
1750 –	£15	£45	£150
1750/6 –	£20	£50	£175
1750 – 5 over 4	£20	£45	£150
1751 –	£25	£55	£200
1758 –	£12	£25	£40

1728 Young Head Shilling

GEORGE III

	F	VF	EF	Unc
1763 'Northumber-land'	£150	£225	£350	£400
1786 proof or pattern	*	*	*	£4000
1787 no hearts	£5	£10	£30	£50
1787 – no stop over head	£10	£25	£60	£85
1787 – no stops at date	£10	£30	£75	£100

SHILLINGS

	F	VF	EF	Unc
1787 – no stops on obv	£125	£350	£750	*
1787 hearts	£5	£10	£30	£50
1798 'Dorrien and Magens'	*	£2250	£3500	£5000
1816	*	£3	£35	£50
1817	*	£3	£35	£50
1817 GEOE	£50	£125	£350	*
1818	£4	£20	£45	£90
1819	*	£4	£40	£55
1819/8	*	*	£60	£90
1820	*	£4	£40	£75

GEORGE IV

	F	VF	EF	Unc
1820 1st hd 1st rev pattern or prf ...	*	*	*	£1750
1821 1st hd 1st rev ...	£10	£30	£95	£170
1821 – proof	*	*	£175	£350
1823 – 2nd rev	£20	£50	£160	*
1824 – –	£8	£25	£95	£180
1825 – –	£15	£35	£95	£200
1825 2nd hd	£10	£25	£90	£150
1826 –	*	£20	£85	£120

George IV 1824 shilling

	F	VF	EF	Unc
1826 – proof	*	*	£100	£170
1827	£10	£50	£150	£250
1829	*	£30	£120	£200

WILLIAM IV

	F	VF	EF	Unc
1831 proof	*	*	*	£300
1834	£10	£30	£85	£150
1835	£10	£35	£120	£200
1836	£15	£25	£85	£150
1837	£25	£75	£175	*

William IV 1837 shilling

VICTORIA

	F	VF	EF	Unc
1838	£8	£18	£65	£130
1839	£8	£20	£65	£130
1839 2nd YH	£8	£20	£65	£130
1839 – proof	*	*	*	£225
1840	£12	£35	£100	£160
1841	£12	£35	£100	£160
1842	£10	£20	£60	£95
1843	£12	£30	£90	£140
1844	£8	£20	£55	£95
1845	£8	£20	£60	£110
1846	£8	£20	£55	£95
1848/6	£30	£80	£350	*
1849	£12	£25	£70	£120

SHILLINGS

	F	VF	EF	Unc
1850	£150	£500	*	*
1850/46	£150	£500	£950	*
1851	£25	£100	£300	*
1852	£8	£20	£65	£95
1853	£8	£20	£65	£90
1853 proof	*	*	*	£375
1854	£60	£175	£450	*
1855	£8	£20	£60	£90
1856	£8	£20	£60	£90
1857	£8	£20	£60	£90
1857 F:G:	*	*	*	*
1858	£8	£20	£60	£90
1859	£8	£20	£60	£90
1860	£10	£25	£80	*
1861	£10	£25	£80	*
1862	£15	£35	£100	*

Victoria 1839 shilling

	F	VF	EF	Unc
1863	£15	£50	£200	*
1864	£8	£15	£60	£90
1865	£8	£15	£60	£90
1866	£8	£15	£60	£90
1866 BBITANNIAR ...	*	*	£350	*
1867	£8	£15	£70	£110
1867 3rd YH, die no.	£150	£250	*	*
1868	£8	£20	£70	£110
1869	£12	£30	£70	£130
1870	£10	£25	£70	£120
1871	£8	£20	£50	£80
1872	£8	£20	£50	£80
1873	£8	£20	£50	£80
1874	£8	£20	£50	£80
1875	£8	£20	£50	£80
1876	£10	£25	£60	£100
1877 die no.	£8	£20	£45	£75
1877 no die no	*	*	*	*
1878	£8	£20	£45	£75
1879 3rd YH	£45	£100	£200	*
1879 4th YH	£8	£20	£45	£75
1880	£6	£15	£35	£65
1880 longer line below SHILLING	*	*	*	*
1881	£6	£15	£35	£70
1881 longer line below SHILLING	£6	£15	£40	£70
1881 – Large rev lettering	£6	£15	£35	£70
1882	£10	£35	£75	£150
1883	£6	£15	£35	£65
1884	£6	£15	£35	£65
1885	£6	£15	£35	£65
1886	£6	£15	£35	£65
1887	£7	£20	£65	£110
1887 JH	*	*	£12	£25
1887 proof	*	*	*	£80
1888	*	£6	£25	£50
1889	£40	£100	£300	*
1889 large JH	*	*	£25	£50
1890	*	*	£25	£50
1891	*	*	£25	£50
1892	*	*	£25	£50

Victoria Jubilee Head and Old Head shillings

	F	VF	EF	Unc
1893 OH	*	*	£15	£30
1893 – proof	*	*	*	£100
1893 small obv letters	*	*	£18	£35
1894	*	*	£20	£45
1895	*	*	£18	£40
1896	*	*	£18	£40
1897	*	*	£18	£35
1898	*	*	£18	£35
1899	*	*	£18	£35
1900	*	*	£18	£35
1901	*	*	£15	£30

EDWARD VII

	F	VF	EF	Unc
1902	*	*	£20	£30
1902 matt prf	*	*	*	£30

Edward VII 1905 shilling

	F	VF	EF	Unc
1903	*	£15	£65	£140
1904	*	£12	£60	£120
1905	£40	£120	£375	*
1906	*	*	£25	£50
1907	*	*	£25	£60
1908	£8	£20	£55	£130
1909	£8	£20	£55	£130
1910	*	*	£20	£35

GEORGE V

	F	VF	EF	Unc
1911	*	*	£10	£18
1911 proof	*	*	*	£35
1912	*	*	£15	£45
1913	*	*	£25	£60
1914	*	*	£8	£15
1915	*	*	£8	£15
1916	*	*	£8	£15
1917	*	*	£10	£20
1918	*	*	£8	£18
1919	*	*	£12	£30
1920	*	*	£12	£30
1921	*	*	£20	£40

George V nickel trial shilling, 1924

	F	VF	EF	Unc
1922	*	*	£12	£35
1923	*	*	£10	£25
1923 nickel	*	*	£300	£550
1924	*	*	£10	£20
1924 nickel	*	*	£300	£550
1925	*	*	£12	£60
1926	*	*	£10	£35
1926 mod eff	*	*	£10	£25
1927 –	*	*	£10	£30
1927 new type	*	*	£6	£20
1927 – proof	*	*	*	£20
1928	*	*	*	£10
1929	*	*	£4	£12
1930	*	*	£8	£20
1931	*	*	£4	£12
1932	*	*	£4	£12
1933	*	*	£4	£12
1934	*	*	£5	£25
1935	*	*	*	£7
1936	*	*	*	£5
GEORGE VI				
1937 Eng	*	*	*	£5
1937 Eng prf	*	*	*	£7
1937 Scot	*	*	*	£3
1937 Scot prf	*	*	*	£6
1938 Eng	*	*	£2	£15
1938 Scot	*	*	£2	£12
1939 Eng	*	*	*	£5
1939 Scot	*	*	*	£5
1940 Eng	*	*	*	£5
1940 Scot	*	*	*	£5
1941 Eng	*	*	*	£4
1941 Scot	*	*	£2	£5
1942 Eng	*	*	*	£3
1942 Scot	*	*	*	£4
1943 Eng	*	*	*	£3
1943 Scot	*	*	*	£4
1944 Eng	*	*	*	£3
1944 Scot	*	*	*	£3
1945 Eng	*	*	*	£3
1945 Scot	*	*	*	£2
1946 Eng	*	*	*	£2
1946 Scot	*	*	*	£2
1947 Eng	*	*	*	£3
1947 Scot	*	*	*	£3

Reverses: English (left), Scottish (right)

	F	VF	EF	Unc
1948 Eng	*	*	*	£2
1948 Scot	*	*	*	£2
1949 Eng	*	*	*	£4
1949 Scot	*	*	*	£4
1950 Eng	*	*	*	£5
1950 Eng prf	*	*	*	£6
1950 Scot	*	*	*	£5
1950 Scot prf	*	*	*	£6
1951 Eng	*	*	*	£5
1951 Eng prf	*	*	*	£6
1951 Scot	*	*	*	£5
1951 Scot prf	*	*	*	£6
ELIZABETH II				
1953 Eng	*	*	*	£1
1953 Eng prf	*	*	*	£5
1953 Scot	*	*	*	£1

SHILLINGS

	F	VF	EF	Unc
1953 Scot prf	*	*	*	£5
1954 Eng	*	*	*	£1
1954 Eng	*	*	*	£1
1955 Eng	*	*	*	£1
1955 Scot	*	*	*	£1
1956 Eng	*	*	*	£2
1956 Scot	*	*	*	£6
1957 Eng	*	*	*	£2
1957 Scot	*	*	*	£5
1958 Eng	*	*	*	£6
1958 Scot	*	*	*	£1

Reverses: English (left), Scottish (right)

	F	VF	EF	Unc
1959 Eng	*	*	*	£1
1959 Scot	*	*	*	£20
1960 Eng	*	*	*	£1
1960 Scot	*	*	*	£2
1961 Eng	*	*	*	£1
1961 Scot	*	*	*	£5
1962 Eng	*	*	*	*
1962 Scot	*	*	*	*
1963 Eng	*	*	*	*
1963 Scot	*	*	*	*
1964 Eng	*	*	*	*
1964 Scot	*	*	*	*
1965 Eng	*	*	*	*
1965 Scot	*	*	*	*
1966 Eng	*	*	*	*
1966 Scot	*	*	*	*

Sixpences

CROMWELL	F	VF	EF
1658	*	*	of the
			highest rarity
1658 Dutch copy	£650	£1250	£2500

CHARLES II	F	VF	EF
1674	£25	£90	£250
1675	£120	£75	£250
1675/4	£30	£100	£275
1676	£30	£100	£275
1676/5	£30	£100	£275
1677	£20	£95	£250
1678/7	£30	£100	£275

Charles II 1678 sixpence

	F	VF	EF
1679	£30	£100	£275
1680	£40	£120	£300

SIXPENCES

	F	VF	EF
1681	£20	£70	£225
1682	£40	£120	£275
1682/1	£20	£75	£225
1683	£20	£75	£200
1684	£25	£90	£275

James II 1688 sixpence

JAMES II
	F	VF	EF
1686 early shields	£45	£150	£300
1687 –	£40	£150	£350
1687/6	£40	£150	£350
1687 later shield	£40	£150	£300
1687/6	£45	£175	£375
1688 –	£50	£200	£400

WILLIAM AND MARY
	F	VF	EF
1693	£45	£200	£400
1693 3 upside down	£55	£225	£450
1694	£70	£250	£500

William and Mary 1694 sixpence

WILLIAM III
	F	VF	EF
1695 1st bust early harp ...	£10	£35	£95
1696 – –	£5	£20	£65
1696 – – no obv stops	£10	£35	£95
1696/5	£15	£50	£125
1696 – – B	£10	£35	£100
1696 – – C	£10	£35	£100
1696 – – E	£15	£50	£110
1696 – – N	£10	£40	£100
1696 – – y	£10	£35	£90
1696 – – Y	£15	£50	£110
1696 – later harp	£15	£70	£165
1696 – – B	£25	£90	£200
1696 – – C	£30	£100	£225
1696 – – N	£25	£90	£200
1696 2nd bust	£100	£225	£475
1697 1st bust early harp ...	£5	£20	£65
1697 – – B	£10	£35	£100
1697 – – C	£15	£50	£100
1697 – – E	£15	£50	£100
1697 – – N	£10	£35	£100
1697 – – y	£15	£50	£100
1697 2nd bust	£30	£110	£250
1697 3rd bust later harp ...	£5	£20	£65
1697 – – B	£15	£40	£120
1697 – – C	£30	£60	£125
1697 – – E	£20	£50	£125
1697 – – Y	£20	£50	£110
1698 – –	£15	£40	£90
1698 – – plumes	£30	£80	£175
1699 – –	£45	£125	£275
1699 – – plumes	£35	£85	£225

William III 1699 sixpence, plumes

	F	VF	EF
1699 – – roses	£50	£125	£300
1700	£10	£25	£75
1701	£15	£30	£110

ANNE
	F	VF	EF
1703 VIGO	£20	£50	£100
1705	£25	£90	£175
1705 plumes	£20	£80	£160
1705 roses & plumes	£20	£60	£130
1707 –	£20	£55	£95
1707 plain	£15	£35	£75
1707 E	£15	£45	£125

Anne 1707 sixpence, E below bust

	F	VF	EF
1707 plumes	£20	£45	£125
1708 plain	£10	£30	£65
1708 E	£20	£60	£175
1708/7 E	£50	£120	£225
1708 E★	£20	£70	£200
1708/7 E★	£50	£120	£225
1708 Edin bust E★	£20	£75	£200
1708 plumes	£20	£55	£175
1710 roses & plumes	£20	£60	£200
1711	£10	£30	£65

George I 1717 sixpence

GEORGE I
	F	VF	EF
1717	£25	£95	£250
1720/17	£25	£95	£250
1723 SS C, Small letters on obv	£15	£30	£85
1723 SS C, large letters on both sides	£15	£30	£85
1726 roses & plumes	£30	£125	£300

GEORGE II
	F	VF	EF
1728 YH	£25	£85	£250
1728 – plumes	£20	£75	£150
1728 – r & p	£20	£65	£175
1731 – –	£20	£65	£175
1732 – –	£20	£65	£175
1734 – –	£25	£65	£200
1735 – –	£25	£70	£175
1736 – –	£20	£60	£175
1739 – roses	£15	£50	£125

	F	VF	EF
1741 – –	£15	£45	£125
1743 OH	£15	£45	£125
1745 – –	£15	£45	£125
1745/3 – –	£25	£55	£175
1745 – LIMA	£10	£30	£85
1746 – LIMA	£10	£30	£85
1746 – plain proof	*	*	£350

George II 1746 sixpence

	F	VF	EF
1750	£10	£30	£90
1751	£15	£40	£100
1757	£5	£10	£30
1757	£5	£10	£30
1758/7	£10	£25	£40

GEORGE III

	F	VF	EF	Unc
1787 hearts	£8	£15	£20	£35
1787 no hearts	£8	£15	£20	£35
1816	£8	£15	£25	£55
1817	£8	£15	£25	£55
1818	£8	£18	£40	£95
1819	£8	£15	£25	£65
1819 small 8	£10	£20	£50	£125
1820	£8	£15	£30	£75
1820 1 inverted	£30	£100	£225	£450

GEORGE IV

	F	VF	EF	Unc
1820 1st hd 1st rev (pattern or proof)	*	*	*	£1000
1821 1st hd 1st rev	£6	£18	£60	£100
1821 – – BBITANNIAR	£65	£125	£300	£550
1824 1st hd 2nd rev	£6	£18	£55	£100
1825 – –	£6	£18	£65	£100
1826 – –	£15	£60	£150	£275
1826 2nd hd 3rd rev	£5	£14	£60	£95

George IV 1825 sixpence

	F	VF	EF	Unc
1826 – – proof	*	*	*	£175
1827	1£15	£45	£130	£250
1828	£8	£20	£95	£175
1829	£6	£20	£85	£150

WILLIAM IV

	F	VF	EF	Unc
1831	£6	£20	£80	£100
1831 proof	*	*	*	£175
1834	£6	£30	£50	£100
1835	£6	£20	£70	£125
1836	1£15	£35	£95	£150
1837	1£12	£30	£95	£150

VICTORIA

	F	VF	EF	Unc
1838	£5	£10	£50	£85
1839	£5	£10	£50	£85
1839 proof	*	*	*	£150

SIXPENCES

	F	VF	EF	Unc
1840	£5	£10	£45	£80
1841	£5	£10	£45	£80
1842	£5	£10	£60	£110
1843	£5	£10	£50	£85
1844	£5	£10	£50	£85
1845	£5	£10	£50	£85
1846	£3	£8	£40	£80
1848	£15	£75	£300	£500
1848/6	£10	£50	£200	£400
1848/7	£10	£50	£200	£400
1850	£5	£15	£55	£110
1850 5 over 3	£15	£30	£150	£300
1851	£4	£12	£40	£85
1852	£4	£12	£40	£80
1853	£5	£15	£40	£75
1853 proof	*	*	*	£200
1854	£40	£100	£350	*
1855	£4	£12	£40	£70
1856	£4	£12	£40	£75
1857	£4	£12	£45	£75
1858	£4	£12	£45	£70
1859	£4	£12	£40	£70
1859/8	£4	£12	£45	£75
1860	£5	£15	£45	£75
1862	£20	£60	£250	£425
1863	£12	£40	£175	£350
1864	£5	£12	£40	£80
1865	£6	£14	£45	£85
1866	£5	£12	£40	£80
1866 no die no.	*	*	*	*
1867	£8	£20	£50	£95
1868	£8	£20	£50	£95
1869	£8	£25	£75	£130
1870	£8	£20	£60	£100
1871	£5	£12	£40	£75
1871 no die no.	£5	£12	£40	£75
1872	£5	£12	£40	£75
1873	£5	£12	£40	£70
1874	£5	£12	£40	£70
1875	£5	£12	£40	£75
1876	£6	£20	£55	£90
1877	£5	£12	£40	£70
1877 no die no.	£5	£12	£40	£70
1878	£5	£10	£35	£75
1878 DRITANNIAR	£35	£100	£250	*
1879 die no.	£8	£20	£55	£110
1879 no die no.	£5	£10	£35	£70
1880 2nd YH	£4	£10	£25	£60
1880 3rd YH	£3	£8	£20	£50
1881	£4	£10	£20	£50
1882	£8	£20	£50	£100
1883	£4	£10	£20	£50
1884	£4	£10	£20	£50
1885	£4	£10	£20	£50
1886	£4	£10	£20	£50
1887 YH	£4	£10	£20	£50
1887 JH shield rev	£2	£5	£10	£18

1887 Jubilee Head sixpence, withdrawn type

	F	VF	EF	Unc
1887 – proof	*	*	*	£75
1887 – new rev	£2	£5	£10	£15
1888	£3	£5	£10	£15
1889	£3	£7	£12	£30

SIXPENCES

	F	VF	EF	Unc
1890	*	£3	£12	£35
1891	*	£3	£12	£35
1892	*	£3	£12	£35
1893	£100	£300	£750	*
1893 OH	*	£3	£15	£35
1893 proof	*	*	*	£85
1894	*	£3	£20	£35
1895	*	£3	£20	£35
1896	*	£3	£20	£35
1897	*	£3	£18	£30
1898	*	£3	£18	£30
1899	*	£3	£20	£35
1900	*	£3	£18	£30
1901	*	£3	£18	£30

EDWARD VII

	F	VF	EF	Unc
1902	*	£2	£10	£20
1902 matt proof	*	*	*	£25
1903	*	£5	£25	£50
1904	*	£6	£28	£65
1905	*	£6	£28	£55
1906	*	£3	£15	£45
1907	*	£5	£15	£45
1908	*	£7	£28	£65
1909	*	£4	£22	£50
1910	*	£4	£15	£30

GEORGE V

	F	VF	EF	Unc
1911	*	*	£8	£30
1911 proof	*	*	*	£40
1912	*	*	£15	£45
1913	*	*	£20	£45
1914	*	*	£8	£20
1915	*	*	£8	£20
1916	*	*	£8	£20
1917	*	*	£15	£40
1918	*	*	£7	£15
1919	*	*	£8	£20
1920	*	*	£10	£35
1920 debased	*	*	£10	£35
1921	*	*	£8	£30
1922	*	*	£8	£30
1923	*	*	£8	£40
1924	*	*	£8	£30
1925	*	*	£8	£30
1925 new rim	*	*	£8	£20
1926 new rim	*	*	£10	£30
1926 mod effigy	*	*	£8	£20
1927	*	*	£5	£20
1927 new rev prf	*	*	*	£20
1928	*	*	*	£10
1929	*	*	*	£10
1930	*	*	*	£10
1931	*	*	*	£10
1932	*	*	£6	£15
1933	*	*	*	£10
1934	*	*	£3	£10

George V 1929 sixpence

	F	VF	EF	Unc
1935	*	*	*	£8
1936	*	*	*	£8

GEORGE VI

	F	VF	EF	Unc
1937	*	*	*	£2
1937 proof	*	*	*	£4
1938	*	*	£2	£6
1939	*	*	*	£3
1940	*	*	*	£3
1941	*	*	*	£3
1942	*	*	*	£2
1943	*	*	*	£2
1944	*	*	*	£1
1945	*	*	*	£1
1946	*	*	*	£1
1947	*	*	*	£1
1948	*	*	*	£1
1949	*	*	*	£2
1950	*	*	*	£2
1950 proof	*	*	*	£3.50
1951	*	*	*	£2
1951 proof	*	*	*	£3.50
1952	*	£2	£8	£20

ELIZABETH II

	F	VF	EF	Unc
1953	*	*	*	£0.50
1953 proof	*	*	*	£2
1954	*	*	*	£2
1955	*	*	*	£0.60
1956	*	*	*	£0.60
1957	*	*	*	£0.30
1958	*	*	*	£2
1959	*	*	*	£0.20
1960	*	*	*	£1.50
1961	*	*	*	£1.50
1962	*	*	*	£0.25
1963	*	*	*	*
1964	*	*	*	*
1965	*	*	*	*
1966	*	*	*	*
1967	*	*	*	*

Groats (fourpences)

William IV 1836 groat
Earlier dates are included in Maundy sets

WILLIAM IV

	F	VF	EF	Unc
1836	*	*	£25	£50
1836 proof	*	*	*	£350
1837	*	£8	£35	£65

Victoria 1842 groat

VICTORIA

	F	VF	EF	Unc
1838	*	£5	£20	£50
1838 8 over 8 on side	*	£10	£35	£60
1839	*	£8	£25	£60
1839 proof	*	*	*	£125
1840	£2	£10	£30	£60
1840 narrow 0	*	£12	£40	*
1841	£3	£10	£35	£70
1841 I for last 1	*	*	*	*
1842	*	£8	£30	£50

	F	VF	EF	Unc
1842/1	£4	£15	£60	*
1843	*	£5	£25	£45
1844	*	£8	£35	£60
1845	*	£8	£35	£60
1846	*	£8	£35	£60
1847/6	£25	£50	£120	*
1848 small date ...	*	£8	£120	£50
1848 large date ...	*	£8	£25	£50
1848/6	*	£10	£35	*
1848/7	*	£8	£25	£55
1849	*	£8	£25	£60
1849/8	*	£8	£45	£80
1851	£15	£50	£150	*
1852	£40	£100	£250	*
1853	£35	£75	£200	*
1853 proof	*	*	*	£250
1854	*	£8	£25	£50
1854 5 over 3	*	£8	£30	£700
1855	*	£8	£25	£50
1857 proof	*	*	*	£700
1862 proof	*	*	*	£450
1888 JH	£5	£10	£30	£40

Silver threepences

Earlier dates are included in Maundy sets

WILLIAM IV

	F	VF	EF	Unc
1834	*	£6	£38	£80
1835	*	£6	£35	£80
1836	*	£6	£35	£80
1837	£5	£15	£45	£100

Victoria threepence of 1848

VICTORIA

1838	*	£8	£35	£85
1839	*	£10	£45	£100
1840	*	£10	£50	£100
1841	*	£10	£45	£95
1842	*	£10	£45	£95
1843	*	£10	£45	£95
1844	*	£12	£55	£100
1845	*	£4	£35	£75
1846	*	£15	£85	£120
1847	*	*	£400	£800
1848	*	*	£400	£750
1849	*	£12	£50	£100
1850	*	£4	£30	£65
1851	*	£8	£40	£85
1852	*	*	£275	*
1853	*	£12	£55	£120
1854	*	£8	£40	£85
1855	*	£12	£55	£100
1856	*	£10	£50	£100
1857	*	£10	£50	£100
1858	*	£8	£35	£75
1858/6	*	*	*	*
1859	*	£4	£30	£65
1860	*	£8	£35	£75
1861	*	£4	£30	£65
1862	*	£8	£40	£80
1863	*	£10	£50	£100
1864	*	£8	£80	£80
1865	*	£10	£50	£100
1866	*	£8	£40	£80
1867	*	£8	£40	£85

SILVER THREEPENCES

	F	VF	EF	Unc
1868	*	£8	£40	£65
1868 RRITANNIAR	£20	£50	£200	*
1869	£10	£30	£100	*
1870	*	£6	£30	£65
1871	*	£7	£35	£70
1872	*	£5	£25	£60
1873	*	£5	£25	£60
1874	*	£5	£25	£55
1875	*	£5	£25	£55
1876	*	£5	£25	£55
1877	*	£5	£25	£55
1878	*	£5	£25	£55
1879	*	£5	£25	£55
1880	*	£6	£30	£60
1881	*	£6	£30	£60
1882	*	£8	£35	£80
1883	*	£5	£25	£55
1884	*	£5	£25	£55
1885	*	£5	£20	£50
1886	*	£5	£20	£50
1887 YH	*	£6	£25	£55
1887 JH	*	£2	£5	£8
1887 proof	*	*	*	£40
1888	*	£2	£7	£20
1889	*	£2	£6	£15
1890	*	£2	£6	£15
1891	*	£2	£6	£15
1892	*	£3	£10	£20
1893	£12	£40	£100	£225
1893 OH	*	*	£4	£15
1893 OH proof	*	*	*	£50
1894	*	£2	£8	£20
1895	*	£2	£8	£20
1896	*	£2	£6	£20
1897	*	*	£5	£20
1898	*	*	£5	£20
1899	*	*	£5	£20
1900	*	*	£5	£20
1901	*	*	£5	£15

EDWARD VII

1902	*	*	£4	£10
1902 matt proof ...	*	*	*	£12
1903	*	£1.50	£6	£20
1904	*	£6	£14	£35
1905	*	£6	£14	£35
1906	*	£3	£10	£30
1907	*	£1.50	£5	£20
1908	*	£1.50	£6	£22
1909	*	£2	£6	£22
1910	*	£1.25	£4	£18

George V 1927 threepence, acorns on reverse

GEORGE V

1911	*	*	£3	£12
1911 proof	*	*	*	£25
1912	*	*	£3	£12
1913	*	*	£3	£12
1914	*	*	£2	£10
1915	*	*	£2	£10
1916	*	*	£1.50	£8
1917	*	*	£1.50	£8
1918	*	*	£2	£8
1919	*	*	£2	£8

SILVER THREEPENCES

	F	VF	EF	Unc
1920	*	*	£2	£10
1920 debased	*	*	£2	£10
1921	*	*	£2	£12
1922	*	*	£2	£12
1925	*	£1	£6	£18
1926	*	£3	£10	£25
1926 mod effigy ...	*	£1	£6	£20
1927 new rev prf ...	*	*	*	£30
1928	*	£2	£6	£20
1930	*	£1.50	£5	£12
1931	*	*	£1	£6
1932	*	*	£1	£6
1933	*	*	£1	£6
1934	*	*	£1	£6
1935	*	*	£1	£6
1936	*	*	£1	£6

GEORGE VI

	F	VF	EF	Unc
1937	*	*	£0.75	£1.50
1937 proof	*	*	*	£5
1938	*	*	£0.50	£1
1939	*	£1	£3	£5
1940	*	*	£1	£2
1941	*	*	£1	£2
1942	£1	£2	£6	£8
1943	£1	£3	£7	£9
1944	£1.50	£5	£12	£20
1945[2]	*	*	*	*

[1]Threepences issued for use in the Colonies.
[2]All specimens of 1945 were thought to have been melted down but it appears that one or two still exist.

Small silver for Colonies

These tiny coins were struck for use in some of the Colonies – they were never issued for circulation in Britain. However, they are often included in collections of British coins and it is for this reason that prices for them are given here.

TWOPENCES

Other dates are included in Maundy sets.

VICTORIA

	F	VF	EF	Unc
1838	*	£2	£15	£35
1838 2nd 8 like S ...	*	£6	£25	£60
1848	*	£2	£15	£35

THREEHALFPENCES

WILLIAM IV ... ...

	F	VF	EF	Unc
1834	*	£5	£25	£50
1835	*	£5	£25	£50
1835/4	*	£10	£30	£85
1836	*	£5	£25	£50
1837	£10	£25	£100	£200

VICTORIA

	F	VF	EF	Unc
1838	*	£2	£15	£30
1839	*	£1.25	£12	£25
1840	*	£5	£20	£50
1841	*	£2	£15	£40
1842	*	£2	£12	£35
1843	*	£1	£12	£30

George V threepence

	F	VF	EF	Unc
1843/34	£2	£10	£25	£75
1860	£1	£5	£20	£45
1862	£1	£5	£20	£45
1870 proof	*	*	*	£375

Maundy sets

EF prices are for evenly matched sets

Charles II 1677 Maundy set

CHARLES II

	F	VF	EF
1670	£60	£95	£200
1671	£60	£85	£200
1672	£65	£90	£240
1673	£60	£95	£200
1674	£60	£95	£200
1675	£65	£110	£220
1676	£65	£110	£220
1677	£60	£85	£200
1678	£75	£125	£275
1679	£65	£110	£220
1680	£60	£95	£200
1681	£75	£125	£275
1682	£65	£110	£220
1683	£60	£95	£200
1684	£65	£110	£220

JAMES II

	F	VF	EF
1686	£70	£100	£250
1687	£65	£100	£225
1688	£70	£100	£250

WILLIAM AND MARY

	F	VF	EF
1689	£250	£450	£700
1691	£90	£150	£300
1692	£100	£175	£350
1693	£100	£175	£350
1694	£90	£150	£300

WILLIAM III

	F	VF	EF
1698	£75	£125	£275
1699	£85	£175	£325
1700	£85	£175	£325
1701	£75	£130	£300

ANNE	F	VF	EF
1703	£70	£120	£250
1705	£70	£120	£250
1706	£60	£100	£200
1708	£75	£125	£275
1709	£65	£110	£225
1710	£75	£125	£275
1713	£65	£110	£225

GEORGE I

	F	VF	EF
1723	£75	£125	£275
1727	£70	£120	£250

GEORGE II

	F	VF	EF
1729	£60	£90	£180
1731	£60	£90	£180
1732	£55	£80	£160
1735	£55	£80	£160
1737	£55	£80	£160
1739	£55	£80	£160
1740	£55	£80	£160
1743	£55	£90	£180
1746	£50	£75	£150
1760	£70	£100	£200

GEORGE III

	F	VF	EF	Unc
1763	£50	£75	£140	£175
1766	£50	£80	£150	£175
1772	£50	£20	£150	£175
1780	£50	£80	£150	£175
1784	£50	£80	£150	£175
1786	£50	£80	£150	£175
1792 wire type	£75	£125	£200	£275

William and Mary 1694 Maundy set

		F	VF	EF
1795	*	£60	£90	£150
1800	*	£60	£90	£140
1817	*	£65	£100	£150
1818	*	£65	£100	£150
1820	*	£65	£100	£150

GEORGE IV

		F	VF	EF
1822	*	£60	£90	£130
1823	*	£55	£80	£120
1824	*	£55	£85	£125
1825	*	£55	£80	£120
1826	*	£55	£80	£120
1827	*	£55	£80	£120
1828	*	£55	£80	£120
1829	*	£55	£80	£120
1830	*	£55	£80	£120

WILLIAM IV

		F	VF	EF
1831	*	£65	£100	£175
1831 proof	*	*	*	£300
1832	*	£65	£100	£200
1833	*	£60	£90	£150
1834	*	£60	£90	£150
1835	*	£60	£90	£150

MAUNDY SETS

		F	VF	EF	Unc
1836		*	£65	£110	£220
1837		*	£65	£110	£220

VICTORIA

	F	VF	EF	Unc
1838			£60	£95
1839			£65	£100
1839 proof			*	£100
1840			£65	£100
1841			£70	£110
1842			£75	£125
1843			£70	£110
1844			£70	£110
1845			£60	£95
1846			£75	£125
1847			£7	£110

George IV 1825

1848	£70	£110
1849	£75	£125
1850	£55	£90
1851	£55	£90
1852	£60	£95
1853	£60	£95
1853 proof	*	£400
1854	£55	£95
1855	£50	£90
1856	£50	£95
1857	£50	£95
1858	£50	£95
1859	£50	£95
1860	£50	£90
1861	£50	£90
1862	£50	£90
1863	£50	£90
1864	£50	£90
1865	£50	£90
1866	£50	£90
1867	£50	£90
1868	£50	£90
1869	£50	£90
1870	£45	£75
1871	£45	£75
1872	£45	£75
1873	£45	£75
1874	£45	£75
1875	£45	£75
1876	£45	£75
1877	£45	£75
1878	£45	£75
1879	£45	£75
1880	£45	£75
1881	£45	£75
1882	£45	£75
1883	£45	£75
1884	£45	£75
1885	£45	£75
1886	£45	£75
1887	£45	£75
1888 JH	£50	£80

MAUNDY SETS

	EF	Unc
1889	£50	£75
1890	£50	£75
1891	£50	£75
1892	£50	£75
1893 OH	£40	£55
1894	£45	£60
1895	£40	£55
1896	£40	£55
1897	£40	£55
1898	£40	£55
1899	£40	£55
1900	£40	£75
1901	£40	£55

EDWARD VII
	EF	Unc
1902	£40	£55
1902 matt proof	*	£50
1903	£35	£50
1904	£35	£50
1905	£35	£50
1906	£35	£50
1907	£35	£50
1908	£35	£50
1909	£50	£70
1910	£50	£70

GEORGE V
	EF	Unc
1911	£40	£70
1911 proof	*	£75
1912	£40	£70
1913	£40	£70
1914	£40	£75
1915	£40	£65
1916	£40	£65
1917	£40	£65
1918	£40	£65
1919	£40	£65
1920	£40	£65
1921	£40	£65
1922	£40	£65
1923	£40	£65
1924	£40	£65
1925	£40	£65
1926	£40	£65
1927	£40	£65
1928	£40	£65
1929	£40	£65
1930	£40	£65
1931	£40	£65
1932	£40	£65
1933	£40	£65
1934	£40	£65
1935	£45	£65
1936	£50	£65

GEORGE VI
	EF	Unc
1937	*	£55
1938	*	£55
1939	*	£60
1940	*	£60
1941	*	£60
1942	*	£60
1943	*	£60
1944	*	£60
1945	*	£60
1946	*	£60
1947	*	£65
1948	*	£65
1949	*	£65
1950	*	£65
1951	*	£65
1952	*	£65

ELIZABETH II
	EF	Unc
1953	£200	£300
1954	*	£60
1955	*	£60
1956	*	£60
1957	*	£60
1958	*	£60
1959	*	£60
1960	*	£65
1961	*	£60
1962	*	£60
1963	*	£60
1964	*	£60
1965	*	£60
1966	*	£60
1967	*	£60
1968	*	£60
1969	*	£60
1970	*	£65
1971	*	£60
1972	*	£60
1973	*	£60
1974	*	£60
1975	*	£60
1976	*	£60
1977	*	£60
1978	*	£60
1979	*	£60
1980	*	£65
1981	*	£60
1982	*	£60
1983	*	£60
1984	*	£60
1985	*	£60
1986	*	£60
1987	*	£60
1988	*	£60
1989	*	£60
1990	*	£70
1991	*	£65
1992	*	£65
1993	*	£65
1994	*	£65
1995	*	£65
1996	*	£65
1997	*	£70
1998	*	£80
1999	*	£100

1925 Maundy (part set)

Nickel-brass threepences

1937 threepence of Edward VII, extremely rare

1937-dated Edward VIII threepences, struck in 1936 ready for issue, were melted after Edward's abdication. A few, however, escaped into circulation to become highly prized collectors' pieces. George VI 1937 threepences were struck in large numbers.

EDWARD VIII	F	VF	EF	BU
1937	*	*	£25000	*

GEORGE VI	F	VF	EF	BU
1937	*	*	£1	£2
1938	*	*	£3	£10
1939	*	*	£4	£20
1940	*	*	£2	£4
1941	*	*	£1	£3
1942	*	*	£1	£2
1943	*	*	£1	£2
1944	*	*	£1	£3
1945	*	*	*	£3
1946	£2	£10	£50	£150
1948	*	*	£4	£6
1949	£2	£10	£50	£125
1950	*	*	£8	£25
1951	*	*	£8	£25
1952	*	*	*	£1.50

Elizabeth II 1953 nickel-brass threepence

ELIZABETH II	F	VF	EF	BU
1953	*	*	*	£1
1954	*	*	*	£2
1955	*	*	*	£2
1956	*	*	£1	£2
1957	*	*	*	£2
1958	*	*	£2	£4
1959	*	*	*	£2
1960	*	*	*	£1.25
1961	*	*	*	*
1962	*	*	*	*
1963	*	*	*	*
1964	*	*	*	*
1965	*	*	*	*
1966	*	*	*	*
1967	*	*	*	*

Copper twopence

George III 1797 'cartwheel' twopence

GEORGE III	F	VF	EF	BU
1797	£8	£40	£200	£1000

Copper pennies

GEORGE III	F	VF	EF	BU
1797 10 leaves	£3	£10	£100	£450
1797 11 leaves	£3	£10	£100	£450

1797 'cartwheel' penny

	F	VF	EF	BU
1806	£3	£8	£60	£150
1806 no incuse curl	£3	£8	£60	£150
1807	£3	£8	£60	£150

1806 penny of George III

GEORGE IV	F	VF	EF	BU
1825	£5	£15	£90	£250
1826	£3	£12	£80	£300
1826 thin line down St Andrew's cross	£5	£15	£85	£225
1826 thick line	£5	£15	£85	£250
1827	£100	£400	£1000	*

COPPER PENNIES

William IV 1831 penny

WILLIAM IV	F	VF	EF	BU
1831	£6	£30	£225	*
1831.w.w incuse ...	£8	£40	£275	*
1831.w.w incuse ...	£10	£50	£300	*
1834	£10	£50	£275	*
1837	£15	£75	£350	*

Victoria 1841 copper penny

VICTORIA	F	VF	EF	Unc
1839 proof	*	*	£125	£225
1841	£12	£30	£75	*
1841 no colon				
after REG	£3	£15	£50	£120
1843	£12	£40	*	*
1843 no colon				
after REG	£15	*	*	*
1844	£3	£15	£50	£120
1845	£8	£20	£75	£175
1846 DEF far				
colon	£3	£15	£50	£120
1846 DEF close				
colon	£3	£15	£50	£120
1847 DEF close				
colon	£3	£15	£50	£120
1847 DEF far				
colon	£3	£15	£50	£120

	F	VF	EF	BU
1848	£3	£15	£50	£120
1848/6	£15	£35	£100	£200
1848/7	£3	£15	£50	£120
1849	£30	£75	£250	£500
1851 DEF far colon	£3	£15	£50	£120
1851 DEF close colon	£4	£15	£50	£120
1853 OT	£2	£10	£40	£100
1853 colon nearer F	£3	£10	£50	£120
1853 PT	£2	£10	£40	£90
1854 PT	£2	£10	£40	£90
1854/3	£15	£60	*	*
1854 OT	£2	£10	£40	£90
1855 OT	£2	£10	£40	£90
1855 PT	£2	£10	£40	£90
1856 PT	£25	£75	£175	£375
1856 OT	£15	£45	£100	£300
1857 OT	£2	£10	£40	£90
1857 PT	£2	£10	£40	£90
1857 small date ...	£2	£10	£40	£90
1858	£2	£10	£40	£90
1858 small date ...	£3	£10	£45	£100
1858/3 now thought to be 1858 9/8 (see below)				
1858/7	£2	£5	£35	£90
1858/6	£15	£35	£100	*
1858 no ww	£2	£5	£35	£90
1858 no ww (large 1 and 5				
small 8s)	£3	£8	£35	£100
1858 9/8?	£12	£25	£50	£110
1858 9/8? large rose	£12	£30	£65	£125
1859	£3	£10	£35	£100
1859 small date ...	£4	£15	£40	£110
1860/59	*	£350	£850	*

Bronze pennies

For fuller details of varieties in bronze pennies see English Copper, Tin and Bronze Coins in the British Museum 1558-1958 by C. W. Peck; The Bronze Coinage of Great Britain by M. J. Freeman and The British Bronze Penny 1860-1970 by Michael Gouby.

VICTORIA	F	VF	EF	BU
1860 RB, shield crossed with incuse				
treble lines	*	£10	£40	£75
1860 RB, shield crossed with close double				
raised lines	£8	£15	£45	£95
1860 RB, double lines, but farther apart,				
rock to left of				
lighthouse	£10	£50	£125	£300
1860 RB obv/TB rev	£45	£100	£500	*
1860 TB obv/RB rev	£40	£95	£450	*

1860 penny, toothed border on obverse

1860 TB, L.C. WYON on truncation, L.C.W.				
incuse below				
shield	*	£10	£40	£75

	F	VF	EF	BU
1860 TB, same obv but L.C.W. incuse below foot	£20	£50	£250	£450
1860 TB, as previous but heavy flan of 170 grains	*	£300	*	*
1860 TB, LC, WYON below truncation, L.C.W. incuse below shield	*	£6	£40	£80
1860 TB, no signature on obv. L.C.W. incuse below shield	*	£10	£60	£120
1861 L.C. WYON on truncation, L.C.W. incuse below shield	£12	£35	£95	£225
1861 same obv. no signature on rev	*	£6	£40	£80
1861 L.C. WYON below truncation, L.C.W. incuse below shield	*	£6	£40	£80
1861 similar, but heavy flan (170 grains)	*	*	*	£500
1861 same obv but no signature on rev	*	£6	£40	£95
1861 no signature on obv, L.C.W. incuse below shield	*	£8	£45	£85
1861-6/8	£25	£75	£150	£500
1861 no signature either side	£2	£8	£40	£75
1862	£2	£6	£35	£70
1862 sm date figs ...	£15	£50	*	*
1863	£2	£6	£40	£85
1863 slender 3 ...	*	*	*	*
1863 die no. (2, 3 or 4) below date	£125	£250	*	*
1864 plain 4	£8	£40	£225	£650
1864 crossiet 4	£10	£45	£250	£750
1865	*	£10	£50	£85
1865/3	£15	£65	£275	£600
1866	*	£8	£40	£85
1867	*	£10	£45	£95
1868	£6	£30	£100	£300
1869	£20	£125	£500	£1000
1870	£6	£30	£150	£250
1871	£8	£50	£200	£400
1872	*	£8	£40	£80
1873	*	£8	£40	£80
1874 (1873 type) ...	*	£8	£40	£80
1874 H (1873 type)	*	£8	£45	£85
1874 new rev, lighthouse tall and thin	£8	£15	£45	£85
1874 H as previous	£4	£10	£45	£75
1874 new obv/1873 rev	*	£6	£40	£70
1874 H as previous	*	£6	£40	£70
1874 new obv/new rev	*	£6	£40	£70
1874 H as previous	*	£6	£40	£60
1875	*	£8	£40	£65
1875 H	£20	£65	£275	£500
1876 H	*	£6	£25	£50
1877	*	£8	£25	£60
1878	*	£10	£30	£70
1879	*	*	£25	£60
1880	*	*	£30	£80
1881 (1880 obv)	*	*	£30	£60
1881 new obv	*	£15	£50	£100
1881 H	*	*	£25	£60
1882 H	*	*	£25	£60
1882 no H	£75	£300	£800	£2000
1883	*	*	£20	£60
1884	*	*	£20	£50
1885	*	*	£20	£50
1886	*	*	£20	£50
1887	*	*	£20	£50

BRONZE PENNIES

	F	VF	EF	BU
1888	*	*	£20	£50
1889 14 leaves	*	*	£20	£50
1889 15 leaves	*	*	£20	£50
1890	*	*	£20	£45
1891	*	*	£20	£45
1892	*	*	£20	£50
1893	*	*	£20	£50
1894	*	*	£35	£70
1895 2mm	*	£40	£175	£300

Victoria old head penny of 1895

	F	VF	EF	BU
1895	*	*	£5	£35
1896	*	*	£3	£30
1897	*	*	£2.50	£25
1897 higher horizon	£5	£25	£175	£350
1898	*	£1.25	£8	£35
1899	*	£1	£6	£30
1900	*	*	£5	£15
1901	*	*	£3	£12

Edward VII 1902, penny, low horizon

EDWARD VII

	F	VF	EF	BU
1902 low horizon ...	*	£8	£30	£50
1902	*	*	£10	£15
1903	*	*	£10	£25
1904	*	*	£12	£30
1905	*	*	£10	£28
1906	*	*	£10	£25
1907	*	*	£10	£25

BRONZE PENNIES

	F	VF	EF	BU
1908	*	*	£10	£30
1909	*	*	£10	£30
1910	*	*	£10	£25

GEORGE V
	F	VF	EF	BU
1911	*	*	£10	£25
1912	*	*	£10	£25
1912 H	*	*	£20	£50
1913	*	*	£15	£35
1914	*	*	£10	£25
1915	*	*	£10	£25
1916	*	*	£10	£25
1917	*	*	£10	£25
1918	*	*	£10	£25
1918 H	*	£15	£95	£175
1918 KN	*	£20	£120	£250
1919	*	*	£10	£25
1919 H	*	£5	£75	£200
1919 KN	*	£10	£150	£300
1920	*	*	£10	£25
1921	*	*	£10	£25
1922	*	*	£10	£25
1922 rev as 1927 ext. rare		*	*	£750
1926	*	*	£15	£40
1926 mod effigy ...	£5	£40	£350	£700
1927	*	*	£5	£15
1928	*	*	£3	£12
1929	*	*	£3	£12
1930	*	*	£5	£20
1931	*	*	£5	£20
1932	*	*	£8	£35
1933			highest rarity	
1934	*	*	£8	£25
1935	*	*	£2	£5
1936	*	*	*	£4

GEORGE VI
	F	VF	EF	BU
1937	*	*	*	£1
1938	*	*	*	£1
1939	*	*	*	£2
1940	*	*	*	£5
1944	*	*	*	£4
1945	*	*	*	£3
1945 9 double (2 dies)	£2	£5	£20	*
1946	*	*	*	£2
1947	*	*	*	£1
1948	*	*	*	£2
1949	*	*	*	£2

George VI 1948 penny

	F	VF	EF	BU
1950	£2	£5	£10	£20
1951	£2	£5	£8	£15

ELIZABETH II
	F	VF	EF	BU
1953	*	£1	£2	£3
1953 proof	*	*	*	£5

	Fair	F	VF	EF
1961	*	*	*	£0.50
1962	*	*	*	*
1963	*	*	*	*
1964	*	*	*	*
1965	*	*	*	*
1966	*	*	*	*
1967	*	*	*	*

Copper halfpennies

All copper unless otherwise stated

Charles II 1675 halfpenny

CHARLES II
	Fair	F	VF	EF
1672	£5	£25	£80	£350
1672 CRAOLVS	£25	£100	£200	£750
1673	£5	£25	£80	£350
1673 CRAOLVS	£25	£90	£175	£500
1673 no stops on reverse	£10	£40	£100	£400
1673 no stops on obverse	£10	£40	£100	£400
1675	£10	£40	£100	£400
1675 no stops on obverse	£10	£50	£100	£400

James II 1685 tin halfpenny

JAMES II
	Fair	F	VF	EF
1685 (tin)	£30	£75	£250	£800
1686 (tin)	£35	£90	£300	£850
1687 (tin)	£30	£75	£250	£800
1687 D over D	*	*	*	*

WILLIAM AND MARY
	Fair	F	VF	EF
1689 (tin) ET on right	£65	£150	£400	*
1689 (tin) ET on left	*	*	*	*
1690 (tin) dated on edge	£30	£75	£250	£900
1691 (tin) date in exergue and on edge	£30	£75	£250	£900

116 COINS MARKET VALUES

	Fair	F	VF	EF
1691/2 (tin) 1691 in exergue 1692 on edge	£30	£75	£250	£900
1692 (tin) date in exergue and on edge	£30	£75	£250	*
1694	£5	£25	£75	£375

William and Mary 1694 halfpenny

1694 GVLIEMVS ...	*	*	*	*
1694 no stop after MARIA	£15	£45	£95	£400
1694 BRITANNIA with last I over A	£20	£60	*	*
1694 no stop on reverse	£10	£25	£80	£350

WILLIAM III
Type 1 (date in exergue)

1695	£5	£25	£75	£400
1695 thick flan	£25	£75	£150	*
1695 BRITANNIA ...	£5	£25	£75	£400
1695 no stop on reverse	£5	£30	£80	*
1696	£5	£25	£75	£400
1696 GVLIEMVS, no stop on reverse ...	£25	£65	£125	*
1696 TERTVS	£15	£50	£120	*
1696 obv struck from doubled die	£15	£50	£120	*
1697	£5	£25	£80	*
1697 no stops either side	£5	£25	£80	*
1697 I of TERTIVS over E	£15	£50	£125	*
1697 GVLILMVS no stop on reverse ...	£15	£40	£120	*
1697 no stop after TERTIVS	£10	£25	£80	£400
1698	£10	£25	£80	£400

Type 2 (date in legend)

1698	£5	£25	£100	£450
1699	£5	£15	£60	£350
1699 BRITANNIA ...	£5	£15	£60	£350
1699 GVLIEMVS ...	£5	£25	£100	£450

Type 3 (Britannia's hand on knee, date in exergue)

1699	£5	£20	£75	£350
1699 stop after date	£10	£25	£100	£450
1699 BRITANNIA ...	£5	£20	£75	£350
1699 GVLELMVS ...	£10	£25	£100	£450
1699 TERTVS	£20	£50	£150	*
1699 no stop on reverse	£20	£50	£150	*
1699 no stops on obverse	£10	£30	£100	£450

COPPER HALFPENNIES

	FAIR	F	VF	EF
1699 no stops after GVLIELMVS	£5	£20	£75	£400
1700	£5	£15	£65	£400
1700 no stops on obverse	£5	£15	£75	*
1700 no stop after GVLIELMVS	£5	£15	£75	*
1700 BRITANNIA ...	£5	£15	£70	£400
1700 no stops on reverse	£5	£15	£75	*
1700 GVLIELMS ...	£5	£25	£85	*
1700 GVLIEEMVS ...	£5	£25	£85	*
1700 TER TIVS	£5	£15	£75	*
1700 1 of TERTIVS over V	£10	£25	£100	*
1701 BRITANNIA ...	£5	£15	£75	*
1701 no stops on obverse	£5	£15	£75	*
1701 GVLIELMVS TERTIVS	£5	£25	£100	*

GEORGE I
Type 1

1717	£5	£30	£150	£300
1717 no stops on obverse	£10	£40	£200	£40
1718	*	£35	£175	£350
1718 no stop on obverse	£10	£40	£200	£450
1719 on larger flan of type 2	£15	£50	£250	*
1719 – edge grained	£10	£40	*	*

Type 2

1719 both shoulder straps ornate	£5	£20	£85	£300
1719 – edge grained	£10	£40	*	*
1719 bust with left strap plain	£5	£20	£85	£350
1719 – edge grained	£10	£40	*	*
1720	£5	£20	£85	£300
1721	£5	£20	£85	£300
1721/0	£5	£20	£85	*
1721 stop after date	£5	£20	£85	£300
1722	£5	£20	£85	£300
1722 GEORGIVS ...	£5	£20	£85	*
1723	£5	£20	£85	£300
1723 no stop on reverse	£5	£20	£85	£350
1724	£5	£20	£85	£300

George II 1729 halfpenny

GEORGE II
Young Head

1729	£2	£10	£40	£175
1729 no stop on reverse	£2	£10	£35	£150

COPPER HALFPENNIES

	Fair	F	VF	EF
1730	*	£10	£40	£175
1730 GEOGIVS, no stop on reverse ...	£5	£20	£40	£175
1730 stop after date	£5	£20	£30	£175
1730 no stop after REX or on reverse	£5	£20	£50	£175
1731	*	£10	£40	£175
1731 no stop on reverse	*	£15	£35	£150
1732	*	£10	£25	£150
1732 no stop on reverse	*	£15	£35	£150
1733	*	£10	£30	£150
1733 only obverse stop before REX ...	*	£10	£35	£150
1734	*	£10	£30	£150
1734/3	*	£10	£25	£150
1734 no stops on obverse	*	£10	£30	£150
1735	*	£10	£30	£150
1736	*	£10	£30	£150
1737	*	£10	£30	£150
1738	*	£10	£30	£150
1739	*	£10	£30	£150

Old Head

	Fair	F	VF	EF
1740	*	£5	£25	£125
1742	*	£5	£25	£125
1742/0	*	£10	£40	£150
1743	*	£5	£25	£125
1744	*	£5	£25	£125
1745	*	£5	£25	£125
1746	*	£5	£25	£125
1747	*	£5	£25	£125
1748	*	£2	£25	£125
1749	*	£2	£25	£125
1750	*	£5	£25	£125
1751	*	£5	£25	£125
1752	*	£5	£25	£125
1753	*	£5	£25	£125
1754	*	£5	£25	£125

GEORGE III

	F	VF	EF	BU
1770	£1	£20	£125	£300
1771	£1	£20	£110	£250
1771 no stop on reverse	£2	£20	£110	£250
1771 ball below spear head	£2	£20	£110	£250
1772	£2	£20	£110	£250
1772 GEORIVS	£18	£75	£175	£350
1772 ball below spear head	£2	£20	£110	£250
1772 no stop on reverse	£2	£20	£110	£250
1773	£2	£20	£110	£250
1773 no stop after REX	£2	£20	£110	£250
1773 no stop on reverse	£2	£20	£110	£300
1774	£2	£20	£110	£250
1775	£3	£20	£110	£250
1799 5 incuse gunports	*	£5	£30	£75
1799 6 relief gunports	*	£5	£30	£75
1799 9 relief gunports	*	*	£30	£100
1799 no gunports ...	*	*	£30	£85
1799 no gunports and raised line along hull	*	£5	£35	£100
1806 no berries on olive branch	*	*	£25	£75

	F	VF	EF	BU
1806 line under SOHO 3 berries	*	*	£25	£75
1807 similar but double-cut border bead between B and R	*	*	£30	£85

GEORGE IV

	F	VF	EF	BU
1825	*	£2	£50	£110

George IV 1826 halfpenny

	F	VF	EF	BU
1826 two incuse lines down cross	*	£5	£50	£120
1826 raised line down centre of cross ...	*	£5	£50	£120
1827	*	£5	£50	£120

WILLIAM IV

	F	VF	EF	BU
1831	*	£5	£45	£125
1834	*	£5	£45	£125
1837	*	£4	£40	£125

VICTORIA

	F	VF	EF	BU
1838	*	£3	£20	£45
1839 proof	*	*	*	£125
1839 proof, rev inv	*	*	*	£150
1841	*	£3	£20	£45
1843	£3	£10	£50	£100
1844	£1	£5	£40	£85
1845	£18	£40	£250	£650
1846	£2	£5	£40	£60
1847	£1	£10	£40	£60
1848	£1	£5	£40	£60
1848/3	£15	£25	*	*
1848/7	£1	£3	£20	£55
1851	£1	£3	£20	£60
1851 7 incuse dots on and above shield	*	£3	£20	£60
1852	*	£3	£20	£65
1852 7 incuse dots on and above shield	*	£3	£20	£55
1853	*	£3	£20	£45
1853/2	£3	£10	£45	*
1854	*	£3	£15	£45

Victoria 1853 copper halfpenny

	F	VF	EF	BU
1855	*	£3	£15	£45
1856	*	£3	£20	£60
1857	*	£3	£20	£45

	F	VF	EF	BU
1857 7 incuse dots on and above shield	*	£5	£20	£55
1858	*	£5	£20	£55
1858/6	£2	£10	£30	£75
1858/7	£1	£5	£20	£55
1858 small date	£1	£5	£20	£55
1859	£1	£5	£20	£55
1859/8	£3	£10	£50	*
1860	*	*	*	£2000

Bronze halfpennies

VICTORIA

	F	VF	EF	BU
1860	*	£5	£20	£50
1860 TB 7 berries in wreath	*	£5	£25	£60
1860 TB4 berries in wreath	*	£5	£25	£60
1860 TB similar but centres of four of leaves are double incuse lines	£5	£10	£35	£95
1861 obv 4 berries, 15 leaves, raised leaf centres, rev L.C.W. on rock	*	£5	£25	£75
1861 same obv, rev no signature			ext. rare	
1861 same but lighthouse has no vertical lines	£6	£10	£35	£95
1861 obv 4 berries, 4 double incuse leaf centres, rev L.C.W. on rock ...	*	£2	£25	£50
1861 same obv, rev no signature	£5	£8	£35	£100
1861 obv 7 double incuse leaf centres, rev L.C.W on rock	*	£2	£35	£65
1861 same obv, rev no signature	*	£2	£20	£45
1861 obv 16 leaves, rev lighthouse has rounded top	*	£2	£20	£45
1861 same obv, rev lighthouse has pointed top	*	£2	£20	£45
1861 no signature ...	*	£2	£20	£45
1862 L.C.W. on rock	*	£4	£20	£60
1862 letter (A,B or C) left of lighthouse base ...	£50	£125	£350	*
1863	*	£2	£20	£45
1864	*	£4	£25	£60
1865	*	£2	£25	£60
1865/3	£10	£50	£200	*
1866	*	£2	£20	£50
1867	*	£2	£25	£60
1868	*	£2	£25	£60

Victoria 1889 bronze halfpenny

BRONZE HALFPENNIES

	F	VF	EF	BU
1869	*	£5	£25	£85
1870	*	£4	£25	£60
1871	£10	£35	£125	£325
1872	*	£2	£20	£45
1873	*	£5	£25	£65
1874	*	£8	£30	£75
1874H	*	£2	£20	£40
1875	*	£2	£20	£40
1875H	*	£6	£25	£60
1876H	*	£2	£20	£45
1877	*	£2	£20	£45
1878	*	£15	£45	£175
1879	*	£2	£20	£40
1880	*	£2	£20	£40
1881	*	£2	£20	£40
1881H	*	£2	£20	£40
1882H	*	£2	£20	£40
1883	*	£2	£20	£40
1884	*	£2	£20	£40
1885	*	£2	£20	£40
1886	*	£1.50	£20	£40
1887	*	£1	£20	£40
1888	*	£1	£20	£40
1889	*	£1	£20	£40
1889/8	*	£8	£30	£85
1890	*	£1	£20	£50
1891	*	£1	£20	£40
1892	*	£1	£20	£40
1893	*	*	£20	£40
1894	*	£5	£25	£45
1895 OH	*	*	£2	£35
1896	*	*	£2	£30
1897 normal horizon	*	*	£2	£30
1897 higher horizon	*	*	£2	£30
1898	*	*	£5	£30
1899	*	*	£3	£30
1900	*	*	£15	£20
1901	*	*	£1	£10

EDWARD VII

	F	VF	EF	BU
1902 low horizon ...	*	£5	£28	£65
1902	*	*	£5	£15
1903	*	*	£8	£25
1904	*	*	£10	£30
1905	*	*	£6	£20
1906	*	*	£6	£20
1907	*	*	£6	£20
1908	*	*	£6	£20
1909	*	*	£8	£25
1910	*	*	£8	£25

GEORGE V

	F	VF	EF	BU
1911	*	*	£3	£15
1912	*	*	£3	£15

George V 1912 halfpenny

	F	VF	EF	BU
1913	*	*	£5	£20
1914	*	*	£3	£15
1915	*	*	£3	£15

BRONZE HALFPENNIES

	Fair	F	VF	EF
1916		*	£2	£15
1917	*	*	£2	£15
1918	*	*	£2	£15
1919	*	*	£2	£15
1920	*	*	£2	£15
1921	*	*	£2	£15
1922	*	*	£3	£15
1923	*	*	£2	£15
1924	*	*	£3	£15
1925	*	*	£4	£15
1925 mod effigy ...	*	*	£4	£20
1926	*	*	£4	£15
1927	*	*	£2.50	£12
1928	*	*	£2	£12
1929	*	*	£2	£12
1930	*	*	£2	£12
1931	*	*	£2	£12
1932	*	*	£2	£12
1933	*	*	£2	£15
1934	*	*	£2	£15
1935	*	*	£2	£10
1936	*	*	£2	£8

GEORGE VI
	Fair	F	VF	EF
1937	*	*	*	£1
1938	*	*	*	£2
1939	*	*	*	£2
1940	*	*	*	£3
1941	*	*	*	£3
1942	*	*	*	£1
1943	*	*	*	£1
1944	*	*	*	£2
1945	*	*	*	£1
1946	*	*	£2	£4
1947	*	*	*	£3
1948	*	*	*	£1
1949	*	*	*	£1
1950	*	*	*	£4
1951	*	*	*	£5
1952	*	*	*	£2

ELIZABETH II
	Fair	F	VF	EF
1953	*	*	*	£2
1954	*	*	*	£3
1955	*	*	*	£3
1956	*	*	*	£3
1957	*	*	*	£1
1958	*	*	*	£0.50
1959	*	*	*	£0.25
1960	*	*	*	£0.20
1962	*	*	*	*
1963	*	*	*	*
1964	*	*	*	*
1965	*	*	*	*
1966	*	*	*	*
1967	*	*	*	*

Copper farthings

Copper unless otherwise stated

OLIVER CROMWELL
	Fair	F	VF	EF
Patterns only	*	£1250	£3000	*

CHARLES II
	Fair	F	VF	EF
1671 patterns only	*	*	£100	£350
1672	£1	£4	£60	£250
1672 no stop on obverse	£2.75	£6	£75	£275
1672 loose drapery at Britannia's elbow	£2	£6	£75	£275
1673	£1	£5	£60	£250

Oliver Cromwell copper farthing

	Fair	F	VF	EF
1673 CAROLA	*	£35	*	*
1673 BRITANNIA ...	*	*	*	*
1673 no stops on obverse	£2	£5	£85	£300
1673 no stop on reverse	£2	£5	£85	£300
1674	£1	£4	£60	£250
1675	£1	£2.75	£60	£250
1675 no stop after CAROLVS	*	£35	*	£100
1676	*	*	*	*
1679	£1.50	£4	£60	£275
1679 no stop on reverse	*	*	*	*
1684 (tin) various edge readings	£12	£50	£250	£800
1685 (tin)	£15	£70	£275	£825

JAMES II
	Fair	F	VF	EF
1684 (tin)	£30	£80	£275	£800
1685 (tin) various edge readings	£20	£35	£200	*
1686 (tin) various edge readings	£20	£50	£200	*
1687 (tin)	*	*	*	*
1687 (tin) draped bust, various readings	*	*	*	*

WILLIAM AND MARY
	Fair	F	VF	EF
1689 (tin) date in exergue and on edge, many varieties ...	£15	£45	£200	*
1689/90 (tin) 1689 in exergue, 1690 on edge	*	*	*	*
1689/90 (tin) 1690 in exergue, 1689 on edge	*	*	*	*
1690 (tin) various types	£12	£30	£200	£800
1691 (tin) small and large figures	£12	£30	£200	£800
1692 (tin)	£15	£35	£200	£800
1694 many varieties	£2	£15	£75	£350

WILLIAM III
Type 1, date in exergue
	Fair	F	VF	EF
1695	£3	£7	£75	£350
1695 M over V	*	*	*	*
1696	£2	£5	£65	£350
1697	£2	£5	£60	£350

William III 1697 farthing

	Fair	F	VF	EF
1698	£5	£12	£75	*
1699	£2	£5	£65	£400
1700	£2	£5	£50	£375

Type 2, date in legend	Fair	F	VF	EF
1698	£4	£10	£60	£400
1699	£2	£10	£50	£400

Anne 1714 pattern farthing

ANNE
1714 patterns (**F**) ...	£50	£150	£275	£350

George II 1730 farthing

GEORGE II	Fair	F	VF	EF
1730	*	£3	£20	£110
1731	*	£3	£25	£110
1732	*	£5	£25	£110
1733	*	£3	£20	£110
1734	*	£2	£20	£110
1734 no stops on obverse	*	£3	£30	£120
1735	*	£2	£20	£110
1735 3 over 3	*	£8	£35	£150
1736	*	£3	£20	£110
1736 triple tie-riband	*	*	*	*
1737 sm date	*	£2	£20	£110
1737 lge date	*	£3	£25	£110
1739	*	£2	£20	£80
1739/5	*	*	*	*
1741 Old Head	*	£3	£20	£50
1744	*	£2	£20	£45
1746	*	£2	£20	£45
1746 V over U	*	*	*	*
1749	*	£2	£20	£45
1750	*	£2	£20	£45
1754/0	*	£12	£35	£150
1754	*	£2	£20	£40

George I 'dump' farthing of 1717

GEORGE I
'Dump Type'
	Fair	F	VF	EF
1717	£12	£50	£150	£300
1718 silver proof ...	*	*	*	£600

Larger flan
1719 large lettering on obverse	£3	£10	£60	£250
1719 small lettering on obverse	£3	£10	£75	£275
1719 – last A of BRITANNIA over I	*	*	*	*

GEORGE III	F	VF	EF	BU
1771	*	£15	£65	£165
1773	*	£3	£35	£135
1774	*	£3	£35	£135
1775	*	£3	£40	£135
1799	*	*	£5	£40
1806	*	£1	£8	£50
1807	*	£2	£10	£45

GEORGE IV				
1821	*	£1	£30	£60
1822	*	£1	£30	£60
1823	*	£2	£30	£60
1825	*	£2	£30	£60
1825 D of DEI over U	:£2	£5	£50	*
1826 date on rev ...	*	£1	£30	£60
1826 date on obv ...	*	£ 2	£35	£65
1826 I for 1 in date	*	*	*	*
1827	*	£2	£35	£65
1828	*	£2	£40	£90
1829	*	£3	£40	£90
1830	*	£2	£35	£75

WILLIAM IV				
1831	*	£2	£35	£90
1834	*	£2	£35	£90
1835	*	£2	£40	£110
1836	*	£2	£40	£110
1837	*	£2	£35	£90

VICTORIA				
1838	*	£2	£15	£40
1839	*	£2	£12	£35

George I 1719 farthing

	Fair	F	VF	EF
1719 legend continuous over bust	£7	£25	*	*
1720 large lettering on obverse	£3	£10	£50	£250
1720 small lettering on obverse	£2	£5	£45	£250
1721	£2	£4	£40	£250
1721/0	£10	£30	*	*
1722 large lettering on obverse	£ 4	£10	£50	£250
1722 small lettering on obverse	£3	£8	£45	£250
1723	£2	£5	£40	£225
1723 R of REX over R	£8	*	*	*
1724	£5	£10	£50	£300

COPPER FARTHINGS

	F	VF	EF	BU
1840	*	£2	£20	£40
1841	*	£2	£15	£30
1842	*	£4	£25	£45
1843	*	£2	£15	£35
1843 I for 1	*	£5	£35	£100
1844	£10	£50	£250	£650
1845	*	£3	£20	£50
1846	*	£5	£25	£60
1847	*	£2	£20	£50
1848	*	£3	£20	£55
1849	*	£7	£50	£200
1850	*	£2	£25	£50
1851	*	£6	£30	£90
1851 D over D	£10	£50	£250	£650
1852	*	£7	£30	£100
1853 w.w. raised	*	£1	£15	£35
1853 ww inc	*	£2	£20	£40
1854 ww inc	*	£2	£20	£40
1855 ww inc	*	£2	£20	£45
1855 ww raised	*	£4	£25	£50
1856	*	£3	£30	£60
1856 R over E	£10	£50	£250	£650
1857	*	£2	£15	£30
1858	*	£1	£15	£30
1859	*	£7	£30	£70
1860 proof	*	*	*	£3500

Bronze farthings

VICTORIA	F	VF	EF	BU
1860 RB	*	£2	£15	£30
1860 TB/RB (mule)	£25	£60	£100	*
1860 TB	*	£1	£15	£30
1861	*	£1	£12	£30
1862 small 8	*	£2	£12	£25
1862 large 8	*	£3	£15	£30
1863	£8.30	£20	£50	*
1864	*	£2	£12	£30
1865 large 8	*	£1	£12	£30
1865–5/2	*	£3	£15	£30
1865–5/3	*	£2	£18	£35
1865 small 8	*	£1	£10	£30
1865–5/3	*	£2	£18	£35
1866	*	*	£10	£25
1867	*	£1	£10	£25
1868	*	£2	£15	£28
1869	*	£2	£18	£35
1872	*	£2	£18	£28
1873	*	£1	£10	£38
1874 H	*	£2	£10	£25
1874 H both Gs over	£30	*	*	*
1875 5 berries/large date	£5	£10	£30	*
1875 5 berries/small date	*	*	*	*
1875 4 berries/small date	£6	£12	£35	*
1875 H 4 berries/small date	*	*	£10	£25
1876 H	*	£5	£20	£40
1877 proof	*	*	*	£1750
1878	*	*	£10	£25
1879	*	£1	£12	£25
1879 large 9	*	£2	£15	£25
1880 4 berries	*	£2	£15	£25
1880 3 berries	*	£5	£20	£40
1881 4 berries	*	£5	£20	£40
1881 3 berries	*	£2	£10	£18

	F	VF	EF	BU
1881 H 3 berries	*	£2	£10	£20
1882 H	*	£1	£8	£20
1883	*	£3	£12	£30
1884	*	*	£6	£20
1886	*	*	£6	£20
1887	*	*	£15	£22
1890	*	*	£10	£22
1891	*	*	£10	£22
1892	*	£3	£18	330
1893	*	*	£5	£18
1894	*	*	£5	£22
1895	*	£10	£35	£100
1895 OH	*	*	£3	£12

Victoria 1896, Old Head Farthing

	F	VF	EF	BU
1897 bright finish	*	*	£2	£15
1897 black finish higher horizon	*	*	£1	£12
1898	*	*	£2	£15
1899	*	*	£1	£12
1900	*	*	£1	£12
1901	*	*	£1	£10

Edward VII, 1907 Farthing

EDWARD VII	F	VF	EF	BU
1902	*	*	£1	£6
1903 low horizon	*	*	£2	£10
1904	*	*	£2	£10
1905	*	*	£2	£10
1906	*	*	£2	£10
1907	*	*	£2	£10
1908	*	*	£2	£10
1909	*	*	£2	£10
1910	*	*	£3	£12

GEORGE V	F	VF	EF	BU
1911	*	*	*	£4
1912	*	*	*	£4
1913	*	*	*	£4
1914	*	*	*	£4
1915	*	*	*	£4
1916	*	*	*	£4
1917	*	*	*	£4
1918 black finish	*	*	*	£6
1919 bright finish	*	*	*	£2
1919	*	*	*	£2
1920	*	*	*	£4
1921	*	*	*	£3
1922	*	*	*	£4
1923	*	*	*	£4
1924	*	*	*	£4
1925	*	*	*	£4

	F	VF	EF	BU
1926 modified effigy	*	*	*	£4
1927	*	*	*	£4
1928	*	*	*	£2
1929	*	*	*	£2
1930	*	*	*	£2
1931	*	*	*	£2
1932	*	*	*	£2
1933	*	*	*	£2
1934	*	*	*	£3
1935	*	*	£1.50	£5
1936	*	*	*	£1

George VI 1951 farthing (wren on reverse)

GEORGE VI

1937	*	*	*	£1
1938	*	*	*	£2
1939	*	*	*	£1
1940	*	*	*	£2
1941	*	*	*	£1
1942	*	*	*	£1
1943	*	*	*	£1
1944	*	*	*	£1
1945	*	*	*	£1
1946	*	*	*	£1
1947	*	*	*	£1
1948	*	*	*	£1
1949	*	*	*	£1
1950	*	*	*	£1
1951	*	*	*	£1
1952	*	*	*	£1

ELIZABETH II

1953	*	*	*	£0.50
1954	*	*	*	£0.35
1955	*	*	*	£0.35
1956	*	*	*	£1

Fractions of farthings

COPPER HALF FARTHINGS

	F	VF	EF	BU
GEORGE IV				
1828 Britannia breaks legend	£3	£15	£50	£125
1828 Britannia below legend	£5	£20	£75	*
1830 lge date	£3	£20	£60	£150
1830 sm date	£4	£25	£75	*
WILLIAM IV				
1837	£12	£50	£250	*

Victoria 1839 half farthing

BRONZE FARTHINGS

	F	VF	EF	BU
VICTORIA				
1839	*	£2	£15	£50
1842	*	£2	£10	£40
1843	*	*	£1	£10
1844	*	*	£1	£8
1844 E over N	£3	£12	£75	*
1847	*	£3	£10	£40
1851	*	£3	£12	£45
1852	*	£3	£20	£50
1853	*	£4	£35	£75
1854	*	£4	£40	£95
1856	*	£5	£50	£110
1856 large date ...	£6	£25	*	*
1868 bronze proof	*	*	*	£150
1868 copper-nickel proof	*	*	*	£300

COPPER THIRD FARTHINGS

	F	VF	EF	BU
GEORGE IV				
1827	*	£5	£25	£75
WILLIAM IV				
1835	*	£5	£30	£85
VICTORIA				
1844	*	£8	£25	£50
1844 RE for REG ...	£20	£35	£95	*
1844 large G in REG	*	£8	£25	£60

BRONZE THIRD FARTHINGS

	F	VF	EF	BU
VICTORIA				
1866	*	*	£5	£30
1868	*	*	£5	£30
1876	*	*	£8	£35
1878	*	*	£5	£30
1881	*	*	£5	£30
1884	*	*	£2	£15
1885	*	*	£2	£15

Edward VII 1902 third farthing

	F	VF	EF	BU
EDWARD VIII				
1902	*	*	£4	£10
GEORGE V				
1913	*	*	£5	£15

COPPER QUARTER FARTHINGS

	F	VF	EF	BU
VICTORIA				
1839	£3	£10	£20	£50

Victoria 1839 quarter farthing

1851	£4	£12	£28	£60
1852	£3	£10	£20	£50
1853	£5	£12	£25	£60
1868 bronze-proof ...	*	*	*	£200
1868 copper-nickel proof	*	*	*	£350

Decimal coinage

f denotes face value

ELIZABETH II

BRITANNIAS

A United Kingdom gold bullion coin introduced in the autumn of 1987 contains one ounce of 22ct gold and has a face value of £100. There are also half ounce, quarter ounce and one-tenth ounce versions, with face values of £50, £25 and £10 respectively. All are legal tender.

The Britannia coins bear a portrait of The Queen on the obverse and the figure of Britannia on the reverse.

	BU
1987, 1988, 1989, 1991, 1992,	
1993, 1994, 1995, 1996, 1997 1oz, proof ...	**£550**
1987 to 1997 inclusive ½oz, proof	*
1987 to 1997 inclusive ¼oz, proof	*
1987 to 1997 inclusive ⅒oz, proof	**£65**

(½ and ¼oz issued only in sets)

To commemorate the 10th anniversary of the first Britannia issue, new reverse designs were introduced for the gold coins as well as a series of 4 silver coins with denominations from £2 to 20 pence. The silver coins were issued in <u>Proof</u> condition only for 1997.

1997. 1oz, ¼oz and ⅒oz issued individually (all coins issued in 4-coin sets)
1997. 1oz, ¼oz silver coins issued individually (all coins issued in 4-coin sets)
1998. Gold and silver coins issued with new portrait of HM the Queen and first reverse design.

FIVE POUNDS

1984 gold, BU	**£400**
1985 – –	**£425**
1986 – –	**£425**
1987 – new uncoupled effigy	**£425**
1988 – –	**£425**
1989 – BU, 500th anniversary of the sovereign	**£450**
1990 gold, BU	**£435**
1990 Queen Mother's 90th birthday, gold, proof	**£600**
1990 – silver, proof	**£35**
1990 – cu-ni, BU	**£10**
1991 gold, BU	**£450**
1992 gold, BU	**£450**
1993 40th Anniversary of The Coronation	
gold, proof	**£700**
1993 – silver, proof	**£32**
1993 – cu-ni, BU	**£10**
1993 gold BU	**£475**
1994 gold BU	**£500**
1995 gold BU	**£535**
1996 Queen's 70th birthday, gold, proof	**£645**
1996 – silver, proof	**£33**
1996 – cu-ni, BU	**£10**
1996 – gold, BU	**£575**
1997 Golden Wedding, gold, proof	**£650**
1997 – silver, proof	**£32**
1997 – cu-ni, BU	**£10**
1997 – gold, BU	**£535**
1998 Prince Charles 50th Birthday, gold, proof	**£600**
1998 – silver, proof	**£33**
1998 – cu-ni, BU	**£10**
1998 – gold, BU	**£535**
1999 Diana Memorial, gold, proof	**£600**
1999 – silver, proof	**£33**
1999 – cu-ni, BU	**£10**
1999 Millennium, gold, proof	**£600**
1999 – silver, proof	**£33**
1999 cu-ni, BU	**£10**

(Gold versions also listed in FIVE POUNDS section of milled gold.) In 1984 the Royal Mint issued the first of an annual issue of Brilliant Uncirculated £5 coins. These bear the letter 'U' in a circle.

TWO POUNDS

1983 gold, proof	**£225**
1986 Commonwealth Games (Nickel brass)	
unc in folder, BU	**£6**
1986 silver unc	**£15**
1986 – – proof	**£20**
1986 gold, proof	**£225**
1987 gold, proof	**£250**
1988 gold, proof	**£250**
1989 Bill of Rights, in folder, BU	**£6**
1989 – silver, proof	**£23**
1989 Claim of Right, in folder, BU	**£6**
1989 – silver, proof	**£23**
(For 1989 £2 piedforts see sets)	
1989 500th anniversary of the sovereign,	
gold, proof	**£275**
1990 gold, proof	**£250**
1991 proof	**£250**
1993 gold, proof	**£250**
1994 Bank of England, gold, proof	**£425**
1994 gold 'mule', proof	**£600**
1994 silver, proof	**£30**
1994 silver piedfort, proof	**£50**
1994 in folder, BU	**£8**
1985 50th Anniverary of end of Second	
World War, silver, proof	**£27**
1995 ditto, in folder, BU	**£8**
1995 –, silver, piedfort, proof	**£50**
1995 –, gold, proof	**£375**
1995 50th Anniversary of United Nations,	
gold, proof	**£300**
1995 –, in folder, BU	**£6**
1995 –, silver, piedfort, proof	**£50**
1995 –, proof	**£30**
1996 European Football, gold, proof	**£350**
1996 –, silver, proof	**£27**
1996 –, silver, piedfort	**£50**
1996 –, in folder, BU	**£6**
1997 Bimetal, gold, proof	**£350**
1997 –, silver, proof	**£29**
1997 –, in folder, BU	**£6**
1998 Bimetal, silver, proof	**£29**
1998 – silver, piedfort	**£50**
1998 – proof	**£6**
1999 Rugby World Cup, gold, proof	**£300**
1999 – silver, proof	**£30**
1999 – silver, piedfort	**£50**
1999 –, in folder, BU	**£6**

(Gold versions are also listed in TWO POUNDS section of milled gold.)

ONE POUND

1983	**£2**
1983 Unc, in folder	**£5**
1983 silver, proof	**£30**
1983 – – piedfort	**£120**
1983 Scottish reverse	**£2**
1984 – Unc, in folder	**£5**
1984 – silver, proof	**£20**
1984 – – piedfort	**£50**
1985 New portrait, Welsh reverse	**£2**
1985 – – Unc, in folder	**£5**
1985 – – silver, proof	**£22**
1985 – – piedfort	**£50**
1986 – Northern Ireland reverse	**£2**
1986 – Unc, in folder	**£5**
1986 – silver, proof	**£25**
1986 – – – piedfort	**£50**
1987 English reverse	**£2**
1987 – Unc, in folder	**£3**
1987 – silver, proof	**£20**
1987 – – – piedfort	**£50**
1988 Royal Arms reverse	**£2**
1988 – Unc, in folder	**£5**
1988 – silver, proof	**£30**
1988 – – – piedfort	**£50**
1989 Scottish rev as 1984,	
silver, proof	**£20**

1991 Northern Ireland rev as 1986,	
silver, proof	£25
1992 English rev as 1987,	
silver, proof	£25
1993 Royal Coat of Arms (reverse as	
1983), silver, proof	£30
1993 – – – piedfort	£50
1994 Scottish Lion, silver, proof	£35
Ditto, Unc. in folder	£5
1994 – silver, piedfort	£50
1995 Welsh dragon, silver, proof	£25
Ditto, Unc in folder, English version	£5
1995 – silver, piedfort	£50
1996 Northern Ireland Celtic Ring	
Unc in folder	£5
Silver, proof	£27
Silver, piedfort	£50
1997 English Lions Unc, in folder	£5
silver, proof	£25
silver, piedfort	£45
1998 Royal coat of arms/reverse as 1983,	
silver, proof	£25
silver, piedfort	£45
1999 Scottish Lion (reverse as 1994)	
new portrait, silver proof	£25
silver piedfort	£45

Note that the edge inscriptions on £2 and £1 appear either upright or inverted in relation to the obverse. (Sovereign and half sovereign prices are not listed here but in the main listings under milled gold.)

FIFTY PENCE

1969	£1
1970	£1
1973 EEC	£1
1973 – proof	£3
1976-1981	f
1982 rev changed to FIFTY PENCE	
instead of NEW PENCE	f
1983, 1985	f
1992 European Community	f
1992 – silver, proof	£30
1992 – silver, proof piedfort	£55
1992 – gold, proof	£400
1994 Normandy landing	f
1994 – silver, proof	£28
1994 – silver, piedfort	£50
1994 – gold, proof	£400
1997 new size (27.3mm diameter)	
silver, proof	£27
silver, piedfort	£46
1997 old and new size,	
silver proofs	£50
1998 European Presidency	£2
1998 – silver, proof	£25
1998 – silver, piedfort	£45
1998 – gold, proof	£250
1998 National Health Service Commemorative	£2
1998 – silver, proof	£25
1998 – silver, piedfort	£45
1998 – gold, proof	£250
1999 Britannia reverse	*

TWENTY-FIVE PENCE

1972 Silver Wedding	£1
1972 – silver, proof	£25
1977 Jubilee	£1
1977 – silver, proof	£20
1980 Queen Mother's 80th birthday	£1
1980 – in blister pack	£3
1980 – silver, proof	£32
1981 Royal Wedding	£1
1981 – in folder ... ... ·...	£3
1981 – silver, proof	£30

TWENTY PENCE

1982	f
1982 silver, proof piedfort	£40
1983, 1984, 1985, 1987, 1988-1997 ...	f

TEN PENCE

1968	£0.25
1969	£0.25
1970	£0.20
1971	£0.20
1973	£0.20
1974-1977, 1979-1981	f
1992 new size (24.5mm diameter)	
silver, proof, piedfort	£30
1992 old and new size,	
silver, proofs	£30
1992, 1995, 1997 – cu-ni	f

FIVE PENCE

1968-1971	*
1975, 1977-1980, 1987, 1988, 1989	f
1990 silver, proof, old and new	£26
1990, 1991, 1992, 1994–1997 – cu-ni ...	f

TWO PENCE

1971	*
1975-1981	f
1985 new portrait, rev changed to	
TWO PENCE instead of NEW PENCE ...	f
1986-1997	f

ONE PENNY

1971	*
1973-1981	f
1982 rev changed to ONE PENNY	
instead of NEW PENNY	f
1983, 1984	f
1985 new portrait	f
1986-1997	f

HALF PENNY

1971	*
1973-81	*
1982 rev changed to HALFPENNY	
instead of 1/2 NEW PENNY	*
1983	*

Note: Some denominations in the range 50 pence to one penny have only been issued in Royal Mint uncirculated and Proof sets and are difficult to locate as individual coins.

Proof and Specimen Sets

Proof or specimen sets have been issued since 1887 by the Royal Mint in official cases. Prior to that date, sets were issued privately by the engraver. Some sets are of currency coins, easily distinguishable from proofs which have a vastly superior finish. The two 1887 sets frequently come on to the market, hence their place in this list. The 1953 'plastic' set, though made up of currency coins, is official. It was issued in a plastic packet, hence the name. Apart from the seats stated, as being uncirculated, currency or specimen, all those in the following listing are proof sets.

GEORGE IV   FDC
New issue, **1826.** Five pounds to farthing (11 coins) … … … … … … … … … … **£18000**

WILLIAM IV
Coronation, **1831.** Two pounds to farthing (14 coins) … … … … … … … … … **£15000**

VICTORIA
Young head, **1839.** 'Una and the Lion' five pounds plus sovereign to farthing (15 coins) … … … **£27500**
Young head, **1853.** Sovereign to half farthing, including 'Gothic' crown (16 coins) … … … … … **£25000**
Jubilee head, Golden Jubilee, **1887.** Five pounds to Threepence ('full set' – 11 coins) … … … … · **£5500**
As above, currency set (unofficial) … … … … … … … … … … … … … … … **£1400**
Jubilee head, Golden Jubilee, **1887.** Crown to threepence ('short set' – 7 coins) … … … … · **£950**
As above, currency set (unofficial) … … … … … … … … … … … … … … … **£200**
Old head, **1893.** Five pounds to threepence ('full set)' – 10 coins) … … … … … … … … · **£6500**
Old head, **1893.** Crown to threepence ('short set' – 6 coins) … … … … … … … … · … **£1100**

EDWARD VII
Coronation, **1902.** Five pounds to Maundy penny – matt proofs (13 coins) … … … … … … … **£1400**
Coronation, **1902.** Sovereign to Maundy penny – matt proofs (11 coins) … … … … … … … · **£450**

GEORGE V
Coronation, **1911.** Five pounds to Maundy penny (12 coins) … … … … … … … … … **£2250**
Coronation, **1911.** Sovereign to Maundy penny (10 coins) … … … … … … … … … · **£750**
Coronation, **1911.** Halfcrown to Maundy penny (8 coins) … … … … … … … … … · **£300**
New types, **1927.** Crown to threepence (6 coins) … … … … … … … … … … … **£225**

GEORGE VI
Coronation, **1937.** Gold set, five pounds to half sovereign (4 coins) … … … … … … … … **£1400**
Coronation, **1937.** Silver and bronze set, crown to farthing including Maundy money (15 coins) … … **£120**
Mid-century, **1950.** Halfcrown to farthing (9 coins) … … … … … … … … … … …**£40**
Festival of Britain, **1951.** Crown to farthing (10 coins) … … … … … … … … … … …**£50**

ELIZABETH II
Coronation, **1953.** Crown to farthing (10 coins) … … … … … … … … … … … …**£55**
Coronation, **1953.** Currency ('plastic') set, official, halfcrown to farthing (9 coins) … … … … …**£15**
Specimen decimal set, **1968.** 10p, 5p; **1971** 2p, 1p, ½p in wallet (5 coins) … … … … … … …**£1**
Last £sd coins, **1970.** (sets issued 1971-73). Halfcrown to Halfpenny (8 coins) … … … … …**£15**
Proof decimal set, **1971.** (issued 1973), 50p, 10p, 5p, 2p, 1p, ½p (6 coins) … … … … … …**£15**
Proof decimal set, **1972.** 50p, Sliver Wedding, 25p, 10p, 5p, 2p, 1p, ½p (7 coins) … … … … …**£15**
Proof decimal sets, **1973, 1974, 1975, 1976.** 50p, to ½p (6 coins) … … … … … … … …**£9**
Proof decimal set, **1977.** 50p to ½p, plus Jubilee crown (7 coins) … … … … … … … … …**£13**
Proof decimal set, **1978.** 50p to ½p (6 coins) … … … … … … … … … … … … …**£15**
Proof decimal set, **1979.** 50p to ½p (6 coins) … … … … … … … … … … … … …**£15**
Proof decimal set, **1980.** 50p to ½p (6 coins) … … … … … … … … … … … … …**£11**
Proof gold set, **1980.** Five pounds, two pounds, sovereign, half sovereign (4 coins) … … … …**£700**
Commemorative proof coin set, **1981.** Five pounds, sovereign, Royal Wedding Silver crown,
    50p to ½p (9 coins) … … … … … … … … … … … … … … … … … … …**£600**
Commemorative set, **1981.** Sovereign and Royal Wedding silver crown (2 coins) … … … … …**£125**
Proof decimal set, **1981.** 50p to ½p (6 coins) … … … … … … … … … … … … …**£11**
Proof gold set, **1982.** Five pounds, two pounds, sovereign, half sovereign (4 coins) … … … … …**£725**
Proof decimal set, **1982.** 50p to ½p including 20p (7 coins) … … … … … … … … … …**£14**
Uncirculated decimal set, **1982.** 50p to ½p including 20p (7 coins) … … … … … … … … …**£8**
Proof gold set, **1983.** Two pounds, sovereign, half sovereign (3 coins) … … … … … … … …**£325**
Proof decimal set, **1983.** £1 to ½p (8 coins) … … … … … … … … … … … … … …**£18**
Uncirculated decimal set, **1983.** £1 to ½p (8 coins) … … … … … … … … … … … …**£12**
Proof gold set, **1984.** Five pounds, sovereign, half sovereign (3 coins) … … … … … … … …**£575**
Proof decimal set, **1984.** £1 (Scottish rev) to ½p (8 coins) … … … … … … … … … … …**£15**
Uncirculated decimal set, **1984.** £1 (Scottish rev) to ½p (8 coins) … … … … … … … … …**£13**
Proof gold set, **1985.** new portrait. Five pounds, two pounds, sovereign, half sovereign (4 coins) … …**£750**
Proof decimal set, **1985.** new portrait. £1 (Welsh rev) to 1p (7 coins) in de luxe case … … … …**£20**
Proof decimal set, **1985.** As above, in standard case … … … … … … … … … … … …**£15**
Uncirculated decimal set, **1985.** £1 (Welsh rev) to 1p (7 coins) … … … … … … … … … …**£12**
Proof gold set, **1986.** Commonwealth Games two pounds, sovereign, half sovereign (3 coins) … … …**£350**
Proof decimal set, **1986.** Commonwealth Games £2, Northern Ireland £1.50p to 1p (8 coins),
    de luxe case …**£25**
Proof decimal set, **1986.** As above in standard case … … … … … … … … … … … …**£20**
Uncirculated decimal set, **1986.** As above, in folder … … … … … … … … … … … …**£12**
Proof gold Britannia set, **1987.** One ounce, half ounce, quarter ounce tenth ounce (4 coins) … … …**£650**
Proof decimal set, **1987.** Quarter ounce, tenth ounce (2 coins) … … … … … … … … … …**£150**

PROOF AND SPECIMEN SETS

Proof gold set, **1987**. Two pounds, sovereign, half sovereign (3 coins) **£325**
Proof decimal set, **1987**. £1 (English rev) to 1p (7 coins) in de luxe case **£23**
Proof decimal set, **1987**. As above, in standing case **£18**
Uncirculated decimal set, **1987**. As above, in folder **£10**
Proof gold Britannia set, **1988**. One ounce, half ounce, quarter ounce, tenth ounce (4 coins) **£615**
Proof gold Britannia set, **1988**. Quarter ounce, tenth ounce (2 coins) **£150**
Proof gold set, **1988**. Two pounds, sovereign, half sovereign (3 coins) **£325**
Proof decimal set **1988**. £1 (Royal Arms rev) to 1p (7 coins) in de luxe case **£26**
Proof decimal set, **1988**. As above, in standard case **£19**
Uncirculated decimal set, **1988**. As above, in folder **£11**
Proof gold Britannia set, **1989**. One ounce, half ounce, quarter ounce, tenth ounce (4 coins) **£700**
Proof gold Britannia set, **1989**. Quarter ounce, tenth ounce (2 coins) **£150**
Proof gold set, **1989**. 500th anniversary of the sovereign. Five pounds, two pounds, sovereign,
    half sovereign (4 coins) **£900**
Proof gold set, **1989**. 500th anniversary of the sovereign. Two pounds, sovereign, half sovereign (3 coins) **£450**
Proof decimal set, **1989**. Bill of Rights £2. Claim of Right £2.
    £1 (Scottish rev as 1984), 50p to 1p (9 coins) in de luxe case **£32**
Proof decimal set, **1989**. As above, in standard case **£27**
Proof silver, Bill of Rights £2. Claim of Right £2. **1989**. (2 coins) **£40**
Proof silver piedfort, **1989**. £2 as above (2 coins) **£80**
Uncirculated. **1989**. As above (2 coins) in folder **£10**
Uncirculated decimal set, **1989**. £1 (Scottish rev as 1984) to 1p (7 coins) **£15**
Proof gold Britannia set, 199**0** **£775**
Proof gold set, **1990**. Five pounds, two pounds, sovereign, half-sovereign (4 coins) **£800**
Proof gold set, **1990**. Two pounds, sovereign, half sovereign (3 coins) **£375**
Proof silver set, **1990**. Five pence (23.59mm diam) and five pence (18mm diam, new size) **£24**
Proof decimal set, **1990**. £1 (Welsh rev as 1985) to 1p including large and small 5p (8 coins) in deluxe case **£30**
Proof decimal set, **1990**. As above, in standard case **£25**
Uncirculated decimal set, **1990**. £1 (Welsh rev as 1985) to 1p including large and small 5p (8 coins) **£15**
Proof gold Britannia set, **1991**. **£775**
Proof gold set, **1991**. Five pounds, two pounds, sovereign, half sovereign (4 coins) **£900**
Proof gold set, **1991**. Two pounds, sovereign, half sovereign (3 coins) **£450**
Proof decimal set, **1991**. £1 to 1p (7 coins) in deluxe case **£30**
Proof decimal set, **1991**. As above, in standard case **£25**
Uncirculated decimal set, **1991**. (7 coins) **£15**
Proof gold Britannia set, **1992**. **£800**
Proof gold set, **1992**. Five pounds, two pounds, sovereign, half sovereign (4 coins) **£950**
Proof gold set, **1992**. Two pounds, sovereign, half sovereign (3 coins) **£450**
Proof decimal set, **1992**. £1 (English rev as 1987) to 1p (two 50p, new 10p) (9 coins) in deluxe case **£32**
Proof decimal set, **1992**. As above, in standard case **£28**
Proof gold Britannia set, **1993**. **£900**
Proof gold set, **1993**. Five pounds, two pounds, sovereign, half sovereign (4 coins) **£975**
Proof gold set, **1993**. Two pounds, sovereign, half sovereign (3 coins) **£450**
Proof decimal set, **1993**. Coronation Anniversary £5, £1 to 1p (8 coins) in deluxe case **£35**
Proof decimal set, **1993**. As above, in standard case **£30**
Uncirculated decimal set, **1993** (with two 50p, no £5) (8 coins) **£12**
Proof gold Britannia set, **1994**. **£900**
Proof gold set, **1994**. Five pounds, two pounds Bank of England, sovereign, half sovereign (4 coins) **£1025**
Proof gold set, **1994**. Two pounds Bank of England, sovereign, half sovereign (3 coins) **£550**
Proof decimal set, **1994**. £2 Bank of England, £1 (Scottish rev), 50p D-Day to 1p (8 coins) in deluxe case **£34**
Proof decimal set, **1994**. As above, in standard case **£28**
Uncirculated decimal set, **1994**. **£14**
Proof gold Britannia set, **1995**. **£1000**
Proof godl set, **1995**. Five pounds, two pounds Peace, sovereign, half sovereign (4 coins) **£1100**
Proof gold set, **1995**. Two pounds Peace, sovereign, half sovereign (3 coins) **£500**
Proof decimal set, **1995**. Two pounds Peace, £1 (Welsh rev) to 1p (8 coins) in deluxe case **£36**
Proof decimal set, **1995**. As above, in standard case **£29**
Uncirculated decimal set, **1995**. **£12**
Proof gold Britannia set, **1996**. **£1050**
Proof gold set, **1996**. Five pounds, two pounds, sovereign, half sovereign (4 coins) **£1175**
Proof gold set, **1996**. Two pounds, sovereign, half sovereign (3 coins) **£500**
Proof silver decimal set, **1996**. £1 to 1p (7 coins) **£100**
Proof decimal set, **1996**. 60th Birthday £5, £2 Football, £1 Northern Irish rev) to 1p (9 coins) in deluxe case **£38**
Proof decimal set, **1996**. As above, in standard case **£32**
Proof gold Britannia set, **1997**. **£1050**
Uncirculated decimal sert, **1996**. £2 to 1p (8 coins) **£11**
Proof gold set, **1997**. Five pounds, two pounds (bimetal), sovereign, half sovereign (4 coins) **£1175**
Proof gold set, **1997**. Two pounds (bimetal), sovereign, half sovereign **£500**
Proof silver Britannia set, **1997**. Two pounds to 20p **£85**
Proof decimal set, **1997**. Golden Wedding £5, £2 bimetal. £1 (English rev) to 1p, with new 50p **£40**
Proof decimal set, **1997**. As above, in standard case **£35**
Uncirculated decimal set, **1997**. As above but no £5 (9 coins) **£11**
Proof gold Britannia set, **1998**. **£1045**
Proof gold set, **1998**, £5 to half sovereign **£1175**
Proof gold set, **1998**, £2 to half sovereign **£495**
Proof silver set, Britannia **1998**, £2 to 20p **£85**
Proof decimal set, **1998**, Prince Charles, £5 to 1p **£40**
Proof decimal set, **1998**, as above, in standard case **£33**
Uncirculated set, **1998**, as above but no £5 (9 coins) **£11**
Proof silver set, **1998**, 'EU' and 'NHS' 60p (2 coins) **£50**
Proof gold Britannia set, **1999**. **£1050**
Proof gold set, **1999**, £5, £2 Rugby World Cup, sovereign, half sovereign **£1175**
Proof gold set, **1999**, £2 Rugby World Cup, sovereign, half sovereign **£500**
Proof decimal set, **1999**, Diana £5 to 1p **£40**
Proof decimal set, **1999**, as above, in standard case **£35**
Uncirculated set, **1999**, as above but no £5 (8 coins) **£11**

Scottish Coins

THE SCOTTISH MINTS
H = A HOARD

Forres
Inverness
Aberdeen
Montrose
Forfar
Dundee
Perth • H
St Andrews
Stirling H Montrave
Kinghorn
Dumbarton • Linlithgow
Dunbar
Renfrew • Glasgow
Edinburgh
Lanark
Berwick
Kelso
Bamborough
Ayr
Jedburgh
Roxburgh
H Crossraguel
Abbey
Dumfries
Carlisle
Corbridge

Based on a map of actual and supposed mints prepared by Spink and Son Ltd.

The number of mints which have been in operation in Scotland can be seen from the map above. The mints of the first coinage of Alexander III are the greatest number ever working together in Scotland, and it is this area that really attracts the collector of the different mint issues. For this reason, when we deal with this reign later on, we give a price for issues of each mint town, but not for any other reign.

MINT TOWN	KING(S)
ABERDEEN	Alexander III, David II
	Robert III, James I, II, III
AYR	Alexander III
BAMBOROUGH	Henry
BERWICK	David I, Malcom IV,
	William I, Alexander II, III
	Robert Bruce, James III
CARLISLE	David I, Henry
CORBRIDGE	Henry
DUMBARTON	Robert III
DUMFRIES	Alexander III
DUNBAR	William I ?, Alexander III
DUNDEE	William I ?, Alexander III
DUNFERMLINE	William I
FORFAR	Alexander III
FORRES	Alexander III
GLASGOW	Alexander III
INVERNESS	Alexander III
JEDBURGH	Malcom IV
KELSO	Alexander II
KINGHORN	Alexander III
LANARK	Alexander III
LINLITHGOW	James I, II
MONTROSE	Alexander III
PERTH	William I, Alexander III,
	Robert II to James II
RENFREW	Alexander III
ROXBURGH	Alexander III
ST ANDREWS	Alexander III
STIRLING	Alexander III, James I, II
	Mary Stuart

Prices are for the commonest coins in each case. Collectors should expect to pay these amounts and upwards. For further details see The Scottish Coinage, *by I. Stewart (Spink, 1967, reprint 1975) and Standard Catalogue, Volume 2 (Seaby, 1984). Gold coins are indicated. All other coins are silver unless another metal is stated.*

DAVID I 1124-53

	F	VF
Pennies	£500	£1000

Four different groups; struck at the mints of Berwick, Carlisle, Roxburgh and Edinburgh

This superb David I penny of Carlisle realised £1,210 in Spink's Douglas auction in 1997

HENRY 1136-52
(Earl of Huntingdon and Northumberland)

Pennies	£1200	*

Three types; struck at the mints of Corbridge, Carlisle and Barnborough.

MALCOLM IV 1153-65

Pennies	£3500	*

Five types; struck at the mints of Roxburgh and Berwick.

WILLIAM THE LION 1165-1214

Pennies	£65	£140

Three issues; struck at the mints of Roxburgh, Berwick, Edinburgh, Dun (Dunfermline?), Perth

ALEXANDER II 1214-49

Pennies	£700	£1500

Mints of Berwick and Roxburgh, varieties of bust.

Halfpenny and farthing of Alexander III and penny of Robert Bruce

ALEXANDER III 1249-86
1st coinage pennies 1250-80
Mints

Aberdeen	£100	£250
Ayr	£100	£300
Berwick	£40	£120
'DUN'	£140	£400
Edinburgh	£35	£100
Forfar	£130	£375
Fres	£130	£375
Glasgow	£150	£400
Inverness	£150	£400
Kinghorn	£200	£450
Lanark	£150	£400
Montrose	£250	*
Perth	£60	£140

SCOTTISH COINS

	F	VF
Renfrew	£200	*
Roxburgh	£45	£140
St. Andrews	£90	£220
Stirling	£130	£400
'TERWILANER' (uncertain name)	£200	*

2nd coinage c. 1280 –
Many types and varieties

Pennies	£15	£40
Halfpennies	£80	£200
Farthings	£175	£450

JOHN BALIOL 1292-6
1st coinage (rough surface issue)

Pennies	£100	£250
Halfpennies		ext. rare

2nd coinage (smooth surface issue)

Pennies	£120	£300
Halfpennies	£200	£450

Robert Bruce Penny

ROBERT BRUCE 1306-29

Pennies	£300	£650
Halfpennies	£350	£800
Farthings		ext. rare

Probably all struck at Berwick.

David II Groat, Edinburgh Mint

DAVID II 1329-71

Nobles (gold)		ext. rare
Groats	£70	£200
Halfgroats	£50	£160
Pennies	£35	£80
Halfpennies	£150	£350
Farthings	£500	*

Three issues, but these denominations were not struck for all issues. Edinburgh and Aberdeen mints.

ROBERT II 1371-90

Groats	£60	£200
Halfgroats	£90	£200
Pennies	£70	£150
Halfpennies	£140	£400

Some varieties. Struck at mints of Dundee, Edinburgh, Perth.

SCOTTISH COINS

ROBERT III 1390-1406 ... ...

	F	VF
Lion or crowns (gold)	£450	£950
Demy lions or halfcrowns (gold) ...	£375	£850
Groats	£60	£150
Halfgroats	£100	£300
Pennies	£175	£350
Halfpennies	£250	*

Three issues, many varieties. Struck at mints of Edinburgh, Aberdeen, Perth, Dumbarton.

James I Demy or Nine Shilling Piece

JAMES I 1406-37

	F	VF
Demies (gold)	£375	£650
Half demies (gold)	£475	£850
Groats	£130	£270
Billon pennies	£90	*
Billon halfpennies	£120	*

Mints, Aberdeen, Edinburgh, Inverness, Linlithgow, Perth, Stirling.

JAMES II 1437-60

	F	VF
Demies (gold) from	£400	£800
Lions (gold) from	£500	£1250
Half lions (gold) from		Very rare
Groats	£175	£600
Halfgroats	£400	*
Billon pennies	£150	*

Two issues, many varieties. Mints: Aberdeen, Edinburgh, Linlithgow, Perth, Roxburgh, Stirling.

ECCLESIASTICAL ISSUES C 1452-80

	F	VF
Bishop Kennedy copper pennies ...	£75	£170
Copper farthings	£150	*

Different types, varieties

JAMES III 1460-88

	F	VF
Riders (gold) from	£750	£1500
Half riders (gold)	£950	£1800
Quarter riders (gold)	£950	£2000
Unicorns (gold)	£800	£1700
Groats ... ...from	£150	£400

James III groat and James V one-third groat

	F	VF
Halfgroats from	£350	*
Pennies from	£100	£250
Billon placks from	£50	*
Billon half placks from		Very rare

	F	VF
Billon pennies from	£70	*
Copper farthings from	£150	*

Many varieties. Mints: Edinburgh, Berwick, Aberdeen.

James IV Unicorn

JAMES IV 1488-1513

	F	VF
Unicorns (gold)	£700	£1600
Half unicorns (gold)	£600	£1200
Lions or crowns (gold)	£850	£2000
Half lions (gold)	£1500	£3500
Pattern angel (gold)		unique
Groats	£350	£800
Halfgroats	£350	*
Pennies (light coinage) ... ...ext rare		*
Billon placks	£30	£75
Billon half placks	£100	*
Billon pennies	£50	£100

Different types, varieties. Mint: Edinburgh only.

James V 'Bonnet' piece of 1540

JAMES V 1513-42

	F	VF
Unicorns (gold)	£800	£1800
Half unicorns (gold)	£1500	£4500
Crowns (gold)	£550	£1250
'Bonnet' pieces or ducats (gold) ...	£1500	£3250
Two-thirds ducats (gold)	£1900	£3250
One-third ducats (gold)	£2000	£5000
Groats from	£90	£220
One-third groats	£150	£375

James V groat

	F	VF
Billon placks	£25	£100
Billon bawbees	£25	£80
Billon half bawbees	£75	£150
Billon quarter bawbees		unique

Different issues, varieties. Edinburgh mint.

Note: from here on all Scottish coins were struck at Edinburgh.

MARY 1542-67

1st Period 1542-58

	F	VF
Crown (gold)	£950	£2400
Twenty shillings (gold)	£1800	*
Lions or forty-four shillings (gold)	£850	£2000

Extremely rare Francis and Mary ducat which realised £77,000 at a Spink auction in March 1997

Half lions or twenty-two shillings (gold)	£500	£1400
Ryals or £3 pieces (gold) 1555, 1557, 1558	£1750	£4500
Half ryals (gold) 1555,1557,1558 ...	£2700	*
Portrait testoons, 1553	£1200	£3750

Mary, Queen of Scots Half Testoon, 1560, Francis and Mary

	F	VF
Non-portrait testoons, 1555-8	£150	£450
– half testoons, 1555-8	£150	£400
Billon bawbees	£25	£80
– half bawbees	£70	£180
– pennies (facing bust)	£150	£450
– pennies (no bust) 1556	£100	£400
– lions, 1555, 1558	£25	£75
– placks, 1557	£25	£75

2nd period (Francis and Mary) 1558-60

	F	VF
Ducats or sixty shillings (gold) ...	ext. rare	
Non-portrait testoons, 1558-61 ...	£150	£400
– half testoons, 1558-60	£150	£450
Twelvepenny groats (Nonsunt) 1558-9	£90	£250
– lions, 1559-60	£25	£80

3rd period (widowhood) 1560-5

	F	VF
Crown (gold) 1562		
Portrait testoons, 1561-2	£750	£2500
– half testoons, 1561-2	£850	*

4th period (Henry and Mary) 1565-7

	F	VF
Portrait ryals, 1565	ext. rare	
Non-portrait ryals, 1565-7	£200	£550

Mary and Henry 1565 two thirds ryal

	F	VF
– two thirds ryals, 1565-7	£200	£575
– – undated	£400	£950
– one-third ryals, 1565-6	£200	£475
– testoons, 1565	ext. rare	

5th period (2nd widowhood) 1567

	F	VF
– Non portrait ryals, 1567	£200	£475
– two thirds ryals, 1567	£220	£550
– one third ryals, 1566-7	£220	£550

Mints: Edinburgh, Stirling (but only for some bawbees)

JAMES VI

Before English accession 1567-1603

1st coinage 1567-71

	F	VF
Ryals 1567-71	£200	£475
Two-third ryals –	£180	£450
One-third ryals –	£200	£475

Superb gold £20 piece of 1575 realised £30,800 in Spink auction in March 1997

2nd coinage 1571-80

	F	VF
Twenty pounds (gold)	£9000	£20000
Nobles, 1572-7, 1580	£60	£350
Half nobles –	£75	£220
Two merks, 1578-80 –	£950	*
Merks, 1579-80	£900	*

3rd coinage 1580-81

	F	VF
Ducats (gold), 1580	£2750	£5500
Sixteen shillings, 1581	£900	£3000
Eight shillings, 1581	£950	*
Four shillings, 1581	£900	*
Two shillings, 1581	ext. rare	

SCOTTISH COINS

	F	VF
4th coinage 1582-88		
Lion nobles (gold)	£2000	£4500
Two-third lion nobles (gold)	£2500	£6000
One-third lion nobles (gold)	£3000	£7500
Forty shillings, 1582	£2500	£7500
Thirty shillings, 1582-6	£180	£750
Twenty shillings, 1582-5	£130	£400
Ten shillings, 1582-4	£100	£250

James VI twenty shillings, 1582

	F	VF
5th coinage 1588		
Thistle nobles (gold)	£1250	£2750
6th coinage 1591-93		
Hat pieces (gold) 1591-3	£2500	£4750
Balance half merks, 1591-3	£170	£400
Balance quarter merks, 1591	£250	£600
7th coinage 1594-1601		
Riders (gold)	£450	£850
Half riders (gold)	£350	£750
Ten shillings, 1593-5, 1598-1601 ...	£95	£290
Five shillings, 1593-5, 1598-1601 ...	£100	£275
Thirty pennies, 1595-6, 1598-9, 1601	£75	£180
Twelve pennies, 1594-6	£60	£150

James VI Sword and Sceptre piece, 1601

	F	VF
8th coinage 1601-4		
Sword and sceptre pieces (gold) ...	£275	£550
Half sword and sceptre pieces (gold)	£220	£400
Thistle-merks, 1601-4	£50	£150
Half thistle merks –	£40	£120
Quarter thistle-merks –	£35	£100
Eighth thistle-merks, 1601-3	£35	£150
Billon and copper issues		
Billon placks or eight penny groats	£20	£75
Billon half packs	£100	*
Billon hardheads	£25	£80
Billon saltire placks	£125	*

	F	VF
Copper twopence 1597	very rare	
Copper penny 1597	very rare	
After English accession 1603-25		
Units (gold)	£400	£800
Double crowns (gold)	£450	£1200
Britain crowns (gold)	£350	*
Halfcrowns (gold)	£300	*
Thistle crowns (gold)	£250	*
Sixty shillings	£250	£700
Thirty shillings	£75	£200
Twelve shillings	£80	£180
Six shillings	£120	*
Two shillings	£50	*
One shilling	£60	*

James VI Gold Unit
(after English accession)

	F	VF
Sixpences	*	*
Copper twopences	£20	£60
Copper pennies	£30	£70

Charles I Briot Unit, 3rd coinage

	F	VF
CHARLES 1652-49		
1st coinage 1625-36		
Units (gold)	£475	£900
Double crowns (gold)	£950	*
Britain crowns (gold)	ext. rare	
Sixty shillings	£300	£800
Thirty shillings	£70	£200
Twelve shillings	£70	£180
Six shillings	very rare	
Two shillings	£70	*
One shilling	ext. rare	
2nd coinage 1636		
Half merks	£50	£175
Forty penny pieces	£45	£120
Twenty penny pieces	£50	*

3rd coinage 1580-81	F	VF
Units (gold)	£475	£1000
Half units (gold)	£700	£2000
Britain crowns (gold)	£600	£1400
Britain half crowns (gold)	£400	£1200
Sixty shilling	£300	£850
Thirty shilling	£60	£150

Charles I Twelve Shillings, 3rd coinage; Falconer's issue.

Twelve shillings	£50	£170
Six shillings	£50	£150
Half Merks	£50	£170
Forty pennies	£30	£80
Twenty pennies	£25	£60
Three shillings	£50	£120
Two shillings	£50	£120
Copper twopences (lion)	£20	£80
– pennies –		rare
– twopences (CR crowned)	£15	£60
– twopences (Stirling turners) ...	£15	£50

CHARLES II 1660-85	F	VF
1st coinage		
Four merks		
1664 thistle above bust	£275	*
1664 thistle below bust	£300	*
1665	*	*
1670	£190	*
1673	£200	*
1674 F below bust	£300	£700
1675	£200	£500

Two merks		
1664 thistle above bust	£2005	£500

*Charles II silver
two merks 1664*

1664 thistle below bust	£200	*
1670	£150	£450
1673	£150	£450
1673 F below bust	£275	*
1674	£250	*
1674 F below bust	£200	*
1675	£150	£450

Charles II, Merk 1669

Merks		
1664	£40	£150
1665	£40	£150
1666	£100	*
1668	£40	£150
1669	£40	£200
1670	£75	£250
1671	£80	£200
1672	£70	£200
1673	£70	£200
1674	£50	£200
1674 F below bust	£50	£200
1675 F below bust	£50	£200
1675	£100	£250

Half merks		
1664	£50	£150
1665	£50	£150
1666	£75	£200
1667	£50	£150
1668	£50	£150
1669	£75	£200
1670	£100	£275
1671	£120	£300
1672	£50	£180
1673	£50	£180
1675 F below bust	£50	£150
1675	£45	£175

2nd coinage

Dollars		
1676	£200	£450
1679	£200	£450
1680	£250	*
1681	£200	£500
1682	£150	£350

Half dollars		
1675	£170	£450
1676	£200	£500
1681	£150	£450

Quarter dollars		
1675	£75	£200
1676	£80	£250
1677	£80	£250
1678	£50	£250
1679	£90	*
1680	£70	£250
1681	£90	*
1682	£75	£250

Eighth dollars		
1676	£60	£150
1677	£60	£150
1678/7	£90	*
1679	*	*
1680	£80	£175
1682	£100	*

Sixteenth dollars

1677	£35	£90
1678/7	£100	*
1679/7	£100	*
1680	£80	£200
1681	£50	£150

Charles II 1678 Bawbee

Copper twopence CR"		
crowned	£25	£100
Copper bawbees, 1677-9	£40	£120
Copper turners, 1677-9	£25	£100

JAMES VII 1685-9

Sixty shillings 1688 proof only[1]	FDC	£950
– gold proof only[1]	FDC	*
([1]Struck in 1828, not contemporary)		

Forty shillings

1887	£90	£350
1688	£150	£400

James VII 1687 ten shillings

Ten shillings

1687	£90	£300
1688	£100	£320

WILLIAM AND MARY 1689-94

Sixty shillings

1691	£150	£500
1692	£150	£500

Forty shillings

1689	£95	£300
1690	£90	£300
1691	£70	£270
1692	£90	£300
1693	£100	*
1694	£100	*

Twenty shillings

1693	£90	£300
1694	£200	*

Ten shillings

1689	*	*
1690	£100	£250
1691	£80	£200
1692	£50	£120
1694	£170	£400

William and Mary 1694 five shillings

Five shillings	F	VF
1691	£75	£250
1694	£70	£200
Copper bawbee 1691-4	£50	£125
Copper bodle 1691-4	£35	£80

WILLIAM II 1694-1702	F	VF
Pistole (gold) 1701	£1600	£3500
Half pistole (gold) 1701	£1500	£3750

Sixty shillings

1699	*	*

Forty shillings

1695	£80	£300
1696	£60	£250
1697	£80	£300
1698	£60	£250
1699	£100	*
1700	£200	*

Twenty shillings

1695	£50	£200
1696	£50	£200
1697	*	*
1698	£80	£250
1699	*	*

Ten shillings

1695	£90	*
1696	£80	£250
1697	£80	*
1698	£80	*
1699	£100	£350

Five shillings

1695	£50	*
1696	£50	*
1697	£25	£90
1699	£90	*
1700	£50	*
1701	£80	*
1702	£70	£200
Copper bawbee 1695-7	£20	£100
Copper bodle 1695-7	£30	£120

ANNE 1702-14
Pre-Union 1702-7

Ten shillings

1705	£75	£200
1706	£120	£350

Five shillings

1705	£20	£80
1706	£25	£100

Post-Union 1707-14
see under British milled series

JAMES VIII 1688-1766 (The Old Pretender)

Guinea 1716, gold	FDC	£3000
– silver	FDC	£900
– bronze	FDC	£1200
Crown 1709		unique
Crown 1716, silver	FDC	£950
– gold		ext. rare
– bronze		ext. rare

NB: All the 1716-dated pieces were struck in 1828 from original dies.

Irish Coins

Hammered Issues 995-1661

Prices are for the commonest coins in each case. It should be remembered that most of the Irish coins of these times are in fairly poor condition and it is difficult to find specimens in VF condition upwards. For more details see The Guide Book to the Coinage of Ireland AD 995 to the present day, *by Anthony Dowle and Patrick Finn (ref. DF in the following lists):* Seaby's Coins of Scotland, Ireland and the Islands, *which is volume Two of Seaby's Standard Catalogue (ref Sby in price list): and also Patrick Finn's* Irish Coin Values.

All coins are silver unlesss otherwise stated

	F	VF
HIBERNO-NORSEMEN OF DUBLIN 995-1150		
Pennies, imitative of English coins, many types and varieties ...from	£100	£150

Hiberno-Norse penny, c 1015-1035

Hiberno-Norseman of Dublin Penny c1035-1055

JOHN, as Lord of Ireland c 1185-1199

Halfpennies, with profile portrait	extremely rare	
Halfpennies, with facing head	£50	£95
Farthings	£250	£475
Different types,varieties, mints, moneyers.		

JOHN DE COURCY Lord of Ulster 1177-1205

Halfpenny		unique
Farthings	£450	£850
Different types,varieties, mints, moneyers.		

John as King of England, Rex/Triangle Penny

JOHN as King of England and Lord of Ireland c 1199-1216

	F	VF
Rex/Triangle types		
Pennies ... ...from	£40	£100
Halfpennies	£75	£160
Farthings	£350	£750
Different types,varieties, mints, moneyers.		

HENRY III 1216-1272

Pennies (c 1251-1254) ... ...from **£35** **£85**
Dublin only, moneyers DAVI and RICHARD. many varieties.

Edward I Waterford penny

EDWARD I 1272-1307

	F	VF
Pennies ... ...from	£20	£45
Halfpennies	£60	£150

Edward I Farthing, Dublin

Farthings	£140	£350
Dublin,Waterford and Cork. Many different issues.		

EDWARD III 1327-1377

Halfpennies Dublin mint ... ... ext. rare

There were no Irish coins struck for Edward II, Richard II, Henry IV or Henry V.

HENRY VI 1422-1461

Pennies, Dublin mint ... ... ext. rare

Edward IV untitled crown groats

EDWARD IV 1461-1483

Untitled crown groats ... ...from	£300	£600
– pennies	£600	*
Titled crown groats	£950	*
– halfgroats		ext. rare
– pennies		very rare
Cross on rose/-sun groats	£750	*

IRISH COINS

	F	VF
Bust/rose-sun double groats	£1500	£3500
– – groats	£1800	*
– – halfgroats		ext.rare
– – pennies		ext.rare
'English style' groats	£60	£150
– halfgroats	£250	£450
– pennies	£60	£130
– halfpennies		ext.rare
Bust/rose groats	£350	£750
– – pennies	£75	£150
copper issues		
Crown/cross farthing	£850	*
– – half farthing	£600	*
PATRICIUS/SALVATOR		
Farthing	£600	£1200
3 crowns/sun half-farthing		very rare

This is, of course, a very abbreviated listing of the issues of Edward IV which are numerous and complicated, and still pose numismatics many problems. There are also many varieties and different mints.

RICHARD III 1483-1485

	F	VF
Bust/rose-cross groats	£750	£2000
— halfgroat		unique
— penny		unique
Cross and Pellet Penny	£500	*
Three-crown groats	£475	£950
Different mints, varieties, etc.		

HENRY VII 1485-1509
Early issues

	F	VF
Three-crown groats	£70	£175
— halfgroats	£170	£375
— pennies	£350	£700
— halfpennies		ext. rare
Different mints, varieties, etc.		

LAMBERT SIMNEL (pretender) 1487

	F	VF
Three-crown groats	£900	£2000
Different mints, varieties.		

HENRY VII 1485-1509

Henry VII facing bust Groat, Dublin

Later issues

	F	VF
Facing bust groats	£90	£200
— halfgroats		ext. rare
— pennies		very rare
Crowned H pennies		very rare

Many varieties. Mainly Dublin. Waterford is extemely rare.

HENRY VIII 1509-1547

	F	VF
'Harp' groats	£35	£90
— halfgroat	£250	£550

Henry VIII harp groats (with initials HA and HI)

These harp coins carry crowned initials, e.g., HA (Henry and Anne Boleyn), HI (Henry and Jane Seymour), HK (Henry and Katherine Howard), HR (Henricus Rex).

Henry VIII portrait groat

Posthumous issues	F	VF
Portrait groats current for 6 pence	£70	£175
— halfgroats ...current for 3 pence	£95	£250
— pennies current for 3 halfpence	£175	*
— halfpennies current for 3 farthings	£300	*
Different busts, mintmarks etc.		

EDWARD VI 1547-1553

	F	VF
Base shillings 1552 (MDLII)	£650	£1250
— contemporary copy	£50	£170

Mary 1553 shilling

MARY 1553-1558

Shillings 1553 (MDLIII)	£500	£1100
Shillings 1554 (MDLIIII)		ext. rare
Groats		very rare
Halfgroats		ext. rare
Pennies		ext. rare

Several varieties of the shillings and groats.

PHILIP AND MARY 1554-1558

Base shillings	£175	£600
— groats	£50	£150

Several minor varieties.

ELIZABETH I 1558-1603

Base portrait shillings	£170	£650
— groats	£100	£300

Elizabeth I 1561 portrait shilling

	F	VF
Fine silver portrait shillings 1561	£100	£550
— groats –	£275	£650
Base shillings arms-harp	£100	£350
— sixpences –	£80	£200
— threepences –	£150	£400
— pennies –	£20	£80
— halfpennies –	£35	£150

JAMES I 1603-1625
Shillings	£60	£150
— Sixpences	£45	£130

Different issues, busts and mintmarks.

CHARLES I 1625-1649
Siege money of the Irish Rebellion 1642-1649
Siege coins are rather irregular in size and shape.

Kilkenny Money 1642
Copper halfpennies (**F**)	£170	£400
Copper farthings (**F**)	£170	£475

Inchiquin Money 1642-1646
(The only gold coins struck in Ireland)
Gold double pistoles		ext. rare
Gold pistoles (**F**)		ext. rare
Crowns	£950	£2000

Inchiquin shilling

Halfcrowns	£1250	*
Shillings	£1700	*
Ninepences		ext. rare
Sixpences	£1500	*
Groats (**F**)	£1500	*
Threepences ... ... ext. rare		*

Three issues and many varieties.

Ormonde Money 1643
Crowns (**F**)	£300	£650
Halfcrowns (**F**)	£220	£500
Shillings	£95	£200

Ormonde Money, Halfcrown

Ormonde sixpence

	F	VF
Sixpences (**F**)	£90	£200
Groats (**F**)	£70	£180
Threepences	£50	£130
Halfgroats (**F**)	£290	£600

Many varieties.

Rebel Money 1643
Crowns	£2000	*
Halfcrowns	£2500	*

Town Pieces 1645-1647
Bandon
Copper farthings (**F**)	£120	*

Kinsale copper farthing

Kinsale
Copper farthings (**F**)	£100	*

Youghal
Copper farthings (**F**)	£120	£750
Brass twopences		ext. rare
Pewter threepences		ext. rare

IRISH COINS

	F	VF
Cork		
Shillings (**F**)	£1000	*
Sixpences (**F**)	£500	£1000
Copper halfpennies		ext. rare
Copper farthings (**F**)	£100	*
Elizabeth I shillings countermarked		
CORKE (**F**)		ext. rare

Youghal farthing

'Blacksmith's' Money 1649
(Based on English Tower halfcrown)

	F	VF
Halfcrown, varieties	£400	£1200

Dublin Money 1649

	F	VF
Crowns	£1500	*
Halfcrowns	£1250	*

Charles II Armstrong Issue, Farthing

CHARLES II 1660-1685
Armstrong issues 1660-1661

	F	VF
Copper farthings	£45	£300

Charles II to George IV

This series, of which all the issues except Bank of Ireland tokens were struck in base metal, features a large number of varieties, many of which are unpublished, but there is space here for only the main types and best-known variants. A number of rare proofs have also been omitted.

Except for the 'gunmoney' of James II, Irish copper coins are notably hard to find in the top grades, especially the so-called 'Voce populi' issues and specimens of Wood's coinage (which are reasonably common in the lower grades, apart from the rarities).

We have listed some of the 'gunmoney' of James II in only three grades – Fair, Fine and VF. The majority of these hastily produced coins were not well struck and many pieces with little substantial wear are, arguably, not EF in the strictest sense.

Finally, a note on the dating of gunmoney. In the calendar used up to 1723 the legal or civil year commenced on March 25 in Great Britain and Ireland, so December 1689 came before, not after January, February and March 1689. Coins dated March 1689 and March 1690 were struck in the same month.

CHARLES II	Fair	F	VF	EF
St Patrick's coinage				
Halfpenny	£75	£170	*	*
— star in rev legend	£90	£220	*	*
Farthing	£45	£100	*	*
— stars in rev legend	£50	£100	£300	*
— cloud around				
St Patrick	*	*	*	*
— martlet below king	*	*	*	*
— annulet below king	£50	£100	*	*

Charles II St Patrick's Farthing

Regal coinage
Halfpennies

	Fair	F	VF	EF
1680 large letters				
small cross	£25	£60	£140	*
1680 large letters,				
pellets	£5	£25	£130	*
1681 large letters	£5	£25	£120	£250
1681 small letters	*	*	*	*
1682 large letters	*	*	*	*
1682 small letters	£6	£15	£100	£250
1683	£5	£12	£100	£250
1684	£12	£35	£150	*

JAMES II
Regular coinage
Halfpennies

	Fair	F	VF	EF
1685	£1	£10	£100	£250
1686	£1	£10	£100	£250
1687	*	*	*	*
1688	£10	£35	£180	*

Emergency coinage
Gunmoney
Crowns

	Fair	F	VF	EF
1690	£15	£35	£100	*
1690 'chubby'				
horseman, sword				
to E (Sby 6577) ...	£20	£70	£200	*
1690 similar (DF 373)	£20	£50	£180	*

James II Gunmoney Crown

	Fair	F	VF	EF
Large halfcrowns				
1689 July	£4	£20	£70	*
1689 August	£2	£15	£50	*
1689 September ...	£2	£15	£60	*
1689 October	£2	£15	£45	*
1689 November ...	£2	£15	£45	*
1689 December ...	£2	£15	£45	*
1689 January	£2	£15	£50	*
1689 February	£2	£15	£45	*
1689 March	£2	£15	£60	*
1690 March	£2	£15	£50	*
1690 April	£4	£15	£60	*
1690 May	£4	£15	£60	*
Small halfcrowns				
1690 April	*	*	*	*
1690 May	£2	£15	£50	*
1690 June	£2	£15	£45	*
1690 July	£2	£15	£45	*
1690 August	£4	£30	£65	*
1690 September ...	*	*	*	*
1690 October	£75	£250	*	*
Large shillings				
1689 July	£2	£12	£40	£120
1689 August	£2	£12	£40	£120
1689 September ...	£2	£10	£35	£100
1689 October	£4	£20	£60	*
1689 November ...	£2	£10	£40	£100
1689 December ...	£2	£10	£40	£100
1689 January	£2	£10	£40	£100
1689 February	£2	£10	£40	£100
1689 March	£2	£10	£40	£100
1690 March	£2	£10	£40	£100
1690 April	£2	£10	£40	£100
Small shillings				
1690 April	£2	£10	£30	£100
1690 May	£2	£10	£30	£100
1690 June	£2	£10	£30	£100
1690 July	*	*	*	*
1690 August	*	*	*	*
1690 September ...	*	*	*	*

James II Gunmoney, halfcrown, May 1690

Sixpences				
1689 June	£1	£10	£35	£95
1689 July	£1	£10	£35	£95
1689 August	£1	£10	£35	£95
1689 September ...	£1	£10	£35	£95
1689 October	*	*	*	*
1689 November ...	£1	£10	£35	£95
1689 December ...	£1	£10	£35	£95
1689 January	£1	£10	£35	£95
1689 February	£4	£12	£45	£110
1689 March	*	*	*	*
1690 March	*	*	*	*
1690 April	*	*	*	*
1690 May	£12	£20	£90	*
1690 June	*	*	*	*
1690 October	*	*	*	*
Pewter Money				
Crown	£190	£350	£1000	*
Groat	£95	£220	£700	*
Penny large bust ...	£100	£220	*	*
Penny small bust	£100	£220	*	*

	Fair	F	VF	EF

James II Pewter Money, Halfpenny, 1690

Halfpenny large bust	£50	£130	£350	*
Halfpenny small bust	£50	£140	£400	*

Limerick Money halfpenny

Limerick Money				
Halfpenny	£8	£45	£95	*
Farthing reversed N	£10	£50	£100	*
— normal N	£15	£60	£120	*

1693 halfpenny

WILLIAM AND MARY
Halfpennies

1692	£2	£15	£90	*
1693	£2	£25	£100	*
1694	£2	£25	£90	*

WILLIAM III
1696 Halfpenny draped

bust ... ... :	£10	£30	£120	*

1696 Halfpenny crude

undraped bust ... :	£30	£100	£250	*

GEORGE I
Wood's coinage

1722 harp left ... ... :	£15	£70	£200	*
1722 harp right ...	£3	£12	£100	£350
1723	£2	£8	£80	£250

1723 obv Rs altered

Bs	£2	£8	£80	£250

1723 no stop after

date	£2	£8	£80	£250
1723/2	£6	£20	£100	*

1723 star in rev

legend	*	*	*	*

IRISH COINS

	Fair	F	VF	EF
1723 no stop before HIBERNIA	£4	£10	£100	£250
1724 head divides rev legend	£4	£10	£100	£220
1724 legend continuous over head	£5	£15	£140	£350

George I Wood's farthing, 1723

Farthings				
1722 harp left	£20	£70	£350	£600
1723 D: G:	£10	£30	£120	£400
1723 DEI GRATIA ...	£4	£10	£90	£300
1724	£5	£25	£140	£350

GEORGE II
halfpennies

1736	*	£5	£40	£150
1737	*	£5	£40	£150
1738	*	£5	£35	£120
1741	*	£5	£50	£120
1742	*	£5	£40	£120
1743	*	£5	£40	£140
1744	*	£5	£40	£140
1744/43	*	£5	£40	£120
1746	*	£10	£70	£150
1747	*	£5	£40	£140
1748	*	£5	£40	£120
1749	*	£5	£40	£120
1750	*	£5	£40	£120
1751	*	£5	£40	£120
1752	*	£5	£40	£120
1753	*	£5	£40	£120
1755	*	£10	£80	£200
1765	*	£5	£35	£120

Farthings				
1737	*	£4	£40	£100
1738	*	£2	£30	£90
1744	*	£5	£50	£100
1760	*	£5	£40	£80

George III, Voce Populi Halfpenny 1760

GEORGE III
Voce populi coinage
Halfpennies (1760)

	Fair	F	VF	EF
Type 1 (DF 565) ...	£16	£40	£120	£250

	Fair	F	VF	EF
Type 2(DF 566)	£12	£35	£160	*
Type 3(DF 567)	£14	£45	£170	*
Type 4(DF 569)	£12	£40	£170	*
Type 5(DF 570)	£12	£40	£170	*
Type 6(DF 571)	£12	£50	£170	*
Type 7(DF 572)	£12	£40	£170	*
Type 8(DF 573)	£12	£40	£170	*
Type 9(DF 575)	£30	£90	*	*
Type 9, P before head (DF 576)	£14	£60	£200	*
Type 9, P under head (DF 577)	£14	£60	£200	*
Farthings (1760)				
Type 1 loop to truncation	£45	£100	£350	£750
Type 2 no loop ...	*	*	*	*

London coinage
Halfpennies

1766	*	£5	£30	£120
1769	*	£5	£30	£120
1769 2nd type	*	£10	£60	£200
1775	*	£10	£60	£200
1776	£20	£90	£300	*
1781	*	£6	£40	£150
1782	*	£5	£35	£140

George III Halfpenny, 1805

Soho coinage

Penny 1805		£3	£30	£140
Halfpenny 1805 ...		£3	£30	£120
Farthing 1806		£1	£25	£100

Bank of Ireland token coinage

Six shillings 1804 ...	£10	£60	£350	£800

1804 six shilling Bank of Ireland

IRISH COINS

	Fair	F	VF	EF
Thirty pence 1808	£2	£10	£50	£200
Ten pence 1805 ...	£1	£8	£30	£100
Ten pence 1806 ...	£1	£6	£30	£75
Ten pence 1813 ...	£1	£5	£20	£70
Five pence 1805 ...	£1	£5	£15	£60
Five pence 1806 ...	£2	£8	£25	£80

Bank of Ireland ten pence token,1813

GEORGE IV

		F	VF	EF
Penny 1822...	*	£3	£30	£140
Penny 1823...	*	£3	£30	£180
Halfpenny 1822 ...	*	£2	£25	£120
Halfpenny 1823 ...	*	£2	£25	£150

Free State and Republic

Proofs exist for nearly all dates of the modern Irish coinage. However, only a few dates have become available to collectors or dealers and apart from the 1928 proofs, are all very rare. They have therefore been omitted from the list.

TEN SHILLINGS

	F	VF	EF	Unc
1966	*	£2.50	£5	£7.50
1966	*	*	*	£15

HALFCROWNS

1928	£3	£6	£12	£25
1928 proof	*	*	*	£30

Reverse of halfcrown

1930	£3	£10	£75	£250
1931	£6	£20	£100	£300
1933	£3	£15	£80	£250
1934	£5	£20	£40	£150
1937	£30	£75	£300	£750
1939	£3	£6	£15	£50
1940	£3	£5	£10	£40
1941	£4	£6	£20	£50
1942	£4	£6	£20	£45
1943	£70	£150	£600	£1500
1951	*	£1	£5	£30
1954	*	£1	£5	£30
1955	*	£1	£5	£20
1959	*	£1	£5	£15
1961	*	£1	£5	£20

	F	VF	EF	Unc
1961 mule (normal) obv/pre-1939 rev)	£5	£12	£250	*
1962	*	*	*	£5
1963	*	*	*	£5
1964	*	*	*	£5
1966	*	*	*	£3
1967	*	*	*	£3

1937 florin

FLORINS

1928	£2	£4	£8	£20
1928 proof	*	*	*	£30
1930	£3	£6	£50	£250
1931	£3	£10	£80	£250
1933	£10	£30	£80	*
1934	£15	£35	£120	*
1935	£3	£10	£35	£200
1937	£3	£15	£70	£250
1939	£2	£4	£10	£25
1940	£2	£5	£12	£25
1941	£2	£5	£12	£35
1942	£2	£5	£12	£35
1943	£1500	£3000	£6000	£10000
1951	*	*	£3	£15
1954	*	*	£3	£15
1955	*	*	£3	£15
1959	*	*	£3	£15
1961	*	£3	£6	£25
1962	*	*	£3	£15
1963	*	*	£3	£15
1964	*	*	*	£5
1965	*	*	*	£5
1966	*	*	*	£5
1968	*	*	*	£5

SHILLINGS

1928	*	£3	£8	£12
1928 proof	*	*	*	£25
1930	£2	£10	£50	£200
1931	£2	£10	£50	£200
1933	£3	£10	£20	£200
1935	£2	£5	£20	£75
1937	£5	£25	£150	£500
1939	*	£3	£6	£20
1940	*	£3	£8	£25
1941	£2	£5	£8	£25
1942	£2	£5	£8	£25
1951	*	£1	£3	£15
1954	*	*	£3	£15
1955	*	£2	£5	£20
1959	*	*	£3	£15
1962	*	*	*	£5
1963	*	*	*	£4
1964	*	*	*	£5
1966	*	*	*	£4
1968	*	*	*	£4

SIXPENCES

1928	*	£1	£3	£10
1928 proof	*	*	*	£20
1934	*	£1	£8	£35
1935	*	£3	£12	£60
1939	*	£1	£5	£25

COINS MARKET VALUES

	F	VF	EF	Unc
1940	*	£1	£5	£20
1942	*	*	£5	£20
1945	*	£5	£25	£60
1946	£1	£5	£50	£170
1947	*	£2	£20	£50
1948	*	£2	£8	£25
1949	*	*	£5	£25
1950	*	£2	£15	£60
1952	*	£1	£4	£15
1953	*	£1	£4	£15
1955	*	£1	£4	£15
1956	*	*	£3	£10
1958	*	£1	£5	£35
1959	*	*	£2	£6
1960	*	*	£2	£6
1961	*	*	£2	£6
1962	*	*	£3	£30
1963	*	*	*	£3
1964	*	*	*	£3
1966	*	*	*	£3
1967	*	*	*	£3

1968 sixpence

1968	*	*	*	£2
1969	*	*	*	£3

THREEPENCES

1928	*	£1	£3	£8
1928 proof	*	*	*	£12
1933	£1	£3	£20	£150
1934	*	£1	£5	£30
1935	£1	£3	£15	£65
1939	£1	£5	£50	£200
1940	*	*	£5	£25
1942	*	*	£5	£20
1943	*	*	£5	£40
1946	*	*	£5	£15
1948	*	£2	£15	£50
1949	*	*	£5	£20
1950	*	*	£2	£6
1953	*	*	£2	£5
1956	*	*	£1	£4
1961	*	*	*	£3
1962	*	*	*	£3
1963	*	*	*	£3
1964	*	*	*	£3
1965	*	*	*	£3
1966	*	*	*	£3

1967 threepence

1967	*	*	*	*
1968	*	*	*	*

PENNIES

1928	*	*	£3	£10
1928 proof	*	*	*	£30
1931	*	£2	£10	£50

IRISH COINS

	F	VF	EF	Unc
1933	*	£3	£15	£70
1935	*	*	£6	£20
1937	*	*	£9	£60
1938 (unique?)	*	*	*	*
1940	£2	£6	£60	*
1941	*	£1	£6	£15
1942	*	*	£3	£10
1943	*	*	£5	£15
1946	*	*	£3	£10
1948	*	*	£3	£10
1949	*	*	£3	£10
1950	*	*	£3	£10
1952	*	*	£2	£5
1962	*	*	£2	£4
1963	*	*	*	£2
1964	*	*	*	£2
1965	*	*	*	£1
1966	*	*	*	£1
1967	*	*	*	£1
1968	*	*	*	£1

HALFPENNIES

1928	*	£3	£6	£20
1928 proof	*	*	*	£20
1933	£1	£10	£40	£200
1935	*	£5	£15	£50
1937	*	*	£15	£30
1939	£4	£10	£25	£60
1940	*	£3	£20	£35
1941	*	*	£5	£10
1942	*	*	£2	£10
1943	*	*	£3	£10
1946	*	*	£5	£20
1949	*	*	£3	£5
1953	*	*	*	£3
1964	*	*	*	£2
1965	*	*	*	£2
1966	*	*	*	£2
1967	*	*	*	£1.50

FARTHINGS

1928	*	*	£3	£6
1928 proof	*	*	*	£10
1930	*	*	£5	£8
1931	£1	£3	£8	£18
1932	£1	£3	£10	£20
1933	*	£2	£5	£10
1935	*	£5	£12	£25
1936	*	£6	£15	£30
1937	*	£2	£5	£12
1939	*	*	£3	£5
1940	*	£3	£6	£20
1941	*	£1	£3	£5
1943	*	£1	£3	£6
1944	*	£1	£3	£6
1946	*	£1	£3	£5
1949	*	£2	£5	£8
1953	*	*	£3	£5
1959	*	*	£1	£3
1966	*	*	£2	£5

DECIMAL COINAGE
50p, 10p, 5p, 2p, 1p, ½p
All issues face value only.

SETS

1928 (in card case)	*	*	FDC	£120
1928 (in leather case)	*	*	FDC	£200
1966 unc. set	*	*	*	£10
1971 specimen set in folder	*	*	*	£5
1971 proof set	*	*	*	£9

The Anglo-Gallic Series

Chronological table of the Kings of England and France in the period 1154-1453

Henry II 1154-89
He was Duke of Normandy and Count of Anjou, Maine and Touraine. Through his marriage in 1152 with Eleanor of Aquitaine he became Duke of Aquitaine and Count of Poitou. He relinquished both these titles to his son Richard who in 1169 did homage to Louis VII of France. In 1185 he forced Richard to surrender Aquitaine and Poitou to ELEANOR who later – during Richard's absence – actually governed her provinces.

Richard I (Coeur de Lion) 1189-99
After his homage to the French King, he was, in 1172, formally installed as Duke of Aquitaine and Count of Poitou. Although his father forced him in 1185 to surrender Aquitaine and Poitou to his mother he retained actual government. Later Eleanor ruled in his absence.

John 1199-1216
He lost all provinces of the Angevin Empire except Aquitaine and part of Poitou.

Henry III 1216-72
In 1252 he ceded Aquitaine to his son Edward.

Edward I 1272-1307
He governed Aquitaine since 1252. In 1279 he became Count of Ponthieu in the right of his wife, Eleanor of Castile. When she died in 1290 the county went to his son Edward.

Edward II 1307-27
He was Count of Ponthieu as from 1290. In 1325 he relinquished the county of Ponthieu and the Duchy of Aquitaine to his son Edward.

Edward III 1327-77
He was Count of Ponthieu and Duke of Aquitaine as from 1325. At the outbreak of the war in 1337 he lost Ponthieu which was restored to him in 1360. In 1340 he assumed the title of King of France, which he abandoned again in 1360 as a result of the Treaty of Calais. He then obtained Aquitaine in full sovereignty and consequently changed his Aquitanian title from Duke (dux) to Lord (dominus) as the first one implied the overlordship of the French King. He gave Aquitaine as an apanage to his son, the Prince of Wales, better known as Edward The Black Prince, b.1330, d.1376, who was Prince of Aquitaine from 1362 till 1372, although he actually ruled from 1363 till 1371. In 1369, after war broke out again Edward reassumed the French title, which was henceforth used by the Kings of England until the Treaty of Amiens in 1802.

Richard II 1377-99
The son of The Black Prince succeeded his grandfather, Edward III, as King of England and as Lord of Aquitaine.

Henry IV 1399-1413
He adopted the same titles Richard II had, whom he ousted from the throne.

Henry V 1413-22
From 1417 until 1420 he used the title 'King of the French' on his 'Royal' French coins. After the Treaty of Troyes in 1420 he styled himself 'heir of France'.

Henry VI 1422-61
He inherited the title 'King of the French' from his grandfather Charles VI. He lost actual rule in Northern France in 1450 and in Aquitaine in 1453.

Louis VII 1137-80

Philip II (Augustus) 1180-1223

Louis VIII 1223-26
Louis IX (Saint Louis) 1226-70
Philip III 1270-85

Philip IV 1285-1314

Louis X 1314-16
Philip V 1316-22
Charles IV 1322-28

Philip VI (de Valois) 1328-50

John II (The Good) 1350-64

Charles V 1364-80

Charles VI 1380-1422

Charles VII 1422-61

'All Kings of England in the period 1154-1453 had interests in France. They were Dukes or Lords of Aquitaine, Counts of Poitou or Ponthieu, Lords of Issoudun or they were even or pretended to be, Kings of France itself, and, in those various capacities, struck coins. These coins, together with the French coins of their sons, and of their English vassals, are called Anglo-Gallic coins'.

So starts the introduction of the Bourgey-Spink book by E.R. Duncan Elias on this series. We would also like to thank Messrs Bourgey and Spink for allowing us to use some of the illustrations from the book, as well as the chronological table of the Kings of England and France during the period.

The Anglo-Gallic Coins by E.R.D. Elias is still available from Spink and Son Ltd, London (see Some Useful Books on page 11).

Henry II Denier, Aquitaine

HENRY II 1152-68	F	VF
Denier	£40	£120
Obole	£100	£280

RICHARD THE LIONHEART 1168-99
Aquitaine

Denier	£40	£140
Obole	£40	£150

Poitou

Denier	£35	£90
Obole	£60	£220

Issoudun

Denier		ext. rare

ELEANOR 1199-1204

Denier	£40	£120
Obole	£275	*

Edward I Denier au lion, during his father's lifetime

EDWARD I
During the lifetime of his father 1252-72

Denier au lion	£40	£130
Obole au lion	£50	£150

After succession to the English throne 1272-1307

Denier au lion	£120	£250
Obole au lion	£160	*

Edward I Obole au lion, after succession

Denier á la croix longue	£100	£150
Denier au léopard, first type	£45	£90
Obole au léopard, first type	£60	£140
Denier á la couronne		ext. rare

The coinage of PONTHIEU (Northern France) under the Edwards

Edward I	F	VF
Denier	£100	£220
Obole	£120	£250

Edward III		
Denier	£130	£275
Obole		ext. rare

EDWARD II

Gros Turonus Regem		ext. rare
Maille blanche		ext. rare
Maille blanche Hibernie	£65	£160

EDWARD III
Gold coins

Ecu d'or	£1250	£3000
Florin	£4500	£8500
Léopard d'or, 1st issue		ext. rare
Léopard d'or, 2nd issue	£1500	£3500

Edward III Léopard d'or, 2nd issue

Léopard d'or, 3rd issue	£1000	£2500
Léopard d'or, 4th issue	£1750	£4500
Guyennois d'or, 1st type	£10000	£20000
Guyennois d'or, 2nd type	£2250	£4500
Guyennois d'or, 3rd type	£1900	£3750

Silver coins

Gros aquitainique au léopard	£180	£490
Gros tournois à la crois mi-longue	£200	£550
Gros tournois à la croix longue	£100	£290
Sterling	£75	£250
Demi-sterling	£150	£375
Gros au léopard passant		ext. rare
Gros à la couronne	£150	£390
Gros au châtel aquitainique	£150	£390
Gros tournois au léopard au-dessus	£80	£200
Gros à la porte	£80	£20
Gros acquitainique au léopard au-dessous	£180	*
Blanc au léopard sous couronne	£60	£150
Gros au léopard sous couronne	£250	£500
Gros à la couronne avec léopard	£170	£400
Sterling à la tête barbue	£325	£950
Petit gros de Bordeaux		ext. rare
Gros au lion	£160	£475
Demi-gros au lion	£120	£275
Guyennois d'argent (sterling)	£130	£350
Gros au buste	£700	£1500
Demi-gros au buste	£500	£1350

Black coins

Double à la couronne, 1st type	£100	*
Double à la couronne, 2nd type	£100	£200
Double à la couronne, 3rd type	£100	*
Double au léopard	£80	£170
Double au léopard sous couronne	£40	£100
Double guyennois		ext. rare
Denier au léopard, 2nd type	£35	£100
Obole au léopard, 2nd type		ext. rare
Denier au léopard, 3rd type	£45	£120
Denier au léopard, 4th type	£50	£200

THE ANGLO-GALLIC SERIES

	F	VF
Obole au léopard, 4th type	£50	£120
Denier au lion	£35	£80

N.B. Some issues of the deniers au léopard of the 2nd and 3rd type are very rare to extremely rare and therefore considerably more valuable.

The coinage of BERGERAC
Henry, Earl of Lancaster 1347-51

Gros tournois à la croix longue ...	£800	*
Gros tournois à la couronne	£500	*
Gros au châtel aquitainque		ext. rare
Gros tournois au léopard au-dessus	£500	*
Gros à la couronne	£800	*
Gros à fleur-de-lis		ext. rare
Gros au léopard passant		ext. rare
Double		ext. rare
Denier au léopard		ext. rare

Henry, Duke of Lancaster 1351-61

Gros tournois à la couronne avec léopard	£600	*
Gros au léopard couchant	£700	*
Sterling à la tête barbue		ext. rare
Gros au lion		ext. rare

EDWARD THE BLACK PRINCE 1362-72
Gold Coins

Léopard d'or	£950	£2000
Guyennois d'or	£1800	*
Chaise d'or	£1800	£3500
Pavillon d'or 1st issue	£1500	£3000
Pavillon d'or 2nd issue	£1500	£3000
Demi-pavillon d'or		ext. rare
Hardi d'or	£1500	£3000

*Edward the Black Prince
Hardi d'or of Bordeaux*

Silver Coins

Gros	£750	£1500

Edward the Black Prince Demi-Gros

Demi-gros	£90	£200
Sterling	£70	£150
Hardi d'argent...	£35	£70

Edward the Black Prince Hardi d'argent

Black Coins

Double guyennois	£100	£200
Denier au lion	£50	£120
Denier	£50	£120

RICHARD II 1377-99
Gold Coins

Hardi d'or	£1000	£2750
Demi-hardi d'or		ext. rare

Silver Coins

Double Hardi d'argent...	£450	*
Hardi d'argent...	£70	£160

Black Coins

Denier	£70	£150

HENRY IV 1399-1413
Silver Coins

Double Hardi d'argent	£800	*

Henry IV Double Hardi d'argent

	F	VF
Hardi d'argent...	£60	£140
Hardi aux genêts...	ext. rare	

Black Coins

Denier	£40	£120
Denier aux genêts	ext. rare	

HENRY V 1413-22
Gold Coins

Agnel d' or	ext. rare	
Salut d' or	£9000	£25000

Silver Coins

Florette, 1st issue	£100	£250
Florette, 2nd issue	£150	£300
Florette, 3rd issue	£70	£150
Florette, 4th issue	£70	£150
Guénar	£250	£500
Gros au léopard	£300	*

Black Coins

Mansiois	ext. rare	
Niquet	£60	£150
Denier tournois	£60	£140

HENRY VI 1422-53
Gold Coins

Salut d' or	£350	£750
Angelot	£1500	£3000

Henry VI Salut d'or, Paris Mint

Silver Coins

Grand Blanc aux ècus	£40	£140
Petit Blanc	£140	£300
Trésin...	ext. rare	

Henry V Grand Blanc, Paris Mint

Black Coins

Denier Parisis, 1st issue	£60	£140
Denier Parisis, 2nd issue	£60	£140
Denier tournois	£40	£150
Maille tournois	£65	£150

N.B. The prices of the saluts and grand blancs are
for the mints of Paris, Rouen and Saint Lô; coins of
other mints are rare to very rare and consequently
more valuable.

Island Coinages

CHANNEL ISLANDS

From the date of their introduction onwards, proofs have been struck for a large number of Channel Islands coins, particularly in the case of Jersey. Except for those included in the modern proof sets these are mostly at least very rare and in the majority of cases have been omitted from the list. A number of die varieties which exist for several dates of the earlier 19th century Guernsey eight doubles have also been excluded. For further information in both cases the reader is referred to The Coins of the British Commonwealth of Nations, Part I, European Territories *by F. Pridmore, published by Spink and Son Ltd.*

GUERNSEY

TEN SHILLINGS	F	VF	EF	BU
1966	*	*	*	£1
THREEPENCE				
1956	*	*	*	£1
1959	*	*	*	£1
1966 proof only	*	*	*	£1
EIGHT DOUBLES				
1834	*	£12	£30	£100
1858	*	£12	£30	£100
1864	*	£15	£40	*
1868	*	£10	£30	*
1874	*	£10	£30	*
1885 H	*	*	£12	£25
1889 H	*	*	£10	£20
1893 H	*	*	£10	£20
1902 H	*	*	£10	£20
1903 H	*	*	£10	£20
1910 H	*	*	£12	£25
1911 H	*	*	£12	£30
1914 H	*	*	£12	£25
1918 H	*	*	£10	£30
1920 H	*	*	£8	£10
1934 H	*	*	£8	£10
1934 H prooflike	*	*	*	£50
1938 H	*	*	*	£5
1945 H	*	*	*	£5
1947 H	*	*	*	£4
1949 H	*	*	*	£4
1956	*	*	*	£1
1959	*	*	*	£1
1966 proof only	*	*	*	£3
FOUR DOUBLES				
1830	*	*	£20	£60
1858	*	*	£25	£70

Guernsey 1864 four doubles

	F	VF	EF	BU
1864	*	£5	£35	*
1868	*	£5	£35	*

	F	VF	EF	BU
1874	*	*	£30	*
1885 H	*	*	£8	£25
1889 H	*	*	£5	£20
1893 H	*	*	£4	£15
1902 H	*	*	£4	£15
1903 H	*	*	£4	£15
1906 H	*	*	£4	£15
1908 H	*	*	£4	£15
1910 H	*	*	£3	£15
1911 H	*	*	£3	£15
1914 H	*	*	£3	£15
1918 H	*	*	£3	£15
1920 H	*	*	*	£10
1945 H	*	*	*	£4
1949 H	*	*	*	£5
1956	*	*	*	£1
1966 proof only	*	*	*	£1
TWO DOUBLES				
1858	*	£4	£25	*
1868	*	£4	£30	*
1874	*	£4	£20	*
1885 H	*	*	£6	£15
1889 H	*	*	£4	£10
1899 H	*	*	£4	£10
1902 H	*	*	£5	£10
1903 H	*	*	£5	£15
1906 H	*	*	£4	£15
1908 H	*	*	£4	£20
1911 H	*	*	£4	£15
1914 H	*	*	£4	£18
1917 H	*	£10	£30	£60
1918 H	*	*	£2	£6
1920 H	*	*	£3	£8
1929 H	*	*	£2	£5
ONE DOUBLE				
1830	*	*	£10	£25
1868	*	£5	£20	*
1868/30	*	£5	£20	*
1885 H	*	*	£4	£10
1889 H	*	*	£2	£5
1893 H	*	*	£2	£5
1899 H	*	*	£2	£5
1902 H	*	*	£2	£5
1903 H	*	*	£2	£5
1911 H	*	*	£2	£8
1911 H new type	*	*	£2	£8
1914 H	*	*	£3	£8
1929 H	*	*	£1	£2
1933 H	*	*	£1	£2
1938 H	*	*	£1	£2

ISLAND COINAGES

DECIMAL COINAGE

The word 'NEW' was omitted from coins issued after December 1976, being replaced by the word for the denomination.

f denotes face value

TWENTY-FIVE POUNDS

	BU
1994 50th Anniversary Normandy Landings gold	£175
1995 Queen Mother, gold, proof	£200
1996 Queen's 70th Birthday, gold, proof	£200
1996 European Football, gold, proof	£200
1997 Golden Wedding, gold, proof	£200
1988 Royal Air Force, gold, proof	£200
1999 Royal Wedding, gold, proof	£200
1999 Queen Mother, gold, proof	£200

TEN POUNDS

1997 Golden Wedding, silver, proof	£150
1999 Millennium, gold, proof	£350

FIVE POUNDS

1995 Queen Mother, cu-ni	£7
1995 Queen Mother, silver, proof	£37
1996 Queen's 70th Birthday, cu-ni	£7
1996 Queen's 70th Birthday, silver, proof	£37
1996 European Football, cu-ni	£7
1996 European Football, silver, proof	£37
1997 Golden Wedding, cu-ni	£7
1997 Golden Wedding, silver, proof	£40
1997 Castle Cornet, silver, proof	£35
1997 Caernarfou Castle, silver, proof	£41
1997 Leeds Castle, silver, proof	£41
1997 Golden Wedding, gold, BU	£50
1998 Royal Air Force, silver, proof	£40
1999 Millennium, cu-ni	£10
1999 – silver, proof	£32
1999 – Royal Wedding, cu-ni	£10
1999 – silver, proof	£42
1999 Queen Mother, cu-ni	£10
1999 – silver, proof	£42

TWO POUNDS

1985 Liberation 40th Anniversary, crown size, in blister pack	£3.45
1985 – – silver, proof	£28.75
1986 Commonwealth Games, plastic case	£3.50
1986 – in presentation folder	£4
1986 – .500 silver, B. Unc	£15
1986 – .925 silver, proof	£28.75
1987 90th Anniversary of death of William the Conqueror, cu-ni, in presentation folder	£4
1987 gold, proof	£90
1987 – silver, proof	£28.75
1988 William the Second, cu-ni in presentation folder	£4
1988 – – silver, proof	£28.75
1989 Accession of Henry I, cu-ni in presentation folder	£4.25
1989 – silver, proof	£28.75
1989 Royal Visit, cu-ni	£2
1989 – – in plastic case	£3.50
1989 – silver, proof	£28.75
1990 Queen Mother's 90th Birthday, cu-ni	£2
1990 – – in plastic case	£3.50
1990 – silver, proof	£28.75
1991 Henry II, cu-ni	£5
1991 – – silver, proof	£30
1993 40th Anniversary of the Coronation, silver, proof	£28.75
1994 Normandy Landings	f
1994 – silver, proof	£30
1995 50th Anniversary of Liberation, silver, proof	£35
1995 –, silver, piedfort, proof	£60
1995 – cu-ni	£5
1998 Bimetal	f

ONE POUND

1981 copper, zinc, nickel	£2
1981 gold, proof (8 grammes)	£85
1981 gold piedfort (16 grammes)	£250
1983 new specification, new reverse	f
1985 new designs (in folder)	£1.20
1995 Queen Mother, silver, proof	£22
1996 Queen's 70th Birthday, silver, proof	£22
1997 Golden Wedding, silver, proof	£22

1997 Tower of London, silver, proof	£22
1997 Golden Wedding, silver, BU	£10
1998 Royal Air Force, silver, proof	£22
1999 Millennium, gold plated, silver, proof	£27
1999 Royal Wedding, silver, proof	£22
1999 Queen Mother, silver, proof	£22

FIFTY PENCE

1969	£1
1970	£3
1971 proof (from set)	£5
1981	£1
1982	£1
1985 new designs	f
Other dates	f

TWENTY-FIVE PENCE

1972 Silver Wedding (cupro-nickel)	£2
1972 – proof (silver)	£8
1977 Jubilee	£1.50
1977 – silver, proof	£10
1978 Royal Visit (cu-ni)	£1.50
1978 – silver, proof	£8
1980 Queen Mother's 80th birthday (cu-ni)	£1.25
1980 – silver	£10
1981 Royal Wedding (cu-ni)	£1
1981 – silver, proof	£10

OTHER DECIMAL COINAGE

120p, 10p, 5p, 1p, ½p. All issues face value only. *(The 5p and 10p were issued in a reduced size in 1992 and 1993 respectively.)*

SETS

1956 proof	£25
1966 proof	£8
1971 proof	£7.25
1929 proof	£8
1981 proof (including £1)	£10
1985 new designs, £1 to 1p (7 coins)	£6
1985 – £2 Liberation crown to 1p proof *9 coins)	£25
1986 BU set in folder, £1 to 1p (7 coins)	£6
1986 £2 Commonwealth Games to 1p, proof (8 coins)	£25
1987 BU set in folder, £1 to 1p (7 coins)	£6
1987 £2 William the Conqueror to 1p, proof (8 coins)	£25
1988 BU set in folder, £1 to 1p (7 coins)	£7
1988 £2 William the Second to 1p, proof (8 coins)	£25
1989 BU set in folder, £1 to 1p (7 coins)	£8
1989 £2 Henry I to 1p, proof (8 coins)	£26
1990 £2 Queen Mother's 90th Birthday to 1p, poroof (8 coins)	£28
1990 BU set as above (8 coins)	£10
1944 Normandy Landings, £100, £50, £25, £10 gold	£1000
1995 50th Anniversary of Liberation, £100, £50, £25, £10	£1000
1995 Queen Mother, £25 gold, £5 silver, £1 proof (3 coins)	£250
1996 Queen's 70th Birthday, £25 gold, £5 + £1 silver, proof (3 coins)	£250
1997 Golden Wedding, £25 gold, £5 + £1 silver, proof (3 coins)	£250
1997 Three £5 + £1 silver, proof (4 coins)	£135
1998 Royal Air Force, £25 gold, £5 + £1 silver, proof (3 coins)	£250
1999 Royal Wedding, £25 gold, £5 + £1 silver, proof	£250
1999 Queen Mother, £25 gold, £5 + £1 silver, proof (3 coins)	£250

ALDERNEY

TWENTY-FIVE POUNDS

1993 Coronation, gold proof	£225
1997 Golden Wedding, gold, proof	£200

FIVE POUNDS

1995 Queen Mother, cu-ni	£7.50
1995 – silver, proof	£33
1995 – piedfort	£60
1995 – gold, proof	£800
1996 – Queen's 70th Birthday, cu-ni	£7.50
1996 – silver, proof	£35
1996 – piedfort	£60
1996 – gold, proof	£800
1999 Total Eclipse, cu-ni	£8
1999 – silver, proof	£39

TWO POUNDS

1989 Royal Visit, cu-ni	£3
1989 – in plastic case	£5
1989 – silver, proof	£30
1989 – piedfort	£60
1989 gold, proof	£800
1990 Queen Mother's 90th birthday, cu-ni	£3
1990 – in plastic case	£5
1990 – silver, proof	£30
1990 – – – piedfort	£60
1990 – gold, proof	£800
1882 Accession, cu-ni	£3
1992 –, plastic case	£5
1992 –, silver, proof	£30
1992 –, piedfort	£60
1992 –, gold, proof	£800
1993 Coronation, cu-ni	£3
1993 – –, plastics case	£5
1993 – –, silver proof	£35
1993 – –, piedfort	£60
1994 D-Day, cu-ni	£3
1994 –, card pack	£6
1994 –, silver proof	£35
1994 –, piedfort	£60
1995 VE/Liberation, cu-ni	£3
1995 – –, plastic case	£5
1995 –, silver proof	£33
1995 –, piedfort	£60
1995 –, gold proof	£800
1997 Golden Wedding, cu-ni	£3
1997 Golden Wedding, silver, proof	£38
1997 WWF, Puffin, cu-ni	£3
1997 WWF, Puffin, silver, proof	£32
1999 Total Eclipse, cu-ni	£4
1999 Total Eclipse, silver, proof	£34
1999 Total Eclipse, gold, proof	£800

ONE POUND

1993 Coronation, silver, proof	£30
1995 VE/Liberation, silver, proof	£22
1995 –, gold, proof	£300

SETS

1994 £100, £50, £25, £10, D-Day gold, proof (4 coins)	£1000
1994 £50, £25, £10, D-Day gold, proof (3 coins)	£500

JERSEY

CROWN	F	VF	EF	BU
1966	*	*	*	£1
1966 – proof	*	*	*	£3

1/4 OF A SHILLING

	F	VF	EF	BU
1957	*	*	*	£2
1960 proof only	*	*	*	£5
1964	*	*	*	£0.30
1966	*	*	*	£0.75

1/2 OF A SHILLING

	F	VF	EF	BU
1877 H	*	*	£7	£40
1881	*	*	£9	£50
1888	*	*	£8	£40
1894	*	*	£7	£30
1909	*	*	£8	£40
1911	*	*	£5	£25
1913	*	*	£5	£20
1923	*	*	£5	£25
1923 new type	*	*	£7	£20
1926	*	*	£5	£18
1931	*	*	£2	£10
1933	*	*	£3	£10
1935	*	*	£2	£10
1937	*	*	*	£5

ISLAND COINAGES

	F	VF	EF	BU
'1945' (George VI)[1]	*	*	*	£3
'1945' (Elizabeth II)[1]	*	*	*	£2
1946	*	*	*	£4
1947	*	*	*	£3
1957	*	*	*	£0.40
1960	*	*	*	£0.20
1964	*	*	*	£0.15
1966	*	*	*	£0.15

The date 1945 on one-twelfth shillings commemorates the year of liberation from German occupation. The coins were struck in 1949, 1950, 1952 and 1954.

1/13 OF A SHILLING

	F	VF	EF	BU
1841	*	*	£30	£100
1844	*	*	£35	£120
1851	*	*	£40	£100
1858	*	*	£35	£110
1861	*	*	£40	£100
1865 proof only	*	*	*	£350
1866	*	*	£20	£60
1870	*	*	£25	£60
1871	*	*	£25	£60

1/24 OF A SHILLING

	F	VF	EF	BU
1877 H	*	*	£4	£30
1888	*	*	£4	£25
1894	*	*	£4	£25
1909	*	*	£3	£20
1911	*	*	£3	£20
1913	*	*	£3	£20
1923	*	*	£2	£15
1923 new type	*	*	£2	£15
1926	*	*	£2	£15
1931	*	*	£1	£5
1933	*	*	£1	£5
1935	*	*	£1	£5
1937	*	*	£1	£5
1946	*	*	£1	£5
1947	*	*	£1	£5

1/26 OF A SHILLING

	F	VF	EF	BU
1841	*	*	£18	£75
1844	*	*	£18	£75
1851	*	*	£18	£75
1858	*	*	£18	£75
1861	*	*	£16	£65
1866	*	*	£15	£60
1870	*	*	£15	£50
1871	*	*	£18	£50

1/48 OF A SHILLING

	F	VF	EF	BU
1877 H	*	£8	£30	£75

1/52 OF A SHILLING

	F	VF	EF	BU
1841	*	£12	£50	£100
1841 proof	*	*	*	£300
1861 proof only	*	*	*	£400

DECIMAL COINAGE

f denotes face value

FIVE POUNDS

1990 50th Anniversary of the Battle of Britain, silver, proof	£85
1997 Golden Wedding, silver, proof	£38
1997 Golden Wedding, cu-ni	£8
1999 – 2000 Millennium, silver, proof	£40

TWO POUNDS

1981 Royal Wedding, nickel silver (crown size)	f

ISLAND COINAGES

	BU
1981 – in presentation pack	**£2.75**
1981 – silver, proof	**£15**
1981 – gold, proof	**£300**
1985 40th anniversary of liberation, (crown size)	**f**
1985 – in presentation pack	**£3.75**
1985 – silver, frosted proof	**£28.75**
1985 – gold, frosted proof	**£1000**
1986 Commonwealth Games	**£2**
1986 – in presentation case	**£3**
1986 – .500 silver, B. Unc	**£14.95**
1986 – .925 silver, proof	**£28.75**
1987 World Wildlife Fund 25 years cu-ni in blister pack	**£3.25**
1987 – silver, proof	**£30**
1989 Royal Visit cu-ni in de luxe presentation case	**£4**
1989 – silver, proof	**£28.75**
1990 Queen Mother's 90 birthday, cu-ni...	**£4**
1990 – silver, proof	**£28.75**
1990 – gold, proof	**£402.50**
1990 50th Anniversary of the Battle of Britain, silver, proof	**£28.75**
1993 40th Anniversary of the Coronation silver, proof	**£30**
1995 50th Anniversary of Liberation, silver, proof	**£35**
1995 –, silver, piedfort, proof...	**£60**
1995 – cu-ni	**£4**
1996 Queen's 70th Birthday, cu-ni	**£5**
1996 – – – silver, proof	**£33**
1997 Bimetal, BU	**£5**
1997 – – – silver proof	**£25**
1998 – – – new portrait, BU	**£5**

ONE POUND

1981 cu-ni	**£2.25**
1981 silver, proof	**£25**
1981 gold, proof	**£150**

In 1983 Jersey issued a one pound coin with the specification changed to conform with that of the UK one pound coin. The reverse initially bore the emblem of St Helier Parish, but this was changed regularly to represent, in rotation, each of the 12 parishes of Jersey, the others being: St Saviour, St Brelade, St Clement, St Lawrence, St Peter, Grouville, St Martin, St Ouen, Trinity, St John and St Mary, in order of size of the population.

1983 new specification, new designs (both sides), on presentation card (St Helier)	**£4**
1983 silver, frosted proof, in case –	**£23**
1983 gold, frosted proof, in case –...	**£345**
1984 in presentation wallet (St Saviour)	**£4**
1983 silver, frosted proof –	**£23**
1984 gold, frosted proof –...	**£345**
1984 in presentation wallet (St Brelade)	**£4**
1984 silver, frosted proof –	**£23**
1984 gold, frosted proof –...	**£345**
1985 in presentation wallet (St Clement)	**£4**
1985 silver, frosted proof –	**£23**
1985 gold, frosted proof –	**£345**
1985 in presentation wallet (St Lawrence)	**£4**
1985 silver, frosted proof –	**£23**
1985 gold, frosted proof –	**£345**
1986 in presentation wallet (St Peter) ...	**£4**
1986 silver, frosted proof –	**£23**
1986 gold, frosted proof –	**£345**
1986 in presentation wallet (Grouville) ...	**£4**
1986 silver, frosted proof –	**£23**
1986 gold, frosted proof –	**£345**
1987 in presentation wallet (St Martin) ...	**£4**
1987 silver, frosted proof –	**£23**

1987 gold, frosted proof –	**£345**
1987 in presentation wallet (St Quen) ...	**£4**
1987 silver, frosted proof –	**£23**
1987 gold, frosted proof –	**£345**
1988 in presentation wallet (Trinity)	**£4**
1988 silver, frosted proof –	**£23**
1988 gold, frosted proof –	**£345**
1988 in presentation wallet (St John) ...	**£4**
1988 silver, frosted proof –	**£23**
1988 gold, frosted proof –	**£345**
1988 in presentation wallet (St Mary) ...	**£4**
1988 silver, frosted proof –	**£23**
1988 gold, frosted proof –	**£345**

In 1991 Jersey launched a series of six coins featuring ships built on the island during the second half of the 19th century.

1991 Silver, frosted proof 'Tickler'	**£35**
1991 Gold, frosted proof 'Tickler'	**£352**
1991 Silver, frosted proof 'Percy Douglas'	**£25.80**
1991 Gold, frosted proof 'Percy Douglas'	**£352**
1992 Silver, proof 'The Hebe'	**£20**
1992 Gold, frosted proof 'The Hebe'	**£300**
1992 Silver, proof Coat of Arms	**£20**
1992 Gold, frosted proof Coat of Arms ...	**£300**
1992 Silver, proof 'The Gemini'	**£30**
1992 Silver, proof 'The Century'	**£30**
1992 Silver, proof 'The Resolute'	**£25**
1992 Gold, proof 'The Resolute'	**£360**

FIFTY PENCE

1969	**£1**
1983 new obv, new rev...	**f**
1985 40th anniversary of liberation	**f**

TWENTY-FIVE PENCE

1977 Jubilee	**£1.50**
1977 – Silver, proof	**£17.50**

TWENTY PENCE

1982 date on rocks on rev (cased)	**£0.65**
1982, silver, proof, piedfort	**£35**
1983 new obv, with date, rev no date on rocks	**f**
Later dates	**f**

OTHER DECIMAL COINAGE

10p, 5p, 2p, 1p, ½p (to 1982). All face value only.

1983 10p, 5p, 2p, 1p: new obv and rev designs...	**f**
Later dates	**f**

SETS

	BU
1957	**£30**
1960	**£15**
1964	**£10**
1966 (4 coins) proof	**£4**
1966 (2 crowns)	**£7**
1968/7 1 decimal coins	**£2**
1972 Silver Wedding (5 gold, 4 silver coins)	**£400**
1972 – – proof	**£450**
1972 – – (4 silver coins)...	**£25**
1980 50p to ½p	**£2**
1980 – frosted proof	**£15**
1981 £1 to ½p, in presentation pack	**£3**
1981 – base metal, proof	**£13.95**
1983 £1 to 1p (7 coins)	**£3.50**
1983 – silver frosted proof, in album	**£40**
1987 £1 to 1p, in folder (7 coins)	**£6**
1990 50th Anniversary of the Battle of Britain, gold coins with face values of £100, £50, £25 and £10 (4 coins)	**£1035**
1992 £1 to 1p (7 coins)	**£13**
1995 50th Anniversary of Liberation, £100, £50 £25 and £10 (4 coins)	**£1000**
1997 £2 to 1p incl. 2 x 50p (9 coins)	**£15**

ISLE OF MAN

Contemporary forgeries of several of the earlier Isle of Man coins exist.

COPPER AND BRONZE 1709-1839

Isle of Man, Penny, 1786

HALFPENNIES	F	VF	EF	VAC
1709	£12	£30	*	*
1733	£8	£20	£50	£150
1733 proof	£10	£25	£80	£250
1733 silver	*	£60	£120	£300
1758	£8	£15	£50	£175
1758 proof	*	*	*	*
1786	£8	£15	£40	*
1786 plain edge proof	*	*	£110	£250
1798	£8	£15	£50	*
1798 proof	*	*	£65	£125
1798 AE gilt proof ...	*	*	*	*
1813	£8	£20	£40	£125
1813 proof	*	*	£65	£125
1839 proof	*	*	£15	£50
FARTHINGS				
1839	£10	£25	£50	*
1839 proof	*	*	*	*

ISSUES SINCE 1965

Prices for the gold series, £5 to half sovereign, plus 'angels', and platinum 'nobels' are directly governed by day-to-day prices in their respective bullion markets, to which reference should be made for current valuations.
Since 1973 there have been many changes to the designs of the circulating coins and these have often been accompanied by special sets in gold, platinum and silver. In addition there have been many commemorative crowns struck in base metal and in precious metal. A full list of the complete coinage is beyond the scope of this publication.

PENNIES	F	VF	EF	Unc
1709	£15	£40	*	*
1733	£10	£30	£100	*
1733 proof	£20	£60	£120	£275
1733 silver	*	*	£200	£400
1758	£10	£20	£70	£200
1758 proof	*	*	*	*
1758 silver	*	*	£300	£500
1786	£10	£20	£80	£175
1786 plain edge proof	*	*	£150	£300
1798	£15	£40	£100	£200
1798 bronzed proof	*	*	£120	£200
1798 AE gilt proof ...	*	*	£300	*
1798 silver proof	*	*	*	*
1813	£10	£25	£95	*
1813 bronzed proof ...	*	*	£70	£175
1839	*	£15	£50	£100
1839 proof	*	*	*	*

Isle of Man, Halfpenny, proof in Silver, 1733

Dealers who display this symbol are Members of the

BRITISH NUMISMATIC TRADE ASSOCIATION

The primary purpose of the Association is to promote and safeguard the highest standards of professionalism in dealings between its Members and the public. In official consultations the BNTA is the recognised representative of commercial numismatics in Britain.

The BNTA will be organising the following events in 1999 & 2000

COINEX LONDON - 8th/9th October 1999
Hotel Marriott, Grosvenor Sq, W1

SPRING COINEX - 24th/25th March 2000
Old Swan Hotel, Harrogate

COINEX LONDON - 6th/7th October 2000
Hotel Marriott, Grosvenor Sq, W1

For a free Membership Directory and further information, please send a stamped addressed envelope to:

Mrs Carol Carter, General Secretary, BNTA
PO Box 474A, Thames Ditton, Surrey, KT7 0WJ
Tel: 020-8398-4290, Fax: 020-8398-4291, E-mail: bnta@lineone.net

BNTA MEMBERS IN COUNTY ORDER

(Those members with retail premises are indicated with an *)

LONDON AREA
*A.H. Baldwin & Sons Ltd.
Beaver Coin Room
*W. & F.C. Bonham & Sons Ltd.
Chelsea Coins
*Philip Cohen Numismatics
Andre de Clermont
Michael Dickinson
*Dix Noonan Webb
Christopher Eimer
*Glendining's
Harrow Coin & Stamp Centre
Ian Jull
*Knightsbridge Coins
*Lennox Gallery
Lubbock & Son Ltd.
C.J. Martin Coins Ltd.
*Colin Narbeth & Son Ltd.
*George Rankin Coin Co.
*Seaby Coins/C.N.G. Inc.
R.D. Shah
*Simmons Gallery
*Spink & Son Ltd.
Surena Ancient Art & Numismatic
*Vale Coins
*Italo Vecchi
Mark J. Vincenzi
BERKSHIRE
Frank Milward
BUCKINGHAMSHIRE
Europa Numismatics
CORNWALL
Michael Trenerry Ltd.
CUMBRIA
Patrick Finn
DORSET
*Dorset Coin Co. Ltd.
ESSEX
E.J. & C.A. Brooks
GLOUCESTERSHIRE
RJB Coins
HAMPSHIRE
*SPM Jewellers
Raymond Sleet
Studio Coins
West Essex Coin Investments

HERTFORDSHIRE
KB Coins
David Miller
KENT
C.J. Denton
*Peter Morris
LANCASHIRE
*B.J. Dawson (Coins)
*Colin de Rouffignac
*Peter Ireland Ltd.
Liverpool Medal Co.
*R & L Coins
LINCOLNSHIRE
Grantham Coins
NORFOLK
*Clive T. Dennett
Chris Rudd
NORTHUMBERLAND
*Corbitt Stamps Ltd.
OXFORDSHIRE
Simon R. Porter
SHROPSHIRE
*Collectors Gallery
SUFFOLK
*Lockdale Coins Ltd
*Schwer Coins
SURREY
Graeme & Linda Monk
Nigel Tooley Ltd
SUSSEX
*Brighton Coin Co.
WEST MIDLANDS
*Format of Birmingham Ltd.
Mint Coins Limited
WARWICKSHIRE
*Warwick & Warwick Ltd
WORCESTERSHIRE
Whitmore
YORKSHIRE
Airedale Coins
Paul Clayton
Paul Davies Ltd.
*J. Smith

WALES
Lloyd Bennett
*North Wales Coins Ltd.
C. Rumney

British Paper Money

THE prices listed here are only intended as a guide to values of English bank-notes. Notes of Queen Elizabeth II are generally available at a little above face value and previous to that notes tend to increase in value the older they are. Top condition is the most important factor in banknote pricing although it is quite possible to collect a more attractive selection in lower grades; some notes for example are never seen in better then Very Fine. The prices quoted are for Extremely Fine, not uncirculated and a premium can be expected on first class notes - this is especially relevant to notes of John Bradbury and to a lesser extent N.F. Warren Fisher.

We have not listed banknotes prior to 1914 as these are all scarce and only available in grades up to Very Fine. The past year has continued to show a healthy demand for material at every level, the emphasis still remaining on quality followed by rarity. The hobby continues to grow at a sensible pace, the shortage of good material being the only drawback.

Reference numbers are according to Vincent Duggleby's *English Paper Money*. The new (fourth) edition was published by Spink & Son Ltd in October 1990.

TREASURY NOTES

Signed by John Bradbury

First Issue

			VF	EF
T9	10s	Red on white. Prefix 'No'	£140	£300
T8	10s	Red on white. Six digits	£300	£900
T10	10s	Red on white. Five digits	£300	£900
T1	£1	Black on white. Prefix large letters A., B. or C.	£300	£1100
T2	£1	Black on white. As previous but no full stop after serial letter	£800	£1800
T3	£1	Black on white. Six digits	£150	£600
T4	£1	Black on white. Large serial number, 'dot' and five digits	£400	£1400
T5	£1	Black on white. Large serial number, 'dash' and five digits	£350	£1100
T6	£1	Black on white. Double prefix letters	£300	£1250
T7	£1	Black on white. Small type face serial number	£450	£2000

(Serial number with prefix 'No' are referred to as 'dot' if 'No' is followed by a full stop and 'dash' when a dash is used).

Second issue

T13	10s	Red on white. Six digits	£45	£200
T12	10s	Red on white. Five digits	£45	£200
T11	£1	Black on white.	£60	£240
T15	10s	Red on white. Arabic overprint	£225	£900
T14	£1	Black on white. Arabic overprint	from £750	from £3500

Third issue

T20	10s	Green and brown on white Red serial no. with 'dash'	£50	£240

T19	10s	Green and brown on white		
		Red serial no. with 'dot'	£50	£280
T17	10s	Green and brown on white.		
		Black serial no. with 'dot'	£60	£280
T18	10s	Green and brown on white		
		Black serial no. with 'dash'	£60	£240
T16	£1	Green and brown on white	£30	£80

Signed by Norman Fenwick Warren Fisher First issue (overall watermark)
T25	10s	Green and brown on white, 'dot'	£30	£140
T26	10s	Green and brown on white, 'dash'	£15	£90
T24	£1	Green and brown on white	£15	£45

Second issue (boxed watermark)
T30	10s	Green and brown on white	£20	£90
T31	£1	Green and brown on white	£12	£35
T32	£1	Green and brown on white, 'dash'	£15	£35

Third issue (Northern Ireland)
T33	10s	Green and brown on white	£25	£100
T34	£1	Green and brown on white, 'dot'	£15	£60
T35	£1	Green and brown on white, 'dash'	£20	£80

Unissued notes prepared during the Great War (all extremely rare)
T21	5s	Deep violet and green on white (Bradbury)	from £4000
T22	2s 6d	Olive-green and chocolate on white	from £2500
T23	1s	Green and brown on white	from £2250
T27	5s	Violet and green on white (Warren Fisher)	from £2250
T28	2s 6d	Olive-green and chocolate on white	from £2250
T29	1s	Green and brown on white	from £2250

BANK OF ENGLAND NOTES
Cyril Patrick Mahon 1925-29
B210	10s	Red-brown	£15	£60
B212	£1	Green	£10	£30
B215	£5	Black on white	£50	£180

Bank of England £1 serial no. 2 sold at auction by Spink and Son Ltd several years ago for £56,000.

John Bradbury 5 shillings.

Basil Gage Catterns 1929-34

B223	10s	Red-brown	£7	£35
B225	£1	Green (prefix: letter, number, number; e.g.E63)	£8	£20
B226	£1	Green (prefix: number, number, letter)	£10	£20
B228	£5	Black on white	£50	£150

Kenneth Oswald Peppiatt 1934-49

B236	10s	Red-brown (prefix: number, number, letter) 1st period	£3	£20
B251	10s	Mauve 2nd period	£7	£16
B256	10s	Red-brown (prefix: number, number, letter) 3rd period	£5	£15
B262	10s	Red-brown (metal filament) 4th period	£3	£12
B238	£1	Green (prefix: number, number, letter) 1st issue	£3	£7
B248	£1	Pale blue (prefix:A-D) 2nd issue	£6	£7
B249	£1	Blue (shades) 2nd issue	£1	£3
B258	£1	Green (prefix: number, number, letter) 3rd issue	£4	£6
B260	£1	Green (metal filament) 4th issue	£3	£5
B241	£5	Black on white, one straight edge, three deckled	£35	£100
B255	£5	Black on white, straight edges, metal filament, thick paper	£35	£80
B264	£5	Black on white, straight edges, metal filament, thin paper	£35	£80

Unissued notes of the 1939-45 War (very rare)

B253	5s	Olive-green on pale pink background	from £1800	*
B254	2s 6d	Black on pale blue background	from £1500	*

Percival Spencer Beale 1949-55

B266	10s	Red-brown (prefix: letter, number, number, letter)	£2	£8
B265	10s	Red-brown (prefix: number, number, letter)	£3	£10
B268	£1	Green	£2	£5
B270	£5	Black on white		

Leslie Kenneth O'Brien 1955-62

B271	10s	Red-brown (prefix: letter, number, number, letter)	£2	£4
B272	10s	Red-brown (prefix: number, number, letter)	£15	£30
B286	10s	Red-brown, Queen's portrait	£1	£5
B273	£1	Green	£2	£4
B281	£1	Green (prefix: letter, number, number) Queen's portrait	£2	£4
B282	£1	Green (prefix: number, number, letter). Queen's portrait	£2	£4
B284	£1	Green (prefix: letter, number, number, letter). Queen's portrait	£2	£4
B283	£1	Green 'R' variety (letter R found in white space above lower BANK OF ENGLAND panel on reverse)	£100	£225
B275	£5	Black on white	£30	£90
B277	£5	Blue, pale green and orange (solid symbols)	£8	£20
B279	£5	Blue, pale green and orange (symbols for £5 white)	£8	£20

Jasper Quintus Hollom 1962-66

B295	10s	Red-brown (prefix: number, number, letter)	£2	£3
B294	10s	Red-brown (prefix: letter, number, number, letter)	£1	£2
B288	£1	Green	£1	£3
B292	£1	Green, 'G' variety ('G' in same position as 'R' as B283)	£1	£1.50
B297	£5	Blue	£5	£10
B299	£10	Multicoloured	£12	£18

John Standish Fforde 1966-70

B309	10s	Red-brown (prefix: number, number, letter)	£1	£2
B310	10s	Red-brown (prefix: letter, number, number, letter)	£1	£2
B311	10s	Red-brown (prefix: letter, number, number)	£2	£4
B301	£1	Green	£1.50	£2
B303	£1	Green 'G' variety	£1	£1.50
B312	£5	Blue (prefix: letter, number, number)	£6	£8
B314	£5	Blue (prefix: number, number, letter)	£6	£8
B316	£10	Multicoloured	£11	£18
B318	£10	Multicoloured	£22	£45

John Brangwyn Page 1970-1980

B322	£1	Green (prefix: letter, letter, number, number)	f	£1.50
B335	£1	Dark and light green, 1st series, AO1	f	£2
B324	£5	Blue	f	£10
B332	£5	Multicoloured (prefix: letter, number, number). 1st series	f	£7
B334	£5	Multicoloured, L on reverse signifies lithographic printing	f	£6
B326	£10	Multicoloured	f	£14

| B330 | £10 | Multicoloured A-series | f | £14 |
| B328 | £20 | Multicoloured | f | £40 |

David Henry Fitzroy Somerset 1980-1988

B341	£1	Green	£1.50	
B342	£5	Multicoloured	£6	
B344	£10	Multicoloured (prefix: letter, number, number)	£12	
B346	£10	Multicoloured (prefix: letter, letter, number, number)	£12	
B350	£20	Multicoloured	£30	
B352	£50	Olive green, brown, grey	£70	

George Malcolm Gill (1988-1991)

B353	£5	Blue	f	£8
B354	£10	Brown	f	f
B355	£20	Multicoloured	f	f
B356	£50	Multicoloured	f	f
B357	£5	Multicoloured (Series E) AO1	f	£16
		Presentation pair Series D and E £5	£200	
		Presentation pair Series D and E £20	£180	
		Presentation pair Series D and E £10	£120	
B358	£10	Multicoloured	f	f
B359	£20	Multicoloured	f	f
B360	£50	Multicoloured	f	f

G.E.A. Kentfield (1991-)

B-	£5	Multicoloured	f	f
B-	£10	Multicoloured	f	f
B-	£20	Multicoloured	f	f
B-	£50	Multicoloured	f	f

* Exist but no price can be quoted. f - still face value unless special prefix number, i.e. AD1.

John Bradbury hand-painted essay £1